Grade 7

Addison-Wesley Mathematics

Reteaching Workbook

Addison-Wesley Publishing Company

Menlo Park, California ▪ Reading, Massachusetts ▪ New York
Don Mills, Ontario ▪ Wokingham, England ▪ Amsterdam ▪ Bonn
Sydney ▪ Singapore ▪ Tokyo ▪ Madrid ▪ San Juan

ISBN 0-201-27707-7

ABCDEFGHIJKL-HC-96543210

Table of Contents

Name ______________________________

Numbers and Place Value

Place Value Chart

Period names	Trillions			Billions			Millions			Thousands			Units		
Place value names	hundreds	tens	ones	hundreds	tens	ones	hundreds	tens	ones	hundreds	tens	ones	hundreds	tens	ones
Numeral					4	3	2	9	1	2	0	3	1	2	0

We write: 43,291,203,120

Each period is separated by a comma.

We say: "forty-three billion, two hundred ninety-one million, two hundred three thousand, one hundred twenty"

Write the standard numeral.

1. 47,2__ ___ forty-seven **million,** two hundred sixty-three **thousand,** five hundred seven

2. ______________ six **million,** seven hundred forty-five **thousand,** two hundred seventy-five

Fill in the blanks with the missing period names.

3. 2,021,300,918,000 two ______________, twenty-one ______________, three hundred ______________, nine hundred eighteen ______________

Write the standard numeral in words.

4. 2,469,103 ______________________________

Write each standard numeral using expanded notation.

5. 43,298 $(4 \times 10{,}000) + (3 \times \quad) + (2 \times \quad) + (9 \times \quad) + (8 \times \quad)$

6. 168,294 ______________________________

Name ____________________

Relating the Operations

Addition/Multiplication How many times is 4 added to itself in order to arrive at the sum of 24?

$4 + 4 + 4 + 4 + 4 + 4 = 24$ *or* $4 \times ? = 24$

1 2 3 4 5 6

Multiplying is another way of doing repeated addition.

Subtraction/Division How many times is 4 subtracted from 24 in order to arrive at the difference of 0?

$24 - 4 - 4 - 4 - 4 - 4 - 4 = 0$ *or* $24 \div ? = 6$

1 2 3 4 5 6 4

Dividing is another way of doing repeated subtraction.

Addition/Subtraction and Multiplication/Division Remember that addition/subtraction and multiplication/division are inverse operations.

$\square + 18 = 30$ (12) $30 - \square = 18$ (12)

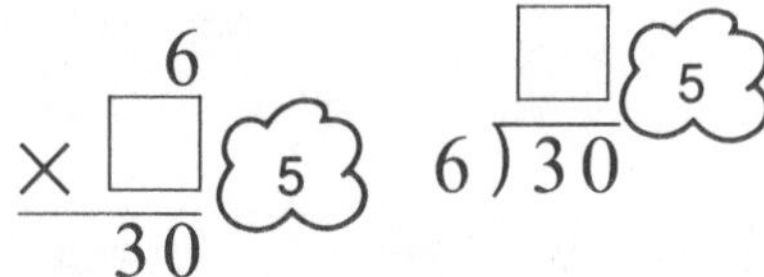

Match the related exercises.

____	**1.** $25 + 25 + 25 = 75$	**a.**	$28 \div 4 = 7$
____	**2.** $18 - 7 = 11$	**b.**	$95 \div 5 = 19$
____	**3.** $61 \times 23 = 1{,}403$	**c.**	$25 \times 3 = 75$
____	**4.** $95 - 19 - 19 - 19 - 19 - 19 = 0$	**d.**	$11 + 7 = 18$
____	**5.** $17 \times 12 = 204$	**e.**	$1{,}403 \div 23 = 61$
____	**6.** $28 - 7 - 7 - 7 - 7 = 0$	**f.**	$204 \div 17 = 12$

7. Write a division problem that would help you solve $17 \times ? = 136$. ____________

8. Write an addition problem that would help you solve $? - 99 = 49$. ____________

Name ______________________________

Order of Operations

Order of Operations
1. Compute inside parentheses first. 2. Do all multiplications and divisions next, left to right. 3. Do all additions and subtractions last, left to right.

Following the order of operations ensures that you get one value for an expression.

Example:

$570 \div (12 - 2) \times 3 + 4 = 570 \div 10 \times 3 + 4$ Work inside parentheses first.

$= 57 \times 3 + 4$ Multiply and divide next.

$= 171 + 4$ Add and subtract last.

$= 175$

Evaluate each expression. Do the operation in dark type first. Decide which answer is correct. Explain.

1. $5 \boldsymbol{\times} 6 - 3 =$ ________ Correct? ________

$5 \times 6 \boldsymbol{-} 3 =$ ________ Correct? ________

Explain. ______________________________

____

2. $100 \boldsymbol{\div} 2 \times 5 =$ ________ Correct? ________

$100 \div 2 \boldsymbol{\times} 5 =$ ________ Correct? ________

Explain. ______________________________

____

3. $(6 + 2) \times 5 \boldsymbol{-} 1 =$ ________ Correct? ________

$(6 \boldsymbol{+} 2) \times 5 - 1 =$ ________ Correct? ________

Explain. ______________________________

____

Name ____________________

Problem Solving Introduction

Use the first 3 steps of the problem solving checklist.

- ▶ Understand the situation.
- ▶ Find data needed.
- ▶ Plan what to do.

Choose the statement that shows how you could solve the problem.

If doughnuts cost $2.40 a dozen, how much will 48 doughnuts cost?

A. Divide 2.40 by 48; then multiply the quotient by 12.
B. Divide 48 by 12; then divide 2.40 by the quotient.
C. Divide 48 by 12; then multiply the quotient by 2.40.

Understand the situation:
You need to know how many dozen doughnuts there are and their total price.

Find data needed:
48 dozen, 12 doughnuts in 1 dozen, $2.40 per dozen

Plan what to do:
Find how many dozen there are by dividing the number of doughnuts by 12. Then multiply the quotient by the price per dozen.

Choose the Correct Response:
Choice C matches your plan.

Choose the statement that shows how you could solve the problem.

1. There were 400 students at a school play. 85 out of every 100 students went to the concession stand at intermission. How many students went to the concession stand?

A. Divide 400 by 100; then multiply the quotient by 85.
B. Divide 400 by 100; then divide the quotient by 85.
C. Divide 400 by 85; then multiply the quotient by 100.

2. Ms. Kay earns $25,704 a year. How much does she earn in 5 months?

A. Divide 25,704 by 5; then multiply the quotient by 12.
B. Multiply 25,704 by 5. Then divide the product by 12.
C. Divide 25,704 by 12; then multiply the quotient by 5.

Name ___________

Using Critical Thinking

Complete the flowcharts.

Example:

Step 1: Write 19.
Step 2: Add 4. $19 + 4 = 23$.
Step 3: Is 23 a multiple of 3?
No. Follow the NO path.
Step 4: Divide by 1. $23 \div 1 = 23$.
Step 5: Return to Add 4. $23 + 4 = 27$.
Step 6: Is 27 a multiple of 3? Yes.
Write 27 as the output.

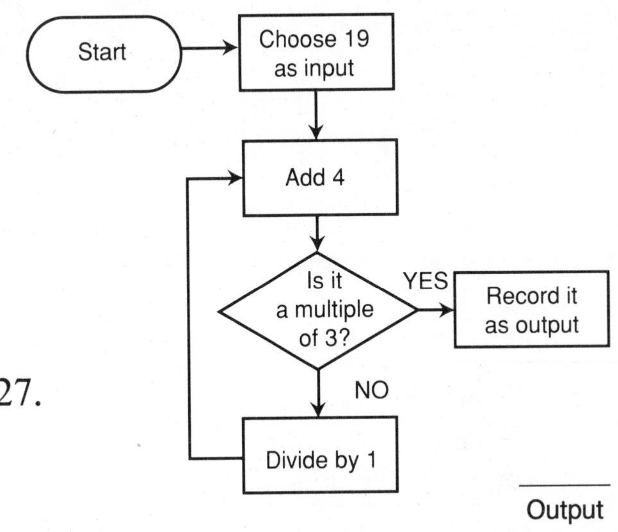

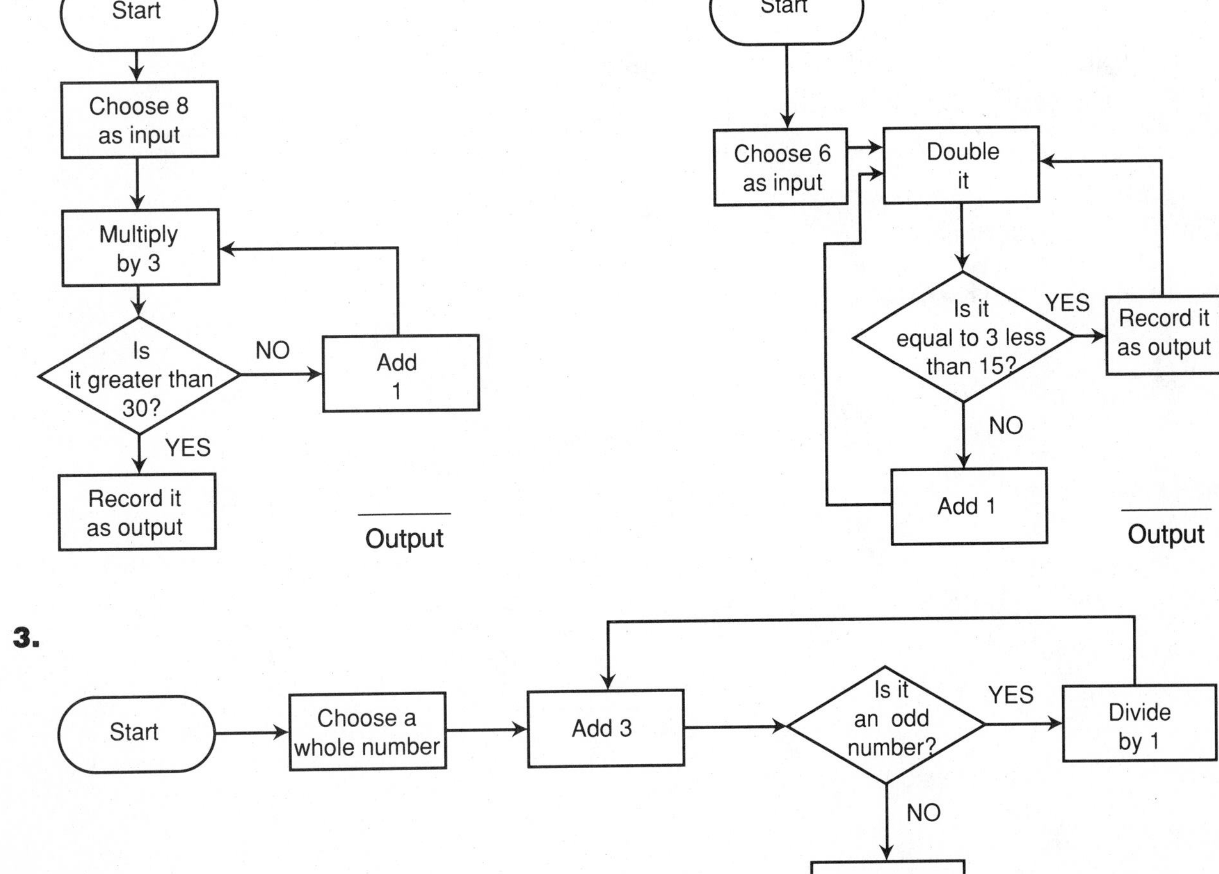

Name ______________________________

Basic Properties

Give your own example of each of the basic properties. Use the right side of this chart.

	Basic Properties	Examples
1.	▶ **Commutative Property**—The sum (product) of two numbers is the same in either order.	
2.	▶ **Associative Property**—You can group addends (factors) in any way and the sum (product) remains the same.	
3.	▶ **Identity for Multiplication**—Any number times one is equal to the number.	
4.	▶ **Identity for Addition**—Any number plus zero is equal to the number.	
5.	▶ **Distributive Property**—Multiplying a sum by a number is the same as multiplying each addend by the number, then adding the products.	

Identify the property used.

6. $18 \times 6 = 6 \times 18 = 108$ ______________________________

7. $0 + 1{,}000 = 1{,}000$ ______________________________

8. $(1.5 + 6) \times 11 = (11 \times 1.5) + (11 \times 6)$ ______________________________

9. $1 \times 1{,}000 = 1{,}000$ ______________________________

10. $(a + b) + c = a + (b + c)$ ______________________________

Solve for *n*. Use the basic properties to help.

11. $8 \times 7 = n \times 8$

$n =$ ________

12. $6 + (10 + 2) = (6 + n) + 2$

$n =$ ________

Name ________________________________

Mental Math Techniques

Count on or back when the number to be added or subtracted is a 1, 2, or 3.

Examples:
Add: 19 + 2. Visualize two blanks after 19; count on to fill them:
19 __20__ __21__.

$$19 + 2 = 21$$

Subtract: 410 − 30. Ignore the ones. Visualize three blanks after 41;
count back to fill them: 41, __40__ __39__ __38__. Restore the ones.

$$410 - 30 = 380$$

Look for **compatible numbers** that can be added or multiplied easily.

Example:
Multiply: 4 × 513 × 25. Link factors that are easy to multiply.

$$4 \times 513 \times 25$$

4 × 25 = 100

$$513 \times 100 = 51{,}300$$
$$4 \times 513 \times 25 = 51{,}300$$

Evaluate using mental math. Count on or back.

1. 11 − 2 = ________ **2.** 489 + 3 = ________ **3.** 212 − 3 = ________

4. 620 − 30 = ________ **5.** 471 + 30 = ________ **6.** 89 + 20 = ________

Evaluate using mental math. Use compatible numbers.

7. 4 × 16 × 5 = ________ **8.** 44 + 18 + 6 = ________

9. 630 + 8 + 62 = ________ **10.** 9 + 608 + 32 = ________

11. 18 + 15 + 2 + 5 = ________ **12.** 2 × 43 × 5 = ________

13. 86 + 19 + 14 = ________ **14.** 5 × 40 × 8 = ________

Name ______________________________

Choosing Estimation Techniques

Substituting compatible numbers or rounding helps in estimation.

Example: 16 oz cost \$4.50. About how much does 1 oz cost?

Accurate: \$4.50 ÷ 16 = ? Difficult to do mentally.

Estimated: \$4.50 ÷ 15 = \$0.30 Easier to do mentally.
15 is close to 16, and it divides evenly into \$4.50.
15 is a **compatible number** with 4.50.
So \$4.50 ÷ 16 is about \$0.30.

Example: About how much do 12 boxes at \$5.75 each cost?

Accurate: \$5.75 × 12 = ?

Estimated: \$6.00 × 10 = \$60.00
Round \$5.75 to \$6.00 and 12 to 10. The rounded numbers are relatively close to the originals and easy to multiply.
So \$5.75 × 12 is about \$60.00.

Estimate using compatible numbers.

1. 76 + 8 ________ **2.** 148 + 52 ________ **3.** 923 − 25 ________

4. 540 ÷ 11 ________ **5.** 24 × 8 ________ **6.** 176 ÷ 6 ________

7. 873 − 126 ________ **8.** 611 ÷ 14 ________ **9.** 19 × 21 ________

Estimate using rounding.

10. 2,695 − 589 ________ **11.** 1,001 − 387 ________ **12.** 54 + 638 ________

13. 498 × 9 ________ **14.** 892 ÷ 29 ________ **15.** 1,699 + 228 ________

16. 1,631 ÷ 41 ________ **17.** 59 × 38 ________ **18.** 846 + 18 ________

Estimate using either technique.

19. 28 × 29 ________ **20.** 681 − 409 ________ **21.** 367 ÷ 42 ________

22. 5,993 + 3,765 ________ **23.** 493 ÷ 11 ________ **24.** 86 × 23 ________

25. 1,205 − 310 ________ **26.** 19 × 82 ________ **27.** 459 ÷ 9 ________

Name ______________________________

Problem Solving: Developing a Plan

Estimates are approximate answers. Use estimates (1) when an approximation is good enough, (2) when an exact answer is too difficult to calculate at the moment, or (3) when an exact answer is impossible to give.

Exact answers are the result of precise calculations.

To make estimates or give exact answers, you normally choose from among three calculation methods—mental math, paper and pencil, or a calculator.

Decide whether an exact answer is needed or if you can estimate. Tell why. Suggest an appropriate calculation method.

Example: You paid for a Mother's Day card with two $1 bills and want to know how much change you will get.
<u>Exact Answer</u> Estimate

Why? You want to receive everything that is owed to you.

Method? Mental math

1. You are deciding how much money to bring with you to buy pizza for a party, so you ask your friend how much it will cost. Exact Answer Estimate

Why? ______________________________

______________________________ Method? ______________________________

2. As treasurer of the school softball team, you are requesting funds for equipment. The school bookkeeper asks you to fill out a Request for Funds form. Exact Answer Estimate

Why? ______________________________

______________________________ Method? ______________________________

Choose a calculation method and evaluate each expression. Write the method you used.

3. 568 ÷ 234 ______________________________

____

4. 275 + 125 ______________________________

____

Name ______________________________

Exploring Algebra: Variables and Algebraic Expressions

A **variable** reserves a place for a number.

$n + 14$

An **algebraic expression** contains at least one variable.

Example: Evaluate $n + 14$ for $n = 6$.

$n + 14$
$6 + 14$ Replace the variable with the number 6.
20 Evaluate the expression.

Evaluate each algebraic expression for the given number or numbers.

1. $x + 12$ for $x = 8$ ________

2. $(3 \times m) - 6$ for $m = 10$ ________

3. $(y \times z) + 5$ for $y = 35$ and $z = 2$ ________

4. $a - 4$ for $a = 25$ ________

Complete each table. Evaluate the expressions for the numbers given.

	a	$a + 3 - 1$
5.	7	
6.	9	
7.	2	

	c	d	$(c \times 3) + d$
8.	0	5	
9.	5	0	
10.	8	6	

Evaluate each algebraic expression for $r = 4$, $s = 6$, and $t = 5$.

11. $r + s + t$ ________

12. $r \times s$ ________

13. $6 + (r \times 2) - t$ ________

14. $(2 \times t) - r$ ________

15. $25 - (r \times t)$ ________

16. $(s \div 2) - 1$ ________

17. $r + 2 - s$ ________

18. $s - (25 \div t)$ ________

19. $(s - t) + 1$ ________

20. $10 - r - s$ ________

Name ______________________________

Understanding Decimals

Decimals can express numbers that fall between whole numbers.

The place value chart shows how to read and write decimals.

thousands	hundreds	tens	ones	tenths	hundredths	thousandths	ten-thousandths	
1,000	100	10	1	$\frac{1}{10}$	$\frac{1}{100}$	$\frac{1}{1000}$	$\frac{1}{10,000}$	place values
		5	1 .	3	0	7	2	standard form

You read:
fifty-one and three thousand seventy-two ten-thousandths.

Expanded form:
$(5 \times 10) + (1 \times 1) + (3 \times 0.1) + (0 \times 0.01) + (7 \times 0.001) + (2 \times 0.0001)$

Give the value of the underlined digits.

1. $0.30\underline{9}$ $\frac{9}{1000}$

2. $4.2\underline{6}03$ ____________

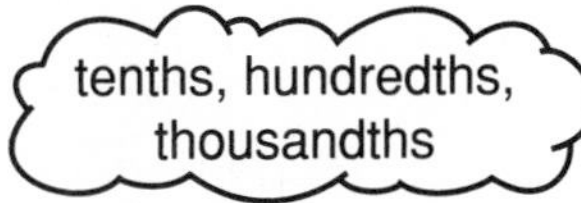

3. $6.\underline{0}35$ ____________

Write each number in standard form.

4. one and twenty-four hundredths

____

5. sixty-seven thousandths

____

6. $(4 \times 1) + (3 \times 0.1) + (6 \times 0.001)$

____

7. $(5 \times 0.01) + 3 \times (0.001)$

____

Name ______________________________

Reviewing Decimal Operations

To multiply decimals:

Multiply as for whole numbers. → Write the product so that it has the same number of decimal places as the sum of the decimal places in the factors.

```
  43.6
× 0.18
  3488
  4360
  7848
```

```
  43.6 ← 1 place
× 0.18 ← 2 places
  3488      2 + 1 = 3
  4360
 7.848 ← 3 places
```

Find the products, sums, or differences.

1. 7.469 ← 3 places
× 3.3 ← 1 place
22407
224070
24.6477 (3 + 1 places)

2. 0.543 ← 3 places
× 5.7 ← 1 place
3801
0
Finish

3. 16.4
× 6.8

4. $32.67
+ 0.95

5. 1.753
− 0.154

6. 14.298
+ 2.503

7. 12.75
× 0.8

8. 2,166 × 0.83
2166
× 0.83

9. 10.854 − 6.9

10. 774.3 + 8.25

Name ______________________

Choosing Estimation Techniques

To estimate the sum of 4,130; 5,689; and 7,220, use front-end estimation.

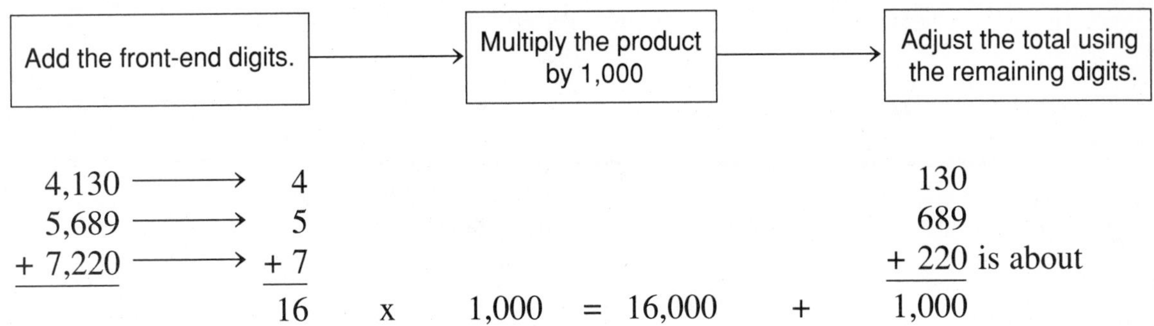

The sum is about 16,000 + 1,000 = 17,000.

To estimate the sum of 162 + 148 + 172 + 159, use clustering.

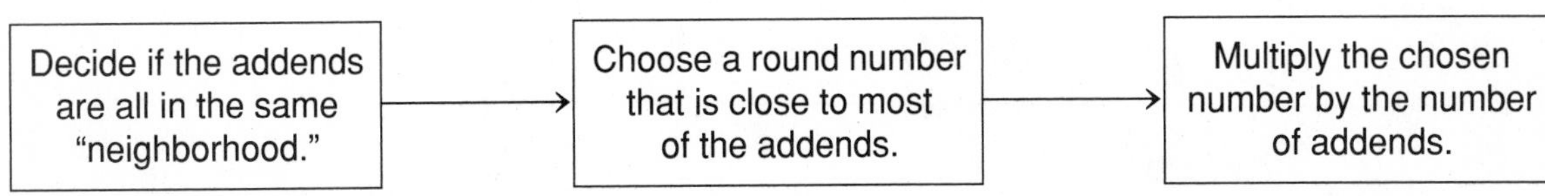

Addends are near 150 or 160. Choose 160. 160 x 4 = 640

The sum is about 640.

Estimate the sums. Use clustering.

1. 52 + 80 + 72 + 63 ____________

2. 14 + 27 + 21 + 19 ____________

3. 9.5 + 8.7 + 9.2 ____________

4. 1.67 + 2.10 + 1.8 ____________

Estimate the sums. Use front-end estimation.

5.
25.6 ⟶
13.9 ⟶
64.2 ⟶
+ 78.5 ⟶

6.
40.89 ⟶
15.70 ⟶
24.35 ⟶
+ 63.62 ⟶

Name ______________________________

Dividing Decimals

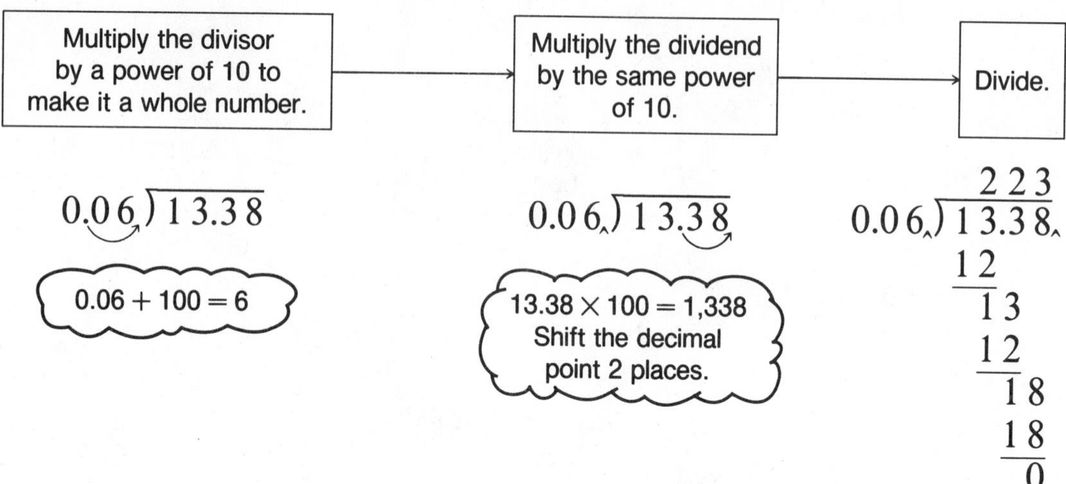

Find the quotients. Round to the nearest tenth.

1. 1.6)0.338 (0.2)

Move the decimal point 1 place.

2. 0.3)0.36 (____)

3. .65)0.0367 (____)

Find the quotients. Round to the nearest hundredth.

4. 0.7)0.3794 (____)

5. 0.32)0.28992 (____)

6. 0.05)0.01780 (____)

Name ______________________________

Problem Solving: Understand the Question

Read each problem. Which question listed is a different way of stating the problem? Circle its letter.

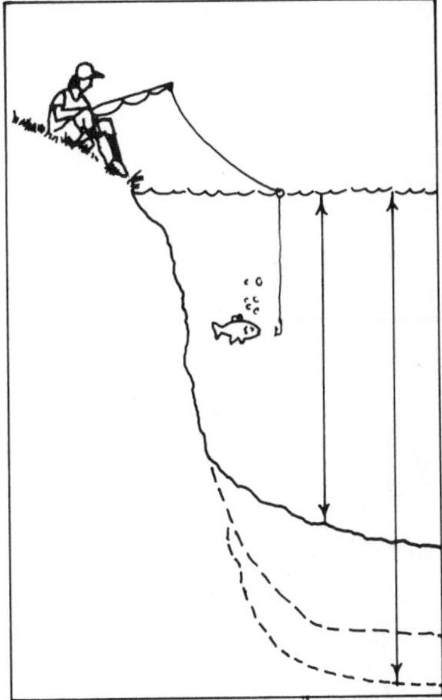

Example: In August, the community lake was 19 feet deep. The lake was dredged and the depth was increased 8.3 feet in September. During the winter dredging, the depth was increased by 4.3 feet. By how many feet was the depth increased?

A What is the present depth of the lake?

B What was the depth of the lake in October?

C How much deeper is the lake now than it was in August?

The answer is **C.** The question is, "How much deeper is it after the winter dredging?"

---

1. The Caspian Sea has a depth of less than 6 meters in the northern region, a depth of about 2 meters near the Volga delta, a depth of up to 975 meters in the southern basin, and a depth of about 790 meters in the northern basin. What is the range in the depths of these areas of the Caspian Sea?

A What is the deepest point?

B What is the difference between its deepest and shallowest points?

C How much deeper is the southern basin than the northern basin?

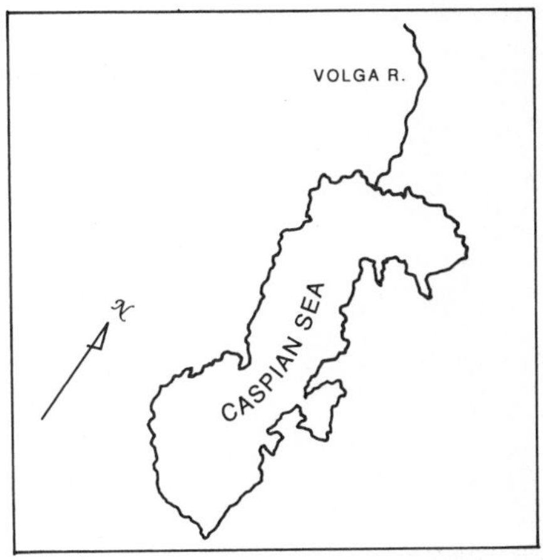

Read the problem below. Write the question in a different way, then solve.

2. The water temperature of the Caspian Sea's northern basin varies from about 30°F in winter to 75°F in summer. What is the temperature range of the waters of the Caspian Sea's basin?

____

____

Name ______________________________

Exponents and Scientific Notation

You can use exponents to write numbers that have repeated factors.

$3^2 = 3 \times 3 = 9$ 3 squared	$3^4 = 3 \times 3 \times 3 \times 3 = 81$ 3 to the fourth power
$3^3 = 3 \times 3 \times 3 = 27$ 3 cubed	$3^5 = 3 \times 3 \times 3 \times 3 \times 3 = 243$ 3 to the fifth power

Writing in scientific notation:

72,000,000 → Place the decimal between the first 2 digits. 7.2000000 7 places → 7.2×10^7 ← The exponent shows the number of places the decimal was moved.

Writing as standard numerals:

4.8×10^5 → Since the exponent is 5, move the decimal 5 places to the right. 4.80000 → 480,000

Give the missing exponent.

1. $5 \times 5 \times 5 \times 5 = 5^{\square}$

2. $10 \times 10 \times 10 \times 10 = 10^{\square}$

3. $6 \times 6 \times 6 = 6^{\square}$

4. $4 \times 4 \times 4 \times 4 \times 4 = 4^{\square}$

Write in scientific notation.

5. 49,000 = 4.9×10^4

6. 62,000,000 = ______

7. 48,000,000 = ______

8. 54,000 = ______

Write as a standard numeral.

9. 9.5×10^2 = 950

10. 8.6×10^6 = ______

11. 7.7×10^5 = ______

12. 3.8×10^4 = ______

Name ______________________________

Exploring Algebra: Understanding Variables

Study each table to understand how its variables are related.

Look for a way to relate the first given number in the top row to the first given number in the bottom row.	→	Test the relationship on other given pairs of numbers.	→	If there is a pattern, use the pattern to complete the table.

Example:

Mike charges $8 for the first swimming lesson. Each lesson after that costs $4. Complete the table.

All lessons cost $4, but the first lesson costs an extra $4.

Let l = the number of lessons
Let c = the cost of the lessons

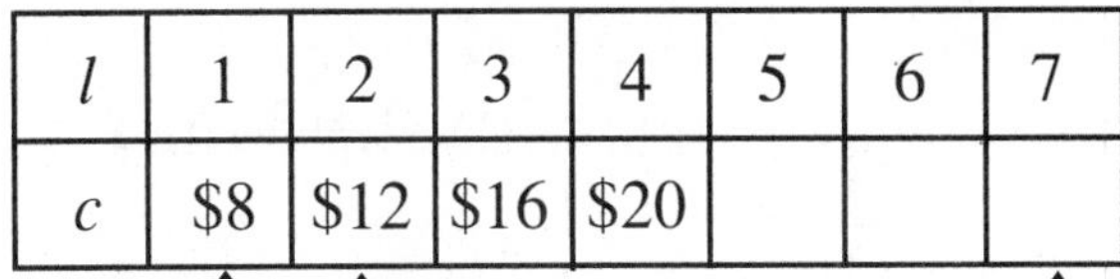

l	1	2	3	4	5	6	7
c	$8	$12	$16	$20			

$(\mathbf{1} \times 4) + 4 = \mathbf{8}$

$(\mathbf{2} \times 4) + 4 = \mathbf{12}$

$(\mathbf{7} \times 4) + 4 = \mathbf{32}$

Example:

Use the blocks to help you complete the table.

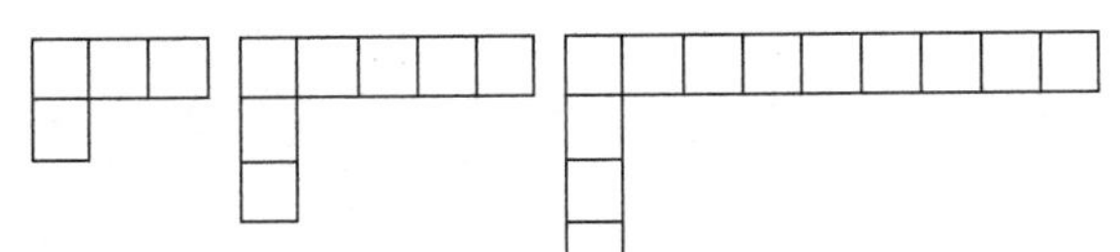

The area is twice the perimeter plus 2.

Let a = area
Let p = perimeter

a	4	7	12	15	18	21	24
p	10	16	26				

Complete the tables to show how the variables are related.

1.

hours (h)	1	2	3	4	5	6
minutes (m)	60	120				

2.

tables (t)	1	2	3	4	5	6
chairs (c)	4	6	8			

3.

cartons (c)	1	2	3	4	5	6
bottles (b)	4	8				

4.

number correct (c)	20	19	18	15	10
score (s)	100	95			

Use with text pages 44–45.

Name ______________________________

Using Critical Thinking: Analyzing Decimal Patterns

To produce a 1-digit number that repeats itself, such as 0.888888 . . . , divide the 1-digit number by 9.

Example: $8 \div 9 = 0.888888 \ldots.$

To produce a 2-digit number that repeats itself, such as 0.393939 . . . , divide the 2-digit number by 99.

Example: $39 \div 99 = 0.393939 \ldots.$

To produce a 3-digit number that repeats itself, such as 0.174174 . . . , divide the 3-digit number by 999.

Example: $174 \div 999 = 0.174174 \ldots.$

Use your knowledge of repeating decimal patterns to decide what two numbers you could divide to obtain the given decimal.

1. 0.373737 . . . = ______________________

2. 0.646464 . . . = ______________________

3. 0.583583 . . . = ______________________

4. 0.111111 . . . = ______________________

5. 0.735735 . . . = ______________________

6. 0.595959 . . . = ______________________

Use your knowledge of repeating decimal patterns to decide what decimal will result when you divide these numbers.

Example: $73 \div 99 = 0.737373 \ldots$

7. $269 \div 999 =$ ______________________

8. $53 \div 99 =$ ______________________

9. $6 \div 9 =$ ______________________

10. $250 \div 999 =$ ______________________

11. $101 \div 999 =$ ______________________

12. $8 \div 9 =$ ______________________

Name ______________________________

Metric Units of Length

The basic unit of length in the metric system is the **meter** (m).
A baseball bat is about 1 meter long.

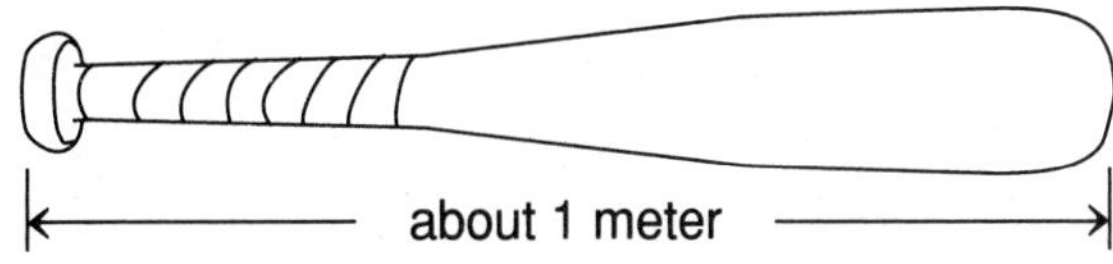

1 kilometer (km) = 1,000 m
1 hectometer (hm) = 100 m
1 dekameter (dam) = 10 m

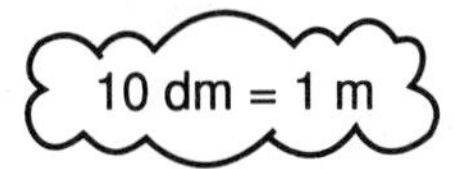

1 decimeter (dm) = 0.1 m
1 centimeter (cm) = 0.01 m
1 millimeter (mm) = 0.001 m

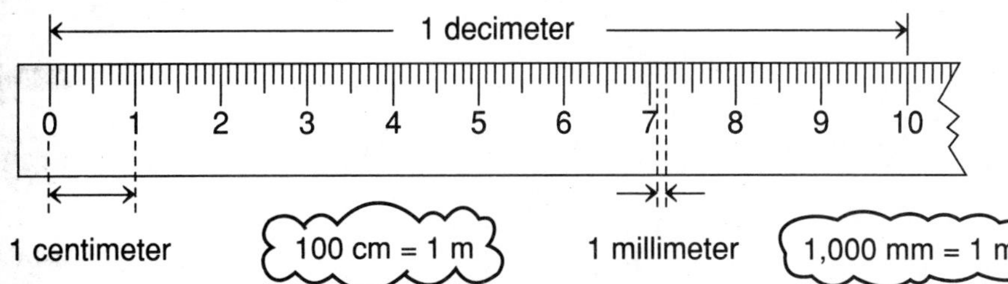

Ring the best estimate of length.

1. the length of a swimming pool

A 100 mm **B** 100 m
C 100 cm **D** 100 km

2. the length of a drinking straw

A 20 mm **B** 20 m
C 20 cm **D** 20 km

3. the distance from New York to Boston

A 330 mm **B** 330 m
C 330 cm **D** 330 km

4. the diameter of a button

A 8 mm **B** 8 m
C 8 cm **D** 8 km

5. the diameter of a table

A 115 mm **B** 115 m
C 115 cm **D** 115 km

6. the height of a full-grown tree

A 12 mm **B** 12 m
C 12 cm **D** 12 km

Write the missing numbers.

7. 100 cm = ______ m

8. 1 m = ______ mm

9. 10 cm = ______ dm

10. 1 m = ______ dm

11. 100 m = ______ hm

12. 10 mm = ______ cm

Write the missing units.

13. 1 km = 1,000 ______

14. 1 dm = 0.1 ______

15. 100 cm = 1 ______

Name ______________________

Precision in Measurement

Which measurement for a paper clip is more precise, 4 cm to the nearest cm or 4.2 cm to the nearest mm? 4.2 cm to the nearest mm

Define the unit of measurement	>	Find the greatest possible error (GPE).	>	Select the measurement with the smaller GPE.

4 cm to the nearest cm	The unit of measurement is cm.	GPE = 0.5 cm	
4 .2 cm to the nearest mm	The unit of measurement if mm.	GPE = 0.5	4.2 cm

4.2 cm to the nearest mm is more precise.

Give the greatest possible error (GPE) of each measurement.

1. 35 cm ________ **2.** 90 km ________ **3.** 16 dm ________

4. 6 mm ________ **5.** 50 m ________ **6.** 10 km ________

In each problem ring the meaurement that is more precise.

7. 85.6 cm to the nearest mm or 1.98 m to the nearest cm

8. 8 km to the nearest km or 19 m to the nearest m

9. 5 mm to the nearest mm or 90 cm to the nearest cm

10. 561 m to the nearest m or 8 km to the nearest km

11. 35.1 cm to the nearest mm or 5.63 m to the nearest cm

12. 83 cm to the nearest cm or 8 m to the nearest m

Name ______________________

Mass and Capacity

Metric Relationships

Weight Units	Capacity Units
milligram (mg)	milliliter (mL)
× ÷ by 1,000	× ÷ by 1,000
gram (g)	liter (L)
× ÷ by 1,000	× ÷ by 1,000
kilogram (kg)	kiloliter (kL)

Follow the direction signs to go from one level to another.

Complete: 12 L = ___?___ mL

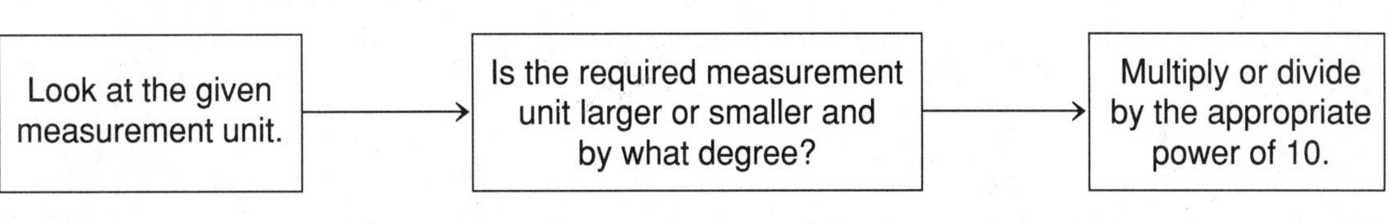

12 L   smaller by 1,000 times   12 L × 1,000 = 12,000 mL

12 L = 12,000 mL

Complete the following statements.

1. 22 g = __________ mg
(Multiply by 1,000.)

2. 350 mL = __________ L
(Divide by 1,000.)

3. 6,500 mg = __________ g
(Divide by 1,000.)

4. 0.8 kL = __________ L
(Multiply by 1,000.)

5. 3.3 kg = __________ g

6. 500 L = __________ kL

7. 504 mg = __________ g

8. 6.03 kg = __________ g

Ring the larger measure in each pair.

9. 350 mg or 3 g

10. 0.5 L or 2,500 mL

11. 8 kL or 16,326 mL

12. 0.03 kL or 3.5 L

13. 950 mg or 1 g

14. 59,000 mg or 0.9 kg

Name ______________________________

Using the Strategies

Use objects or draw a picture to solve the problems.

Example: If 12 toothpicks are arranged to form 6 equal triangles, how many sides will the finished figure have?

Think: Six separate triangles would have 18 sides, so 6 triangles made with 12 toothpicks must share some sides. Also, the question implies that the solution is a single, divided figure.

Use Objects:

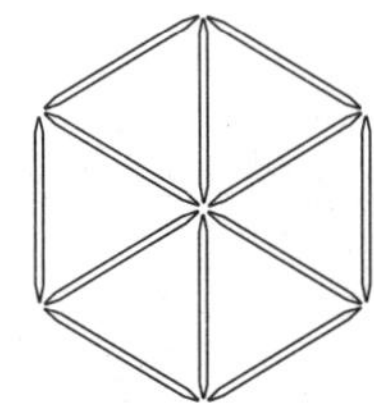

The finished figure has 6 sides.

1. Garnet walked 10 miles in a walkathon. She passed a rest station $\frac{3}{5}$ of the way from the start. How far did she walk from the rest station to the end?

____

2. Mark built a covered wagon replica for social studies class. Its dimensions were 14 inches by 8 inches. He put one cover support at each corner and one every 2 inches on the long sides. How many supports did he use?

____

3. Jon has 6 granola bars, which is $\frac{1}{2}$ as many as Ella has. Ella has $\frac{3}{4}$ as many granola bars as Keri. How many does Keri have?

____

4. Basketball Team A scored 4 more than twice the number of points that Team B scored. If Team A scored 18 points, how many points did Team B score?

____

5. Jayne took the shortest, most direct route across a park. She walked 100 yards. Aldrin followed the paths. He walked 60 yards due north; he then walked east 20 yards more than he walked north. How much farther did Aldrin walk than Jayne?

____

6. Bricks were stacked as shown below. If there are 35 bricks in all, how many are on the bottom row?

____

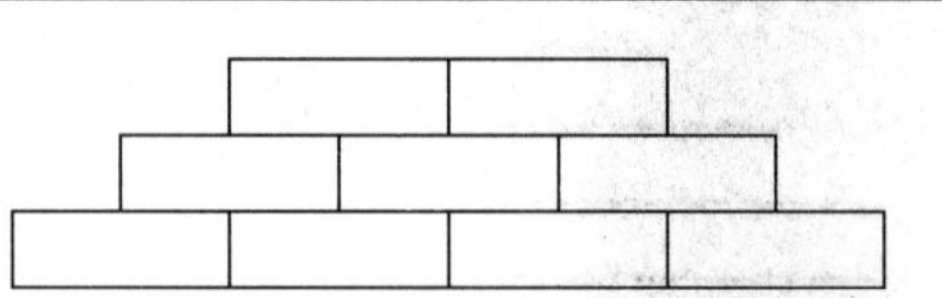

Use with text pages 54–55.

Name ______________________________

Multiple Line Graphs

To read a multiple line graph, decide which graph line you need to look at. Find the month and the corresponding dollar amount to answer the questions.

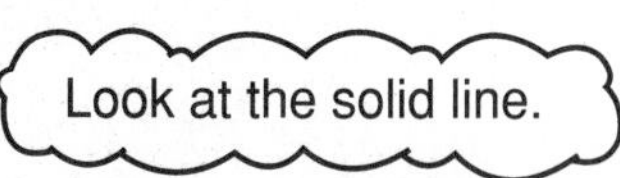

Example: On the average, how much business did the Fashion Store do each day in February?

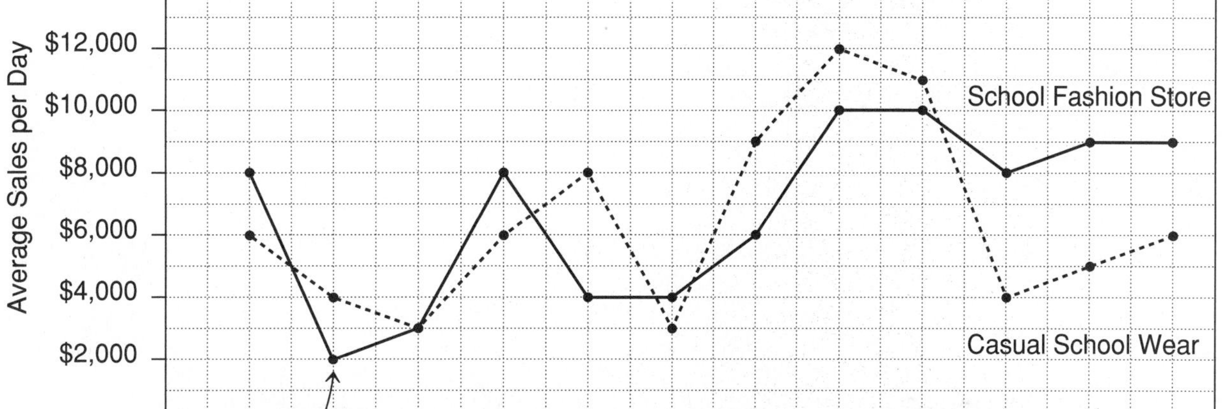

The School Fashion Store did $2,000 worth of business in February.

Interpret the graph to answer the questions.

1. On the average, how much business did Casual School Wear do each day in April?

____

2. In October, how much more business did the School Fashion Store do each day than Casual School Wear?

____

3. During which month did both sell approximately the same amount per day?

____

4. In the graph, a *trend* is a tendency of the data to go in one general direction. What is the trend of the data for both stores from June to August?

____

Name ____________________

Circle Graphs

The circle graph shows how the annual budget for the school newspaper is spent. Examine the graph and answer the questions.

School Newspaper Budget
$4,000

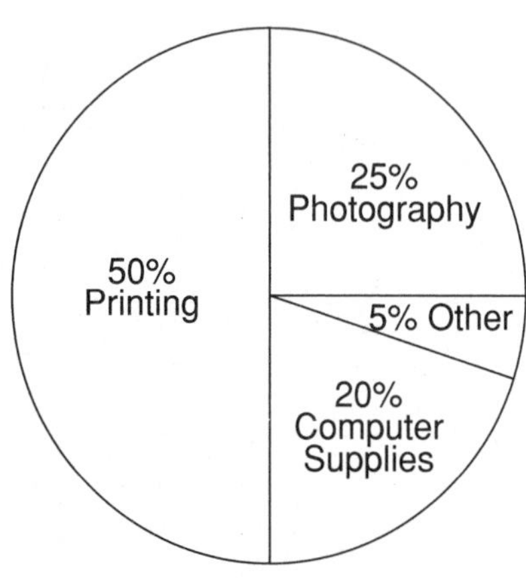

How much is spent on photography?
Think: 25% = $\frac{1}{4}$ and $\frac{1}{4}$ of $4,000 is $1,000.
$1,000 is spent on photography.

1. What percent of the annual budget is spent on printing?

____

2. What percent of the annual budget is spent on computer supplies and photography?

____

3. How much is spent on printing?

____

4. The newspaper spends $\frac{1}{5}$ of its budget on what item?

____

5. How much is spent on computer supplies?

____

6. How much more is spent on photography than on computer supplies?

____

7. Are Other expenses more or less than $\frac{1}{10}$ of the total expenses?

____

8. How much is spent on Other expenses?

____

Name ______________________________

Scattergrams

Students worked each week to prepare projects for the Science Fair. The scattergram shows a correlation between the number of hours spent on a project and the number of points awarded.

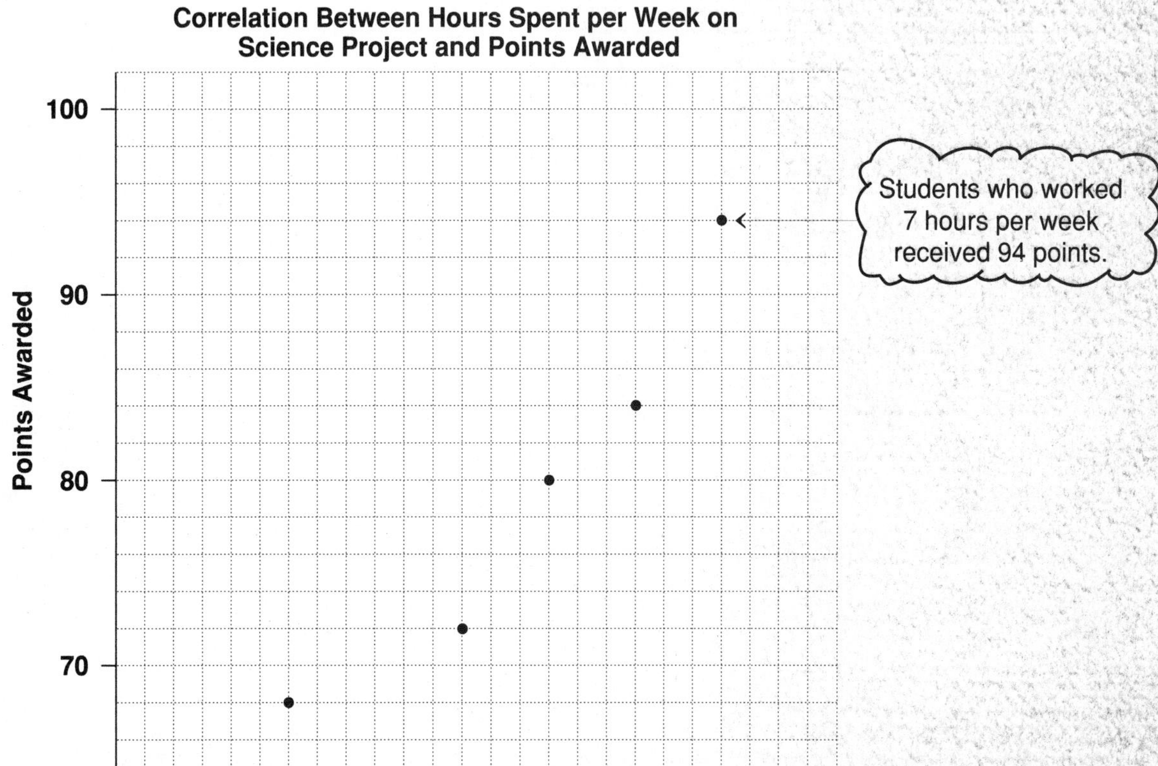

1. How many hours a week were spent on the project that received the lowest rating?

____

2. How many hours a week were spent on the project that was awarded 72 points?

____

3. How many points were awarded the project on which students worked 5 hours a week?

____

4. Does the scattergram have a positive correlation, a negative correlation, or no correlation?

____

Name ______________________________

Choosing Mental Math Techniques

When you replace one number with another to make computation simple and then adjust to the exact answer, you are using **compensation.**

Example: $320 + 47 = ?$

Think: $320 + 50 = 370$. Since 47 is 3 less than 50, $320 + 47$ is 3 less than 370. $370 - 3 = 367$. So, $320 + 47 = 367$.

Complete each exercise below. Use compensation.

1. $58 + 440$

Think: $60 + 440 = 500$. Since 58 is ________ less than ________, $58 + 440$ is ________ less than 500. $500 -$ ________ $=$ ________. So, $58 + 440 =$ ________.

2. 19×7

Think: $20 \times 7 = 140$. Since 19 is ________ less than ________, 19×7 is 1×7 less than 140. $140 - 7 =$ ________. So, $19 \times 7 =$ ________.

3. $600 - 197$

Think: $600 -$ ________ $= 400$. Since 197 is 3 less than ________ but 197 *is subtracted from* 600, $600 - 197$ must be 3 *more than* 400. $400 + 3 =$ ________. So, $600 - 197 =$ ________.

Solve using mental math.

4. $27 + 799 =$ ________

5. $13 \times 12 =$ ________

6. $\$8.97 \times 3 =$ ________

7. $500 - 256 =$ ________

8. $580 + 48 =$ ________

9. $147 - 25 =$ ________

10. $76 - 49 =$ ________

11. $797 \times 2 =$ ________

12. $18 + 45 =$ ________

13. $3 \times 99 =$ ________

14. $42 + 79 =$ ________

15. $400 - 123 =$ ________

Name ______________________________

Using Critical Thinking: Choosing an Appropriate Graph

Match each statement with the appropriate graph at the right.

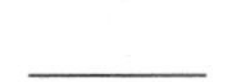 **1.** Bar graphs can be used to compare.

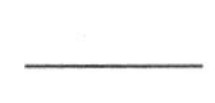 **2.** Line graphs are often used to show trends.

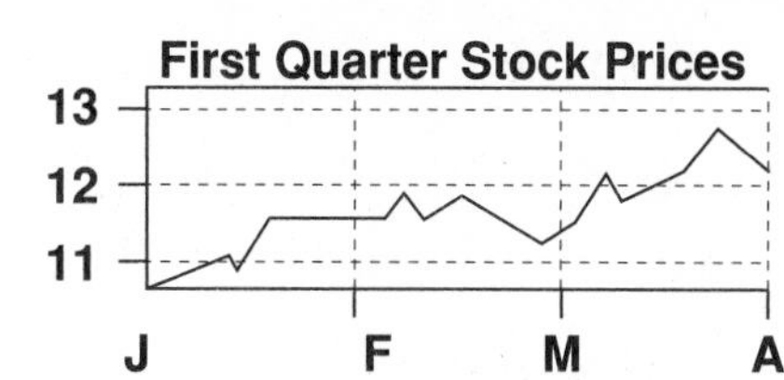

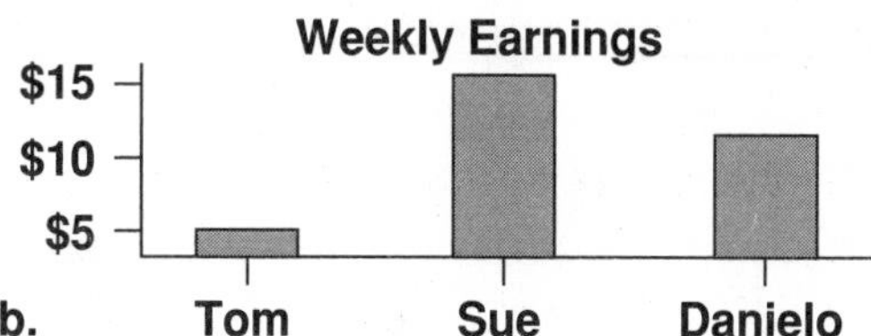

Would a line graph or bar graph be the most appropriate for the data?

3. A month-by-month account of total sales for a department store ______________________

4. A comparison of pollutants emitted by different makes of automobiles ______________________

5. A daily record of heart rates for a hospital patient ______________________

6. A comparison of the number of gallons of water per month produced by certain springs ______________________

7. A warming trend of temperatures over a two-year period ______________________

8. A comparison of the high and low temperatures on a given day in three cities ______________________

9. A comparison of populations in selected cities ______________________

Name ______________________________

Using the Strategies

Solve. Use the strategies Guess and Check or Draw a Picture.

1. Matt's younger brother arranged 36 toy cars in rows that formed a triangle. How many cars were in the longest row? __________

Begin by guessing the answer; use your guess as the number of items in the base of the triangle.
Draw the triangle.
Add or subtract items along one edge of the triangle until you have a total of 36 items.
Count the number of items in the base.

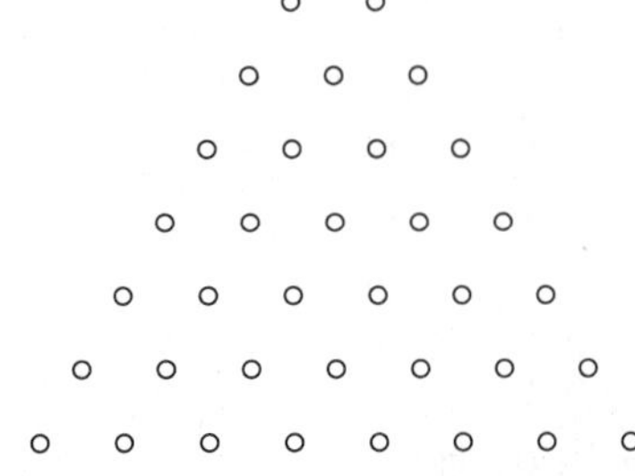

2. One climbing rose plant produced 36 more roses last month than did another. Together they produced 126 roses. How many roses did each plant produce?

____

3. The sum of four consecutive integers is 12. What are the integers?

____

4. Ellen bought 3 audio tapes for a total of \$25.50. Ruby bought 2 tapes for the same unit price as those Ellen bought. How much did Ruby pay?

____

5. Hector bought 3 pairs of new shorts and 4 new shirts. How many different outfits can he wear?

____

Name ______________________________

Mean, Median, and Mode

The **mean** is the average of the numbers

The **median** is the middle number or the average of the two middle numbers when all numbers are arranged in order.

The **mode** is the number that appears morst freqently. Some sets of data have no mode.

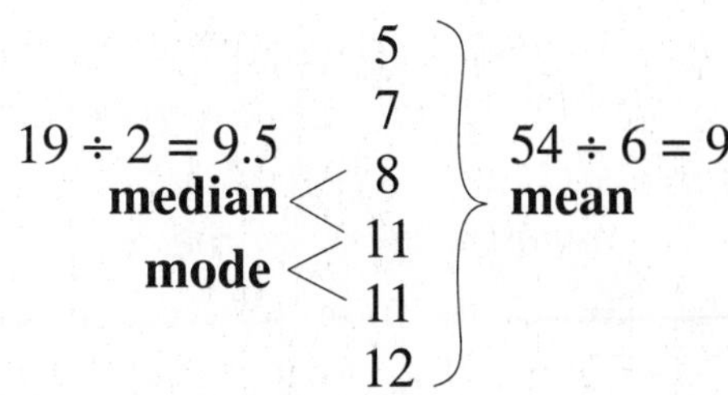

Find the mean, median, and mode for each set of data. Use a calculator.

1. 20, 23, 19, 20, 18, 11

Mean = ______

Median = ______

Mode = ______

2. 56, 60, 67, 52

Mean = ______

Median = ______

Mode = ______

3. 7.5, 6.6, 7.8, 7.5, 8.0

Mean = ______

Median = ______

Mode = ______

4. 89, 91, 92, 92, 95

Mean = ______

Median = ______

Mode = ______

5. 18, 25, 23, 23

Mean = ______

Median = ______

Mode = ______

6. 112, 100, 100

Mean = ______

Median = ______

Mode = ______

Name ______________________________

Stem-and-Leaf Tables

A stem-and-leaf table consists of a stem, which sorts the data, and a leaf, which gives an abbreviated list of the data in the category. To place a 2-digit number in the table, place the tens digit under the stem and the ones digit on the same line under the leaf. Note that in the table the tens digit does not repeat. The ones digit is written as often as it occurs.

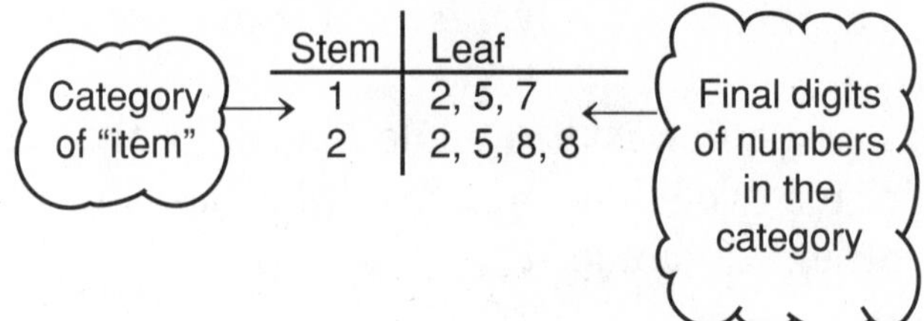

Example: Data: 12, 15, 17, 22, 25, 28, 28

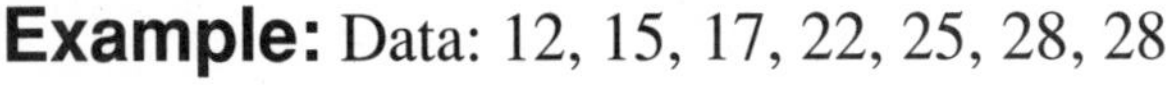

Examine the table below. Answer the questions.

Stem	Leaf
1	2, 4, 3, 5, 5, 3, 7, 5
2	1, 0, 1, 3, 7, 2, 4, 7
3	0, 1, 0, 3, 1, 5 , 3, 7, 8, 8
4	0, 1, 1, 3

1. What is the least number in the table?

____

2. Circle the digits that represent the number 35.

3. What is the most frequent number?

____

4. How many numbers are less than 21?

____

5. How many numbers are greater than 27?

____

6. Are most numbers in the 10–19, 20–29, 30–39, or 40–49 range?

____

7. How many numbers are in this stem-and-leaf table?

____

8. Add 16 to the table. Why is the tens digit not repeated?

____

Name ______________________________

Frequency Tables and Histograms

The frequency table below has been tallied for you. Count the tallies, then enter the number in the frequency column.

Class Grade Point Averages		
Average	Tally	Frequency
1.5–2.0	|	
2.0–2.5	||	
2.5–3.0	~~||||~~ ||	
3.0–3.5	~~||||~~ ~~||||~~ |	
3.5–4.0	~~||||~~ ||	

The graph below is called a histogram. It shows a picture of the data from a frequency table. Each bar rises to the level of its frequency number. The bars always touch one another on a histogram.

Complete the histogram from the data above. Use a ruler.

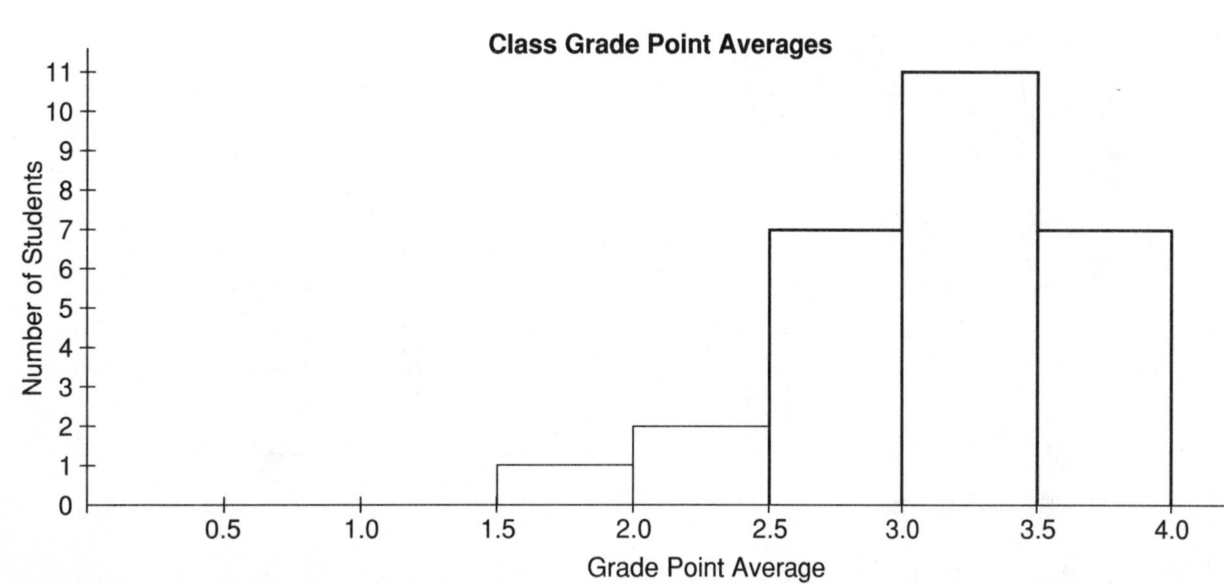

Name ______________________________

Exploring Algebra: More About Variables

Discover the relationship between each number in the top row and the number below it. Write a rule that describes this relationship.

Example:
Examine and complete the table to the right.

Since $5 = 8 - 3$
$7 = 10 - 3$
$8 = 11 - 3$

Then $21 - 3 = 18$
$152 - 3 = 149$

↓	8	10	11	21	152
	5	7	8		

RULE: To find the botom number ______________________________.

1.

↓	6	7	9	12	16	19	35	41
	12	14	18					

RULE: To find the bottom number ______________________________.

2.

↓	6	9	15	21	30	45	51	60
	2	3	5					

RULE: To find the bottom number ______________________________.

3.

↓	5	6	10	12	13	14	15	16
	25	36	100					

RULE: To find the bottom number ______________________________.

Name ________________________________

Problem Solving: Extra Data

These problems have extra data. Decide which data are needed and which are not. Solve the problems. Show your work.

Example:
A rectangular garden is 7 meters long and 5 meters wide. If its length and width are each doubled, its area is quadrupled. If the length and width are each doubled, what will the perimeter be?

What must I find?	the perimeter of a rectangle
What data do I need?	the length (2×7 meters) and the width (2×5 meters), perimeter formula
What data are not needed?	information about the area
I can solve the problem using only the needed data.	$(2 \times 14) + (2 \times 10) = P$ $28 + 20 = P$ $48 = P$

The perimeter is 48 meters.

The manager of an ice cream parlor pays $6.50 for each gallon of ice cream she buys. The wholesaler pays $5 per gallon. The manager can fill 15 cones from 1 gallon of ice cream. Cones cost $0.15 apiece. If she sells 15 cones for $0.90 each, how much profit does she make?

What must I find? ________________________________

What data do I need? ________________________________

____

What data are not needed? ________________________________

I can solve the problem using only the needed data.

The answer is ____________________.

Name ______________________________

Exploring Solid Figures

This rectangular **prism** has:

8 vertices
6 faces
12 edges

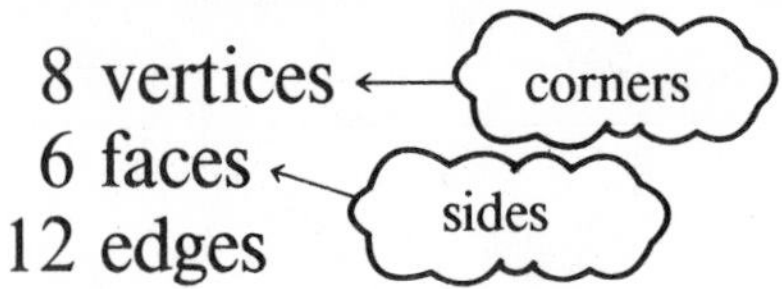

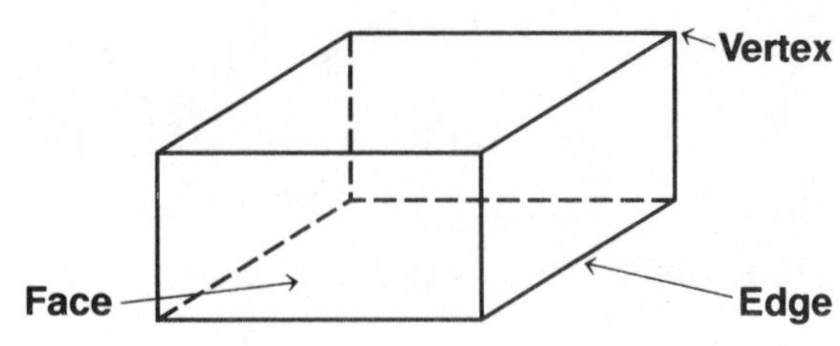

State whether each figure is a prism or a pyramid. Write the number of vertices (V), faces (F), and edges (E) of each figure.

Example:

V 6

F 5

E 9

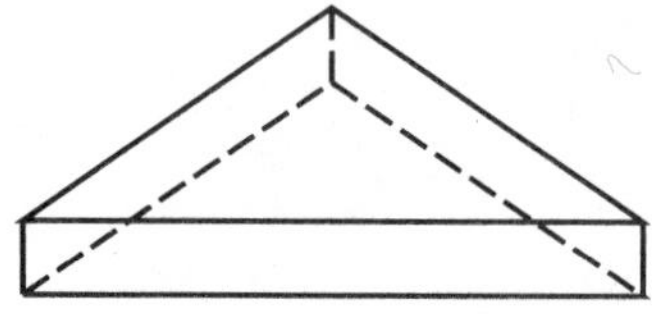

____

1. V ______

F ______

E ______

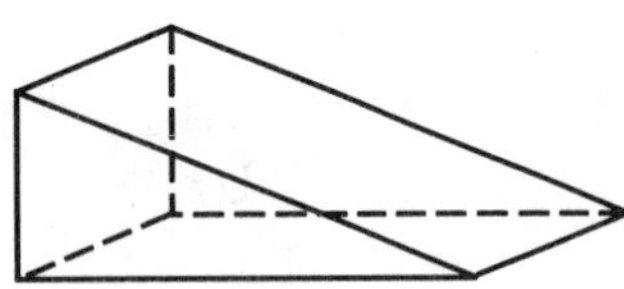

____

2. V ______

F ______

E ______

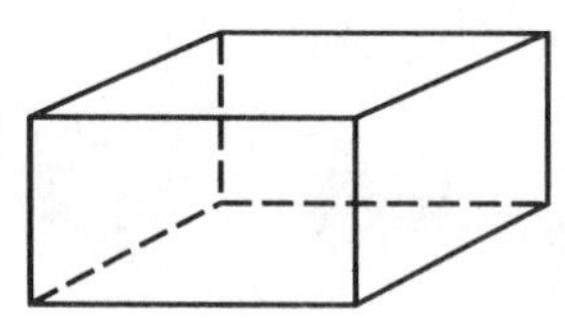

____

3. V ______

F ______

E ______

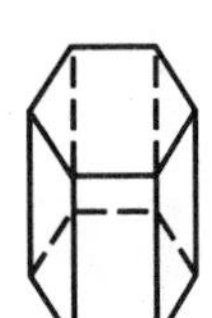

____

4. V ______

F ______

E ______

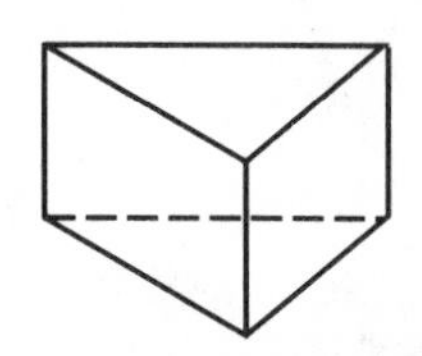

____

5. V ______

F ______

E ______

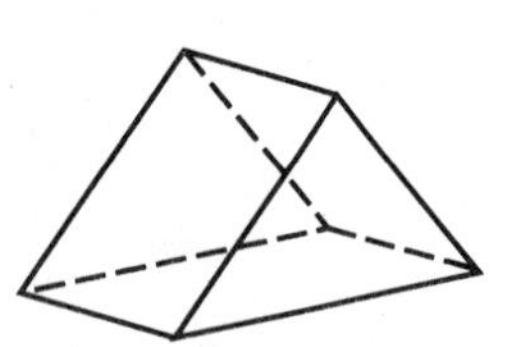

____

6. V ______

F ______

E ______

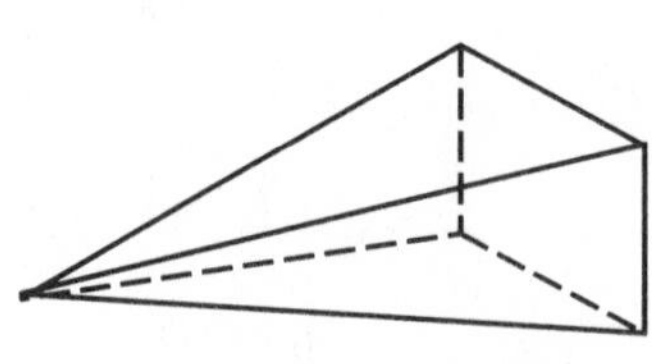

____

7. V ______

F ______

E ______

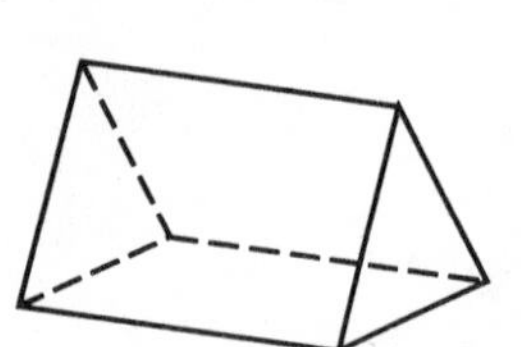

____

8. V ______

F ______

E ______

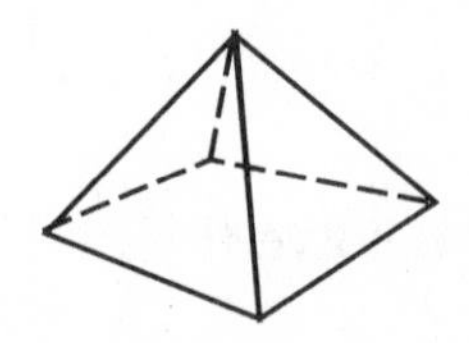

____

Name ______________________________

Visualizing Cross Sections

If you slice through a solid object, the new face that results from the slice is called a **cross section**.

Slice the end off the cheese.

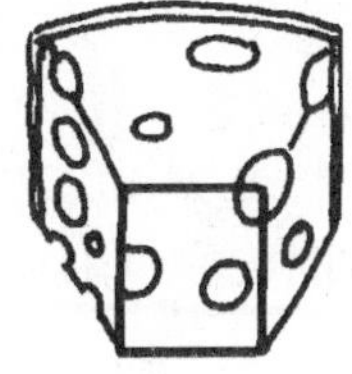

Make a picture of the surface created by the slice

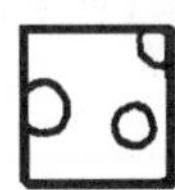

This is the picture —a cross section.

1.

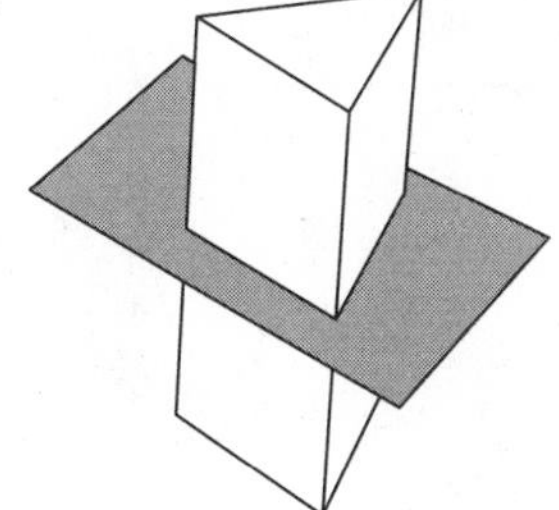

2.

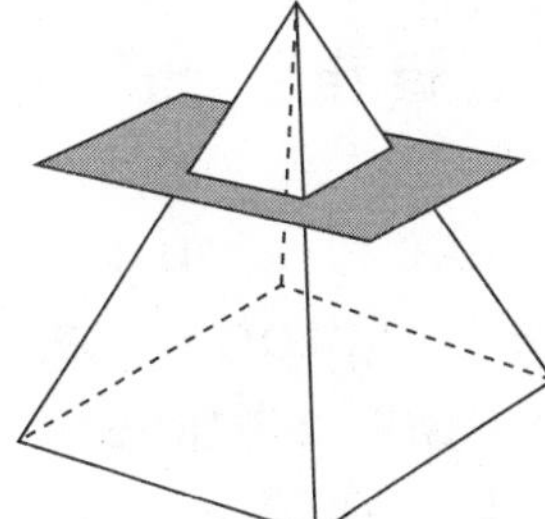

3.

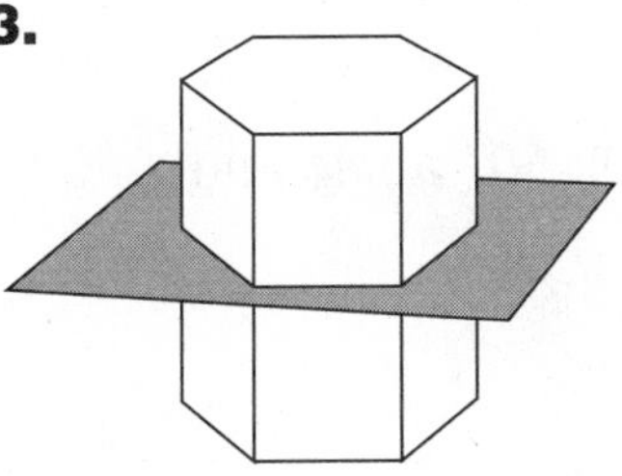

4.

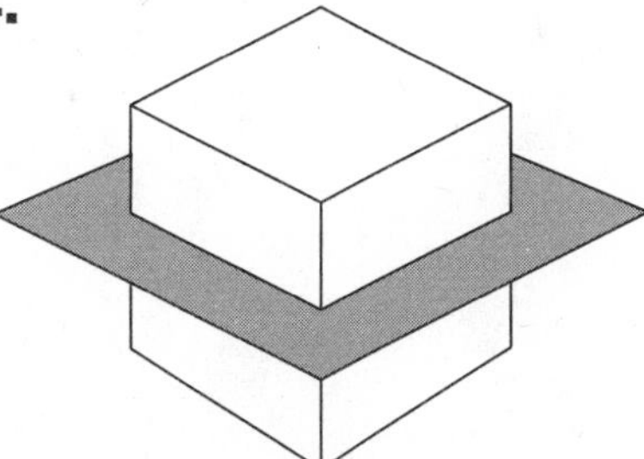

5.

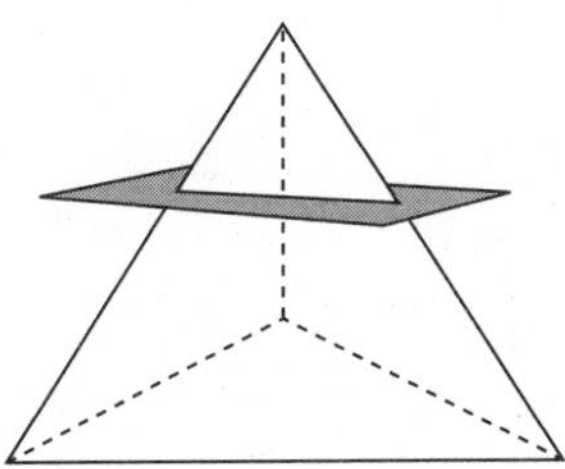

6.

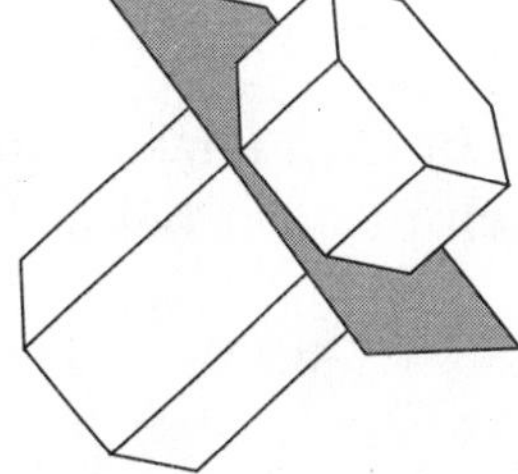

Name ______________________________

Drawing Plane Figures

Use a centimeter ruler and a protractor. Draw and label each geometric figure. For example, draw a 95° angle labeled *CAB*.

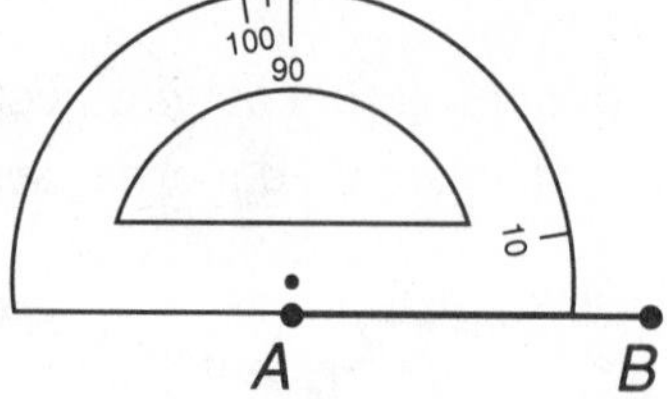

Step 1: Draw a line segment. Label one endpoint *A* and another point on the segment *B*.
Step 2: Place the center of the protractor on Point *A*. Be sure that 0° lies on the line segment.
Step 3: Select the protractor scale that has the number 10° near the 0°.
Step 4: Move along this scale until you find the mark halfway between 90° and 100°. Make a point *C* there.
Step 5: Remove the protractor. Use your ruler to draw a line segment from point *C* to Point *A*.

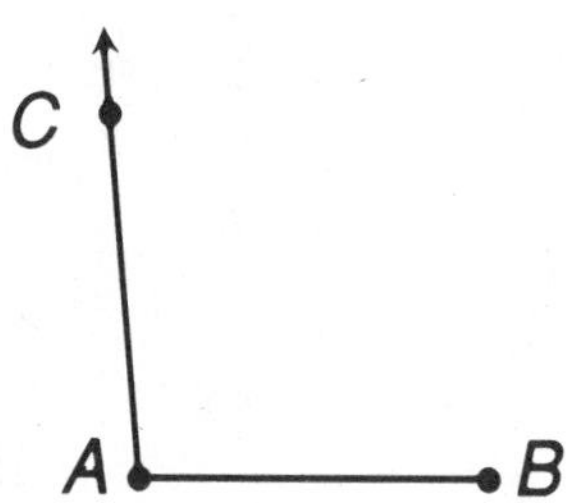

Draw the following:

1. an 80° angle *ABC*

2. a triangle with a 50° angle and a 70° angle

Find the measure of each angle's supplementary angle by subtracting each number below from 180°.

3. 50° ________ **4.** 118° ________ **5.** 89° ________

Find the measure of each angle's complementary angle by subtracting each number below from 90°.

6. 3° ________ **7.** 22° ________ **8.** 60° ________

Name ______________________________

Using Critical Thinking Skills

Equilateral triangle: all sides congruent
Isosceles triangle: at least 2 sides congruent
Scalene triangle: no sides congruent
Acute triangle: all acute angles
Right triangle: 1 right angle, 2 acute angles
Obtuse triangle: 1 obtuse angle, 2 acute angles
Trapezoid: 1 and only 1 pair of opposite sides parallel
Parallelogram: opposite sides parallel and congruent
Rectangle: 4 right angles, opposite sides parallel and congruent
Kite: 2 pairs of adjacent, congruent sides
Square: 4 congruent sides, 4 right angles, opposite sides parallel

Complete the statements below.

1. An acute traingle has __________ acute angles.

2. An equilateral traingle has all sides __________ .

3. An isosceles traingle has at least __________ sides congruent.

4. A scalene triangle has no __________ sides.

Write a statement for each diagram. Tell whether the statement is true or false. Explain why.

Isosceles Triangles

Equilateral Triangles

____

____

____

Squares

Rhombuses

____

____

____

Name ______________________________

Angle Sum Relationships

A triangle has two angles whose measures are 38° and 42°. Find the measure of the third angle.

Step 1: The sum of the measures of the angles of a triangle is 180°.
Step 2: Add 38° and 42°. $38 + 42 = 80$
Step 3: Subtract the sum from 180°. $180 - 80 = 100$
Step 4: m $\angle B = 100°$.
Step 5: Check your answer. $38 + 42 + 100 = 180$

Find the measure of $\angle B$ in each triangle below.

1.

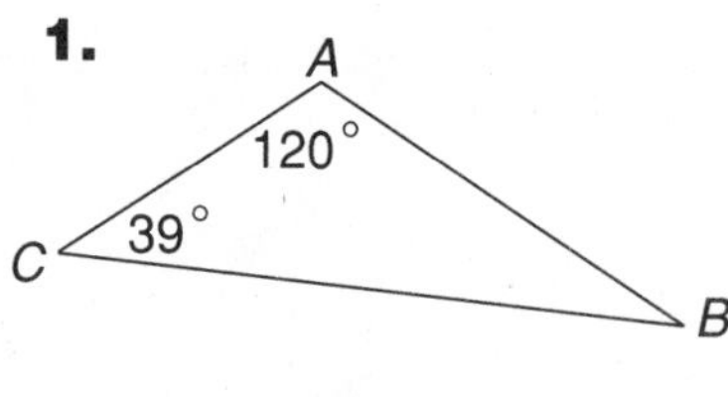

m$\angle B$ = ______

2.

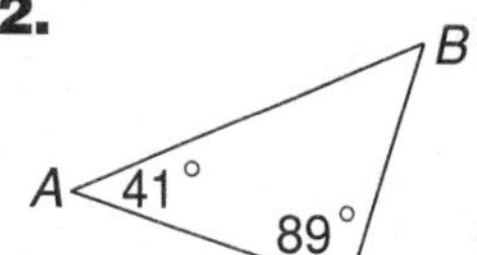

m$\angle B$ = ______

3.

m$\angle B$ = ______

Find the measure of C in each quadrilateral below. Remember that the sum of the measures of a quadrilateral is 360°. Add the measures of the three angles given; subtract the sum from 360°. Check your answer.

4.

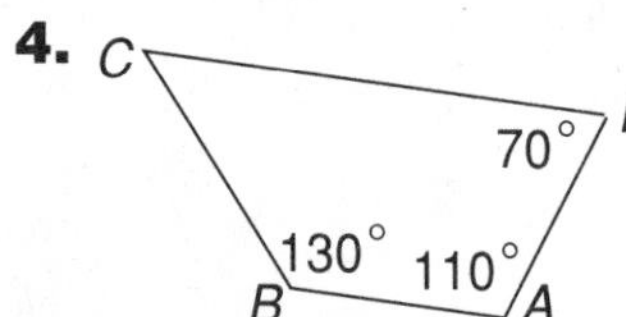

m$\angle C$ = ______

5.

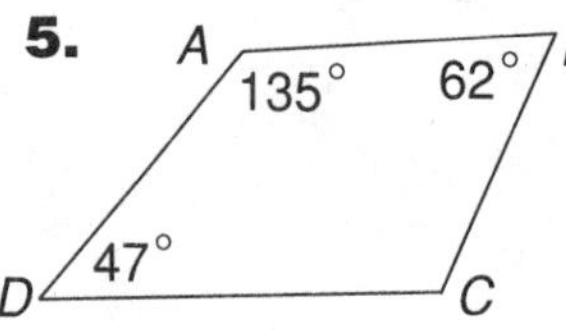

m$\angle C$ = ______

6.

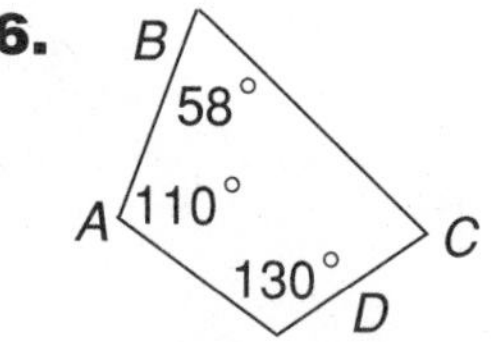

m$\angle C$ = ______

Answer the questions below.

7. Find the measures of the fourth angle of a quadrilateral if the other three measures are 61°, 82°, and 110°. ______

8. The measure of a right angle is 90°. If the measure of one of the acute angles of a right triangle is 31°, what is the measure of the other acute angle? ______

Name ______________________________

Exploring Algebra: Understanding Equations

Complete the equations by supplying the missing numbers.

Examples:

$\square - 39 = 62$

To find the missing number, ask yourself what number is 39 more than 62.
Add 39 and 62. The answer is 101.

$\square \div 20 = 5$

To find the missing number, ask yourself what number is 20 times 5.
Multiply 20 by 5. The answer is 100.

---

1. $\square - 95 = 105$ **2.** $\square + 65 = 81$ **3.** $\square \times 8 = 56$

4. $\square \div 7 = 30$ **5.** $\square - 17 = 92$ **6.** $\square \div 12 = 7$

7. $\square \times 23 = 138$ **8.** $\square \div 40 = 40$ **9.** $87 - \square = 79$

You may use a calculator to decide if each example is true or false. Write true or false.

10. $4.56 + 0.9 = 4.65$ ____________ **11.** $124 \times 84 = 10{,}426$ ____________

12. $6.44 \times 8 = 51.52$ ____________ **13.** $8 - 7.98 = .2$ ____________

14. $900 \div .45 = 2{,}000$ ____________ **15.** $6.42 - .008 = 6.412$ ____________

16. $.03 \times .03 = .09$ ____________ **17.** $78.9 < .789$ ____________

Name ______________________________

Using the Strategies

Use the strategy Guess and Check or Make an Organized List to solve each problem.

Example:

Josie handed 13 coins to Brent. There were only nickels and quarters. The value of the coins was $1.25. How many quarters did she give Brent? How many nickels?

Guess and Check

Try: $4 + 9 = 13$
$4 \times \$.25 + 9 \times \$.05 = \$1.45$ no
Try: $3 + 10 = 13$
$3 \times \$.25 + 10 \times \$.05 = \$1.25$ yes

Make an Organized List

Quarters	Nickels	Value
0	13	$0.65
1	12	$0.25 + $0.60 = $0.85
2	11	$0.50 + $0.55 = $1.05
3	10	$0.75 + $0.50 = $1.25

Josie gave Brent 3 quarters and 10 nickels.

Solve.

1. Mario paid $2.15 for 8 stamps. Some of the stamps cost $0.30; others cost $0.25. How many $0.30 stamps did he buy? ____________
How many $0.25 stamps did he buy?
____

2. The sum of the measures of a triangle is 180°. If the first angle is 1° greater than the second angle and the third angle is 1° smaller than the second angle, what are the measures of the angles?
______ ______ ______

3. Guests at the Sleepy Hollow Ranch ride horses in groups of 2 or 3. One day 4 groups were on the trails; 11 horses were out. How many groups of 2 were on the trails? ____________
How many groups of 3?
____

4. The sum of the lengths of the sides of a triangle is 21 cm. The length of the first side is 2 cm less than the second side; the length of the second side is 2 cm less than the third side. What are the lengths of the sides?
______ ______ ______

Name ______________________________

Parallel and Perpendicular Lines

If two parallel lines, *q and r,* are intersected by a transversal, *t,* eight angles are formed. If the measure of one angle is known, then the measures of all of the other angles can be determined.

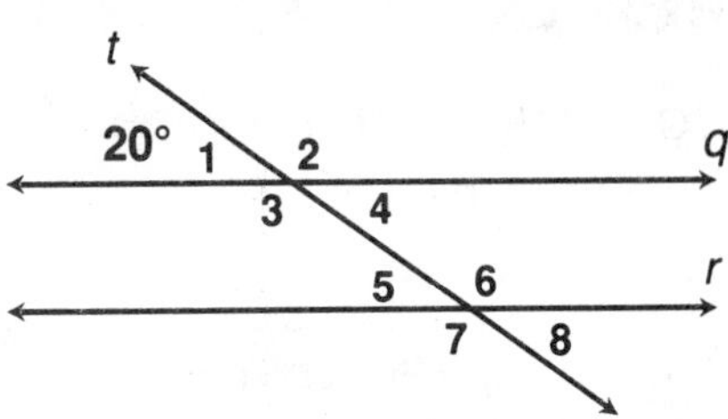

Given $m\angle 1$	→ Determine all angles with the same measure. $m\angle 1 = m\angle 4 = m\angle 5 = m\angle 8$	→ Determine $m\angle 2$. $m\angle 2 = 180° - m\angle 1$	→ Determine all angles with the same measure. $m\angle 2 = m\angle 3 = m\angle 6 = m\angle 7$

Example:

$m\angle 1 = 20°$	→ $m\angle 1 = m\angle 4 = m\angle 5 = m\angle 8$ $= 20°$	→ $m\angle 2 = 180° - 20°$ $= 160°$	→ $m\angle 2 = m\angle 3 = m\angle 6 = m\angle 7$ $= 160°$

---

1. Name two parallel lines. ________

2. Name a transversal. ________

3. $m\angle 1 = 60°$. Find:

$m\angle 2 =$ ________

$m\angle 3 =$ ________

$m\angle 4 =$ ________

$m\angle 5 =$ ________

$m\angle 6 =$ ________

$m\angle 7 =$ ________

$m\angle 8 =$ ________

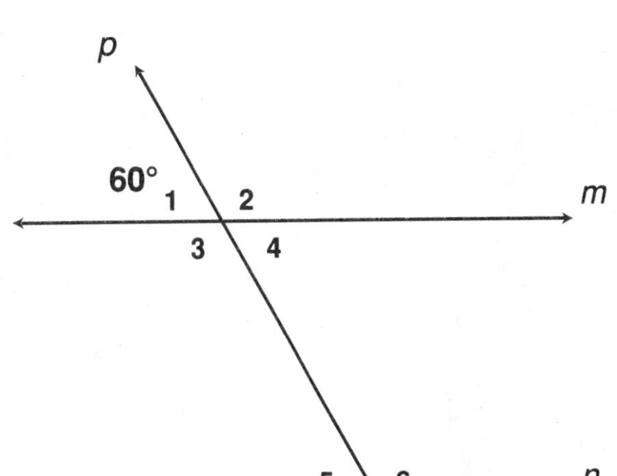

Name ____

Constructing Parallel and Perpendicular Lines

To construct a line perpendicular to a line *t* through point *P*:

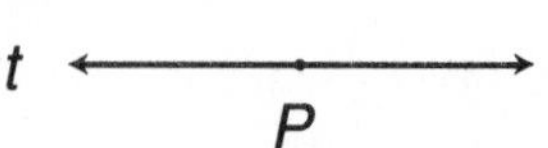

On *t*, draw arcs with center at *P*. Label the points where they cross *t* as *A* and *B*.	→	Draw arcs with centers *A* and *B*. Label the point of intersection *C*.	→	Draw ray *PC*.

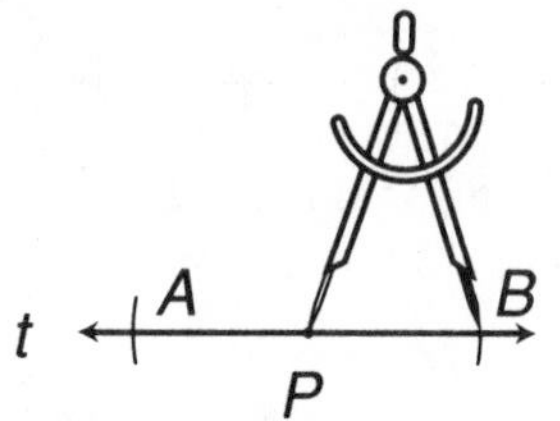

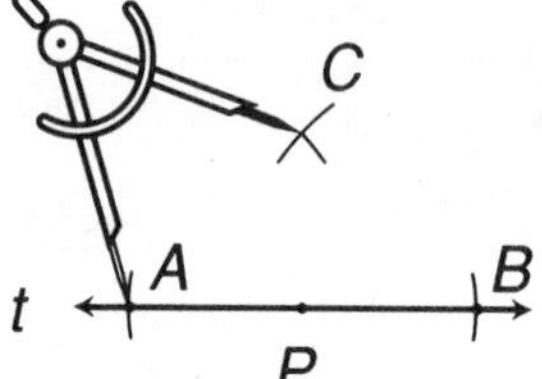

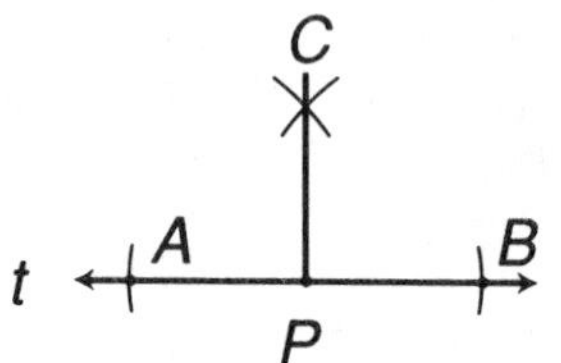

---

1. Construct a line perpendicular to line *s* at *Q*.

To draw a line parallel to a line *m*:

Mark a point *A* on line *m*. Construct a line *n* perpendicular to *m*. Mark a point *B* on line *n*.	→	Construct a line *q* through point *B* so that *q* is perpendicular to *AB*. $q \parallel m$

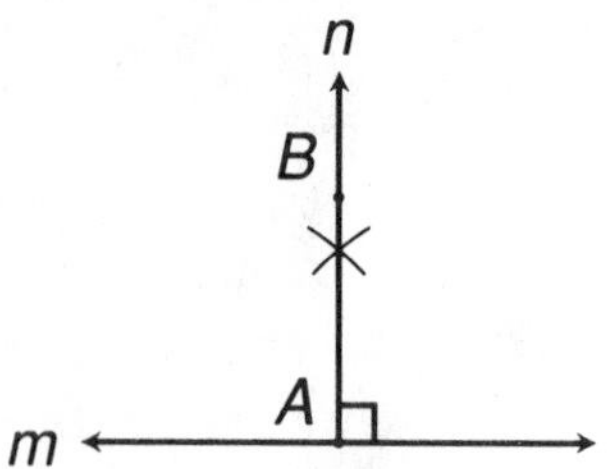

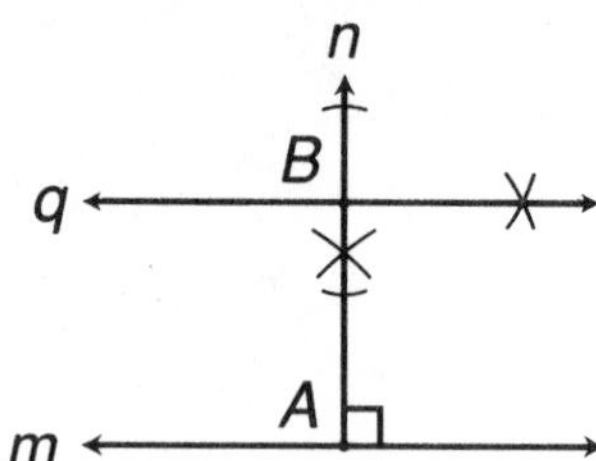

2. Construct a line *q* parallel to line *r*.

Name ___________________________

Constructing Angle and Segment Bisectors

Construct the perpendicular bisector of a segment $\overline{AB}$.

A ———— B

You need two points equally distant from both ends of the line segment, somewhere in the circled areas. → Use a compass, opened to a bit more than half the width of $\overline{AB}$. Make two arcs, one from A, then one from B. Label the arcs' intersections C and D. → Join the points of intersection. $\overline{CD}$ is the ⊥ bisector of $\overline{AB}$ at point M.

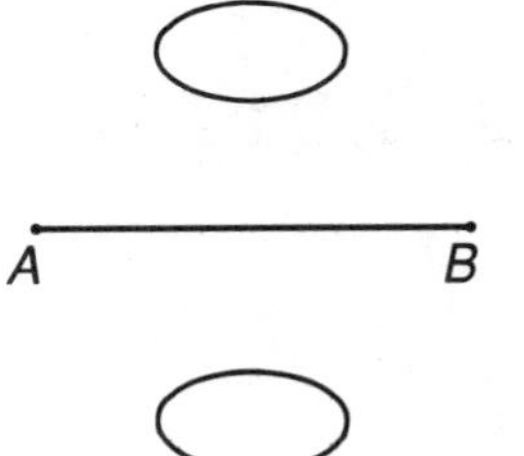

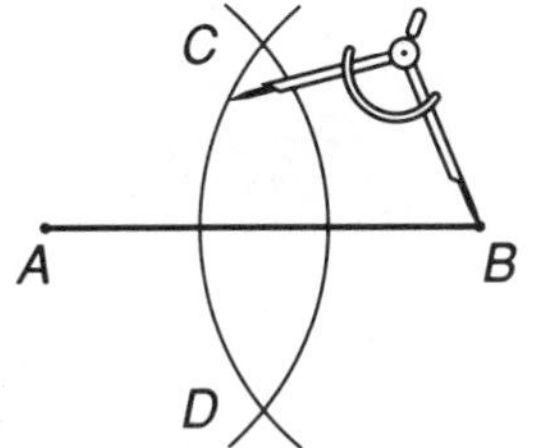

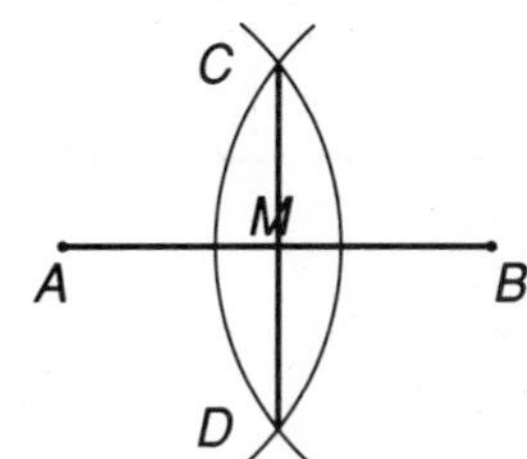

Construct the bisector of an angle O.

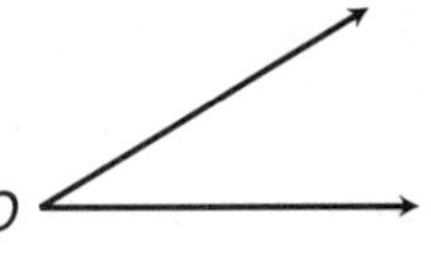

With a compass, mark off equal segments of the angle's rays. Label the intersections X and Y. → With the compass point at X and then Y, draw intersecting arcs. Label this intersection P. → Draw $\overline{OP}$, the angle bisector.

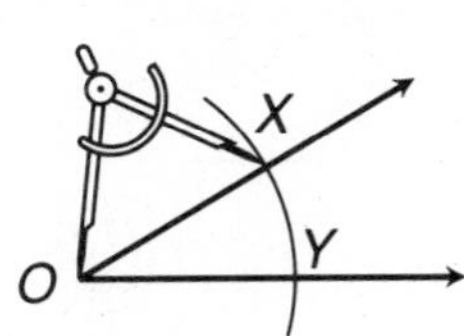

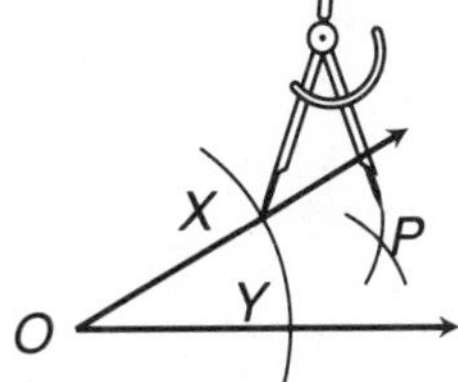

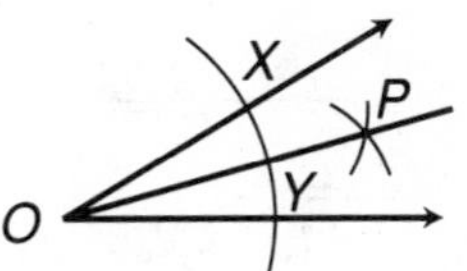

---

1. Draw an angle O and construct its bisector.

2. Draw a segment $\overline{AB}$ and construct its perpendicular bisector.

Name ______________________________

Constructing Triangles

To construct $\triangle ABC$ using a compass and a straightedge.

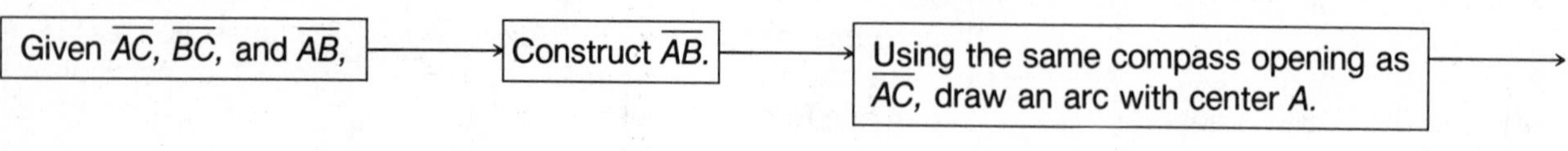

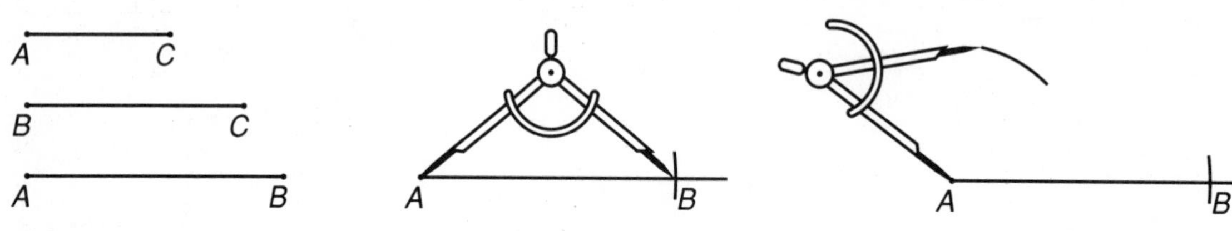

Using the same compass opening as $\overline{BC}$, draw an arc with center B to locate C.

Draw $\overline{AC}$ and $\overline{BC}$.

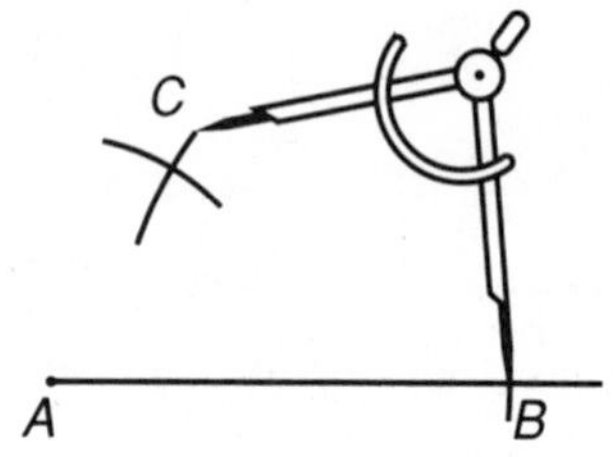

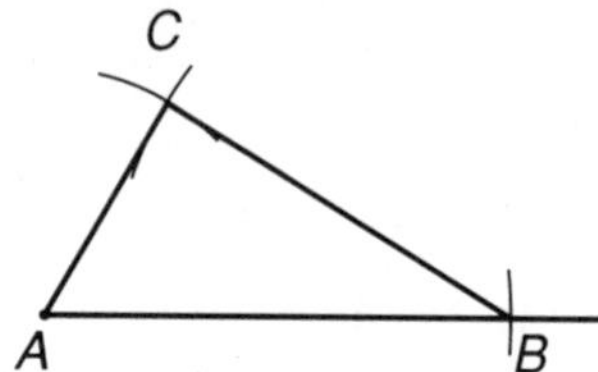

Using $\overline{LM}$, $\overline{MN}$, and $\overline{NL}$, construct $\triangle LMN$.

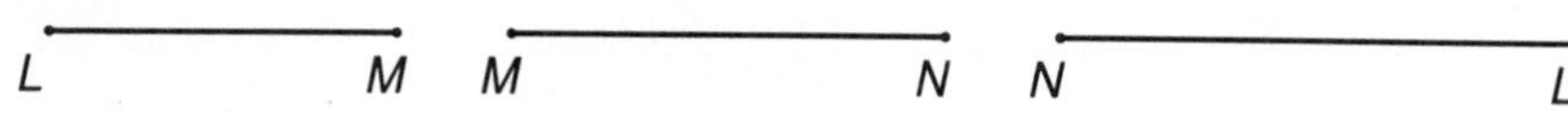

Name ______________________________

Problem Solving: Data from a Chart

This chart at the right shows the number of hours each horse was ridden during this week. Use the chart to solve these problems. Show your work.

Pine Needle Stables

	Hours of Exercise				
	Tue.	Wed.	Thurs.	Fri.	Sat.
Quarter horse	1.5	3.75	2	1.1	2.25
Appaloosa	0.5	3	2.5	1.2	1.75
Arabian	3.25	2.5	1	1.75	3.5

1. How much longer was the Appaloosa ridden on Wednesday than on Saturday?

 3.00 hours on Wed.
– 1.75 hours on Sat.
 1.25 hours difference

____

2. What was the total time the quarter horse was ridden on Friday and Saturday?

__________ __________

3. Last Wednesday the Appaloosa was ridden 2.5 times as long as this Wednesday. How long was the Appaloosa ridden last Wednesday?

____

4. On Wednesday, how much longer was the Appaloosa ridden than the Arabian?

__________ __________

5. Last Saturday the Arabian was ridden 0.5 as long as this Saturday. How long was the Arabian ridden last Saturday?

____

6. What is the total number of hours all three horses were ridden on Friday?

__________ __________

7. The stable charged $6 an hour for a guest to ride the quarter horse on Saturday. One guest rode for 2.25 h. What was the cost of the ride?

____

Name ______________________________

Divisibility

To analyze if a number can be evenly divided by 3, 4, 6, 8, or 9, use the divisibility test.

Factor	Test for Divisibility
3	Is the sum of the digits divisible by 3?
4	Is the number formed by the last two digits divisible by 4?
6	Is the number divisible by both 2 and 3?
8	Is the number formed by the last 3 digits divisible by 8?
9	Is the sum of the digits divisible by 9?

Ring the numbers that are divisible by 3.

Example: (81) 8 + 1 = 9; 9 is divisible by 3.

1. 234 **2.** 196 **3.** 4,746 **4.** 2,977 **5.** 1,346

Ring the numbers that are divisible by 4.

Example: (168) 68 ÷ 4 = 17; 68 is divisible by 4.

6. 472 **7.** 2,608 **8.** 1,453 **9.** 298 **10.** 520

Ring the numbers that are divisible by 6.

Example: (126) 126 ÷ 2 = 63, 126 ÷ 3 = 42; 126 is divisible by 6.

11. 272 **12.** 318 **13.** 3,194 **14.** 738 **15.** 518

Ring the numbers that are divisible by 8.

Example: (1,272) 272 ÷ 8 = 34; 272 is divisible by 8.

16. 154 **17.** 3,288 **18.** 1,075 **19.** 52,320 **20.** 2,224

Ring the numbers that are divisible by 9.

Example: (18,342) 1 + 8 + 3 + 4 + 2 = 18; 18 is divisible by 9.

21. 6,400 **22.** 702 **23.** 8,991 **24.** 530 **25.** 2,277

Use with text pages 126-127.

Name ______________________________

Factors, Primes, and Composites

Prime numbers have exactly two different factors.

13 is prime.

1 × 13 = 13
There are only **2** factors: 1 and 13.

Composite numbers have more than two different factors.

21 is composite.

1 × 21 = 21 3 × 7 = 21
There are **4** factors: 1, 21, 3, and 7.

Complete the following.

	Number	Factors	Exactly 2 Factors?	Prime or Composite?
1.	15	1, 3, 5, 15	no	composite
2.	11	1, 11	yes	
3.	10			
4.	63			
5.	41			
6.	73			
7.	77			
8.	23			
9.	81			
10.	32			
11.	49			
12.	108			
13.	121			
14.	133			
15.	151			

Name ____________________

Prime Factorization

The **prime factors** of a number can be found by making a **factor tree**. Here are two factor trees that show the prime factors of 24.

Start here. → 24

6 · 4

All prime. **2 · 3 · 2 · 2**

Start here. → 24

8 · 3

4 · 2 · 3

All prime. **2 · 2 · 2 · 3**

You get the same prime factors each way.

24 = 2 · 2 · 2 · 3 ← prime factorization

$24 = 2^3 \cdot 3$ ← prime factorization using exponents

Make a factor tree for each number. Write the prime factorization. Then write the prime factorization using exponents.

1. 18

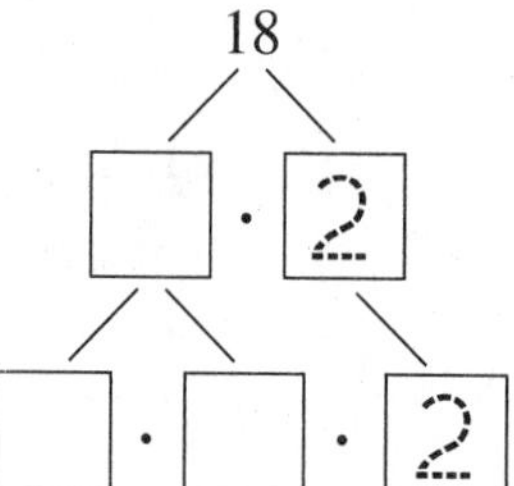

Prime factorization: $3 \cdot 3 \cdot 2 = 3^2 \cdot 2$

2. 32

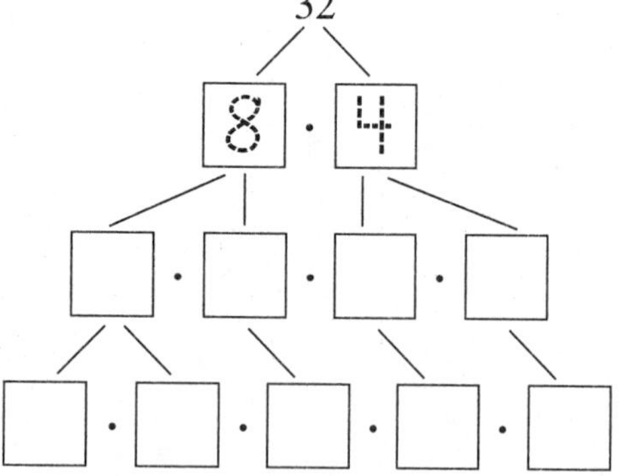

Prime factorization: ____________

Write the prime factorization of each number using exponents.

3. 80 = ____________ **4.** 32 = ____________

5. 48 = ____________ **6.** 50 = ____________

Name ______________________________

Greatest Common Factor

What is the **greatest common factor** (GCF) of 15 and 20?

List all the factors of each number.

15: 1, 3, 5, 15
20: 1, 2, 4, 5, 10, 20

The factors that are the same in both lists are 1 and 5. 5 is the greatest.

Choose the ***greatest*** common factor.

5 is the greatest common factor (GCF).

same in both lists

Which common factor is the greatest?

Find the GCF for each pair of numbers.

	Factors of First Number	Factors of Second Number	Common Factors	GCF
1. 12, 8	1, 2, 3, 4, 6, 12	1, 2, 4, 8	1, 2, 4	4
2. 6, 24	1, 2, 3, 6	____	____	____
3. 6, 13	____	____	____	____
4. 8, 20	____	____	____	____
5. 12, 48	____	____ ____	____	____
6. 16, 40	____	____	____	____
7. 10, 15	____	____	____	____
8. 24, 32	____	____	____	____
9. 12, 30	____	____	____	____
10. 15, 27	____	____	____	____
11. 6, 18	____	____	____	____
12. 18, 30	____	____	____	____
13. 20, 40	____	____	____	____

Name ____________________

Least Common Multiple

What is the least common multiple (LCM) of 9 and 10 ?

List the prime factors of each number.	→	Identify the highest powers listed.	→	Multiply the highest powers of each factor.
$9 = 3 \cdot 3$ $10 = 2 \cdot 5$		$9 = (3^2)$ $10 = (2) \cdot (5)$		$3^2 \cdot 2 \cdot 5 = 90$ (LCM)

Write the prime factorization using exponents.

Use prime factorizations to find the LCM of each pair of numbers.

Identify highest power of each factor.

1. 6 $(2) \cdot (3)$
   15 $3 \cdot (5)$
   LCM $2 \cdot 3 \cdot 5 = 30$

Multiply.

2. 7 ____
   5 ____
   LCM ____

3. 15 ____
   20 ____
   LCM ____

4. 7 ____
   9 ____
   LCM ____

5. 8 ____
   10 ____
   LCM ____

6. 1 ____
   16 ____
   LCM ____

7. 9 ____
   12 ____
   LCM ____

8. 7 ____
   8 ____
   LCM ____

9. 10 ____
   15 ____
   LCM ____

10. 6 ____
    14 ____
    LCM ____

11. 8 ____
    20 ____
    LCM ____

12. 6 ____
    18 ____
    LCM ____

Name ____

Discovering Prime Number Patterns

A prime number is a number with exactly two factors—the number ________ and the number ________. Twin primes are prime numbers that differ by ________.

Ring all the prime numbers in the grid. Put an X on pairs of twin primes.

What number is in two pairs? ________

1	2	3	4	5	6	7	8	9	10
11	12	13	14	15	16	17	18	19	20
21	22	23	24	25	26	27	28	29	30
31	32	33	34	35	36	37	38	39	40
41	42	43	44	45	46	47	48	49	50
51	52	53	54	55	56	57	58	59	60
61	62	63	64	65	66	67	68	69	70
71	72	73	74	75	76	77	78	79	80
81	82	83	84	85	86	87	88	89	90
91	92	93	94	95	96	97	98	99	100

Write all the twin primes from 1 to 100.

1. ______, ______ **2.** ______, ______ **3.** ______, ______ **4.** ______, ______

5. ______, ______ **6.** ______, ______ **7.** ______, ______ **8.** ______, ______

Name ______________________________

Equivalent Fractions

Two fractions that name the same part of a region or set are **equivalent fractions**.

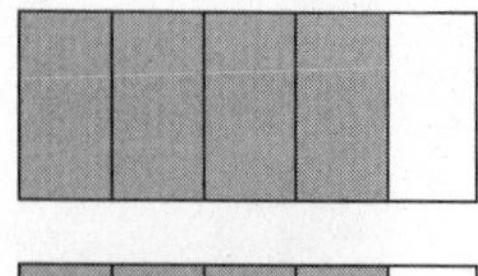

$\frac{4}{5} = \frac{8}{10}$

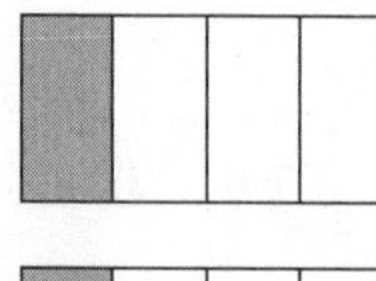

$\frac{1}{4} = \frac{3}{12}$

To make an equivalent fraction, multiply the numerator and denominator of a fraction by the same nonzero number.

$\frac{3}{8} = \frac{?}{16}$

8 x ? = 16

3 x 2

$\frac{3}{8} = \frac{6}{16}$

8 x 2

Write the missing number.

1. $\frac{3}{4} = \frac{15}{20}$

4 x 5

2. 5 x ?

$\frac{5}{6} = \frac{\quad}{12}$

6 x 2

3. $\frac{2}{3} = \frac{\quad}{15}$

3 x ?

4. $\frac{9}{10} = \frac{\quad}{100}$

5. $\frac{1}{3} = \frac{5}{\quad}$

6. $\frac{3}{5} = \frac{\quad}{20}$

7. $\frac{2}{3} = \frac{\quad}{6}$

8. $\frac{2}{3} = \frac{8}{\quad}$

9. $\frac{1}{2} = \frac{\quad}{100}$

10. $\frac{5}{6} = \frac{30}{\quad}$

11. $\frac{3}{4} = \frac{\quad}{24}$

12. $\frac{3}{8} = \frac{\quad}{16}$

13. $\frac{3}{4} = \frac{75}{\quad}$

14. $\frac{3}{20} = \frac{\quad}{60}$

15. $\frac{1}{5} = \frac{2}{\quad}$

16. $\frac{5}{8} = \frac{\quad}{24}$

17. $\frac{7}{8} = \frac{14}{\quad}$

18. $\frac{4}{5} = \frac{\quad}{100}$

19. $\frac{1}{2} = \frac{\quad}{36}$

20. $\frac{5}{16} = \frac{10}{\quad}$

Name ______________________________

Lowest Terms

Find the **lowest-terms fraction** for $\frac{18}{48}$.

Divide the numerator and the denominator by a common factor. → Divide the numerator and the denominator by a common factor. → The fraction is in lowest terms.

$\frac{18 \div 2}{48 \div 2} = \frac{9}{24}$ (lowest terms? no) $\frac{9 \div 3}{24 \div 3} = \frac{3}{8}$ (lowest terms? yes) $\frac{3}{8}$

Dividing by the GCF saves steps. $\frac{18 \div 6}{48 \div 6} = \frac{3}{8}$

Write the lowest-terms fraction.

1. $\frac{8}{12} = \frac{8 \div 4}{12 \div 4} = \frac{2}{3}$ (GCF is 4)

2. $\frac{15}{36} = \frac{15 \div 3}{36 \div 3} =$ (GCF is 3)

3. $\frac{7}{14} = \frac{7 \div 7}{14 \div 7} =$

4. $\frac{2}{14}$

5. $\frac{9}{24}$

6. $\frac{18}{20}$

7. $\frac{5}{20}$

8. $\frac{8}{18}$

9. $\frac{16}{20}$

10. $\frac{7}{28}$

11. $\frac{5}{30}$

12. $\frac{9}{21}$

13. $\frac{6}{8}$

14. $\frac{50}{100}$

15. $\frac{25}{30}$

Name ______________________________

Improper Fractions and Mixed Numbers

Write the improper fraction $\frac{7}{3}$ as a mixed number.

Divide the numerator by the denominator.

$$3\overline{)7}\quad 2\text{ R}1 \longrightarrow 2\frac{1}{2}$$

$$\begin{array}{r} 6 \\ \hline 1 \end{array}$$

$$\frac{7}{3} = 2\frac{1}{3}$$

Write the mixed number $3\frac{2}{5}$ as an improper fraction.

Multiply the whole number by the denominator. Add the numerator. $(5 \times 3) + 2 = 17$

Write the sum over the denominator. $\frac{17}{5}$

$$3\frac{2}{5} = \frac{17}{5}$$

Write each improper fraction as a mixed number or a whole number.

1. $\frac{13}{5} =$ $2\frac{3}{5}$

$5\overline{)13}$ 2 R3, 10, 3

2. $\frac{10}{4} =$ ______ ← Write in lowest terms.

$4\overline{)10}$ 2 R2 $\longrightarrow 2\frac{2}{4} = 2\frac{1}{2}$, 8, 2

3. $\frac{8}{2} =$ ______

4. $\frac{8}{7} =$ ______ 5. $\frac{8}{8} =$ ______ 6. $\frac{19}{6} =$ ______ 7. $\frac{22}{10} =$ ______ 8. $\frac{15}{9} =$ ______

9. $\frac{9}{3} =$ ______ 10. $\frac{11}{5} =$ ______ 11. $\frac{15}{6} =$ ______ 12. $\frac{100}{100} =$ ______ 13. $\frac{16}{9} =$ ______

Write each mixed number as an improper fraction.

14. $6\frac{1}{2} =$ $\frac{13}{2}$

$\frac{(2 \times 6) + 1}{2} = \frac{13}{2}$

15. $4\frac{3}{8} =$ ______

$\frac{(8 \times 4) + 3}{8} = ?$

16. $5\frac{2}{3} =$ ______

$\frac{(3 \times 5) + 2}{?}$

17. $2\frac{7}{8} =$ ______ 18. $5\frac{1}{6} =$ ______ 19. $1\frac{7}{10} =$ ______ 20. $12\frac{3}{8} =$ ______ 21. $7\frac{1}{3} =$ ______

Name ______________________________

Exploring Algebra: More About Equations

The scales are balanced.

One jar weighs the same as two cups.

Four cups weigh the same as two books.

You can add objects of the same weight to both sides of a scale or remove objects of the same weight from both sides, and the scale will remain in balance.

HINT: It is helpful to make a drawing of equivalent weights in "lowest terms" before beginning.

Draw objects on the scale to make it balanced.

1.

1 jar weighs the same as how many books?

2.

3.

4.

Balance these scales. Use the objects above and also add some pencils to each scale. Eight pencils balance two cups.

5.

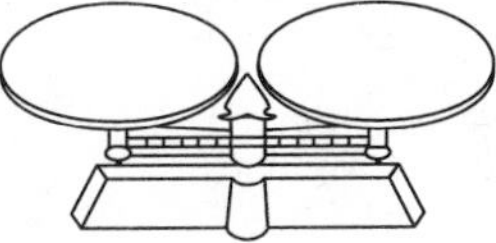

6.

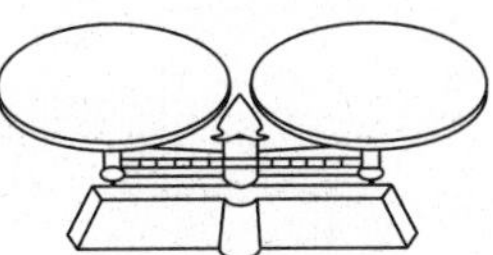

7.

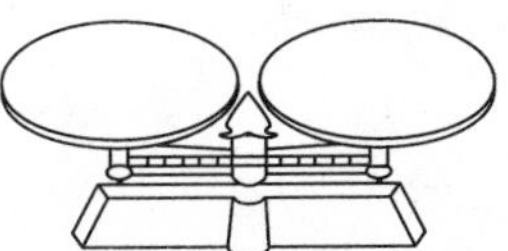

8.

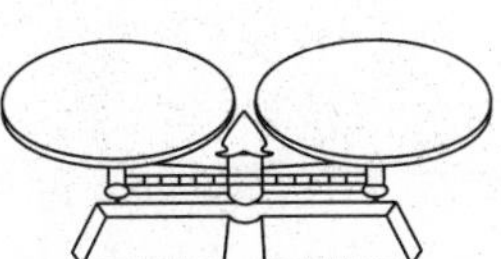

Name ______________________________

Fractions and Decimals

To write a fraction or mixed number as a decimal:

First write an equivalent fraction with a denominator of 10, 100, or 1,000.

$$\frac{3}{25} = \frac{3 \times 4}{25 \times 4} = \frac{12}{100}$$

Then write the fraction as a decimal.

$$\frac{12}{100} = 0.12$$

To write a decimal as a fraction or mixed number:

First write the decimal as a fraction.

$$0.45 = \frac{45}{100}$$

Then write the fraction in lowest terms.

$$\frac{45}{100} = \frac{9}{20}$$

Write each fraction or mixed number as a decimal.

1. $2\frac{2}{5}$ ________ ($2\frac{2 \times 2}{5 \times 2} = 2\frac{4}{10}$)

2. $\frac{4}{25}$ ________ ($\frac{4 \times 4}{25 \times 4} = ?$)

3. $\frac{14}{250}$ ________

4. $\frac{7}{50}$ ________

5. $\frac{9}{10}$ ________

6. $\frac{11}{20}$ ________

7. $1\frac{27}{100}$ ________

8. $\frac{4}{1{,}000}$ ________

9. $3\frac{29}{40}$ ________

Write each decimal as a fraction or mixed number.

10. 0.4 ________ ($\frac{4}{10} = \frac{2}{5}$)

11. 0.27 ________

12. 3.42 ________

13. 2.004 ________

14. 3.2 ________

15. 4.25 ________

16. 0.28 ________

17. 0.006 ________

18. 1.8 ________

Name ____

Terminating and Repeating Decimals

To find a decimal for a fraction, divide the numerator of the fraction by the denominator.

$\frac{7}{20} \longrightarrow 20\overline{)7.00}$ quotient 0.35

```
     0.35
20)7.00
    60
    100
    100
      0
```

The remainder is 0. The decimal is a **terminating decimal.**

$\frac{1}{6} \longrightarrow 6\overline{)1.0000}$ quotient $0.1666 \longrightarrow 0.1\overline{6}$

Place a bar over the digit that repeats.

```
    0.1666
6)1.0000
   6
   40
   36
    40
    36
     4
```

Since the remainders of 4 repeat, the digits of the quotient repeat. The quotient is a **repeating decimal.**

Find the decimal for each fraction. Use a bar to show repeating decimals.

Write as a repeating decimal.

2 digits repeat.

1. $\frac{4}{25}$

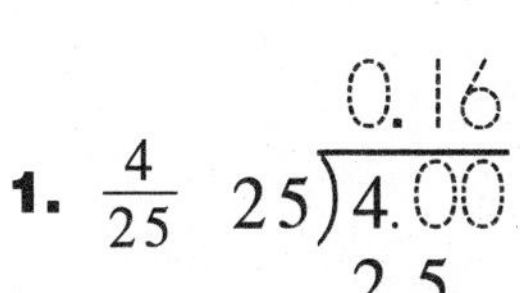

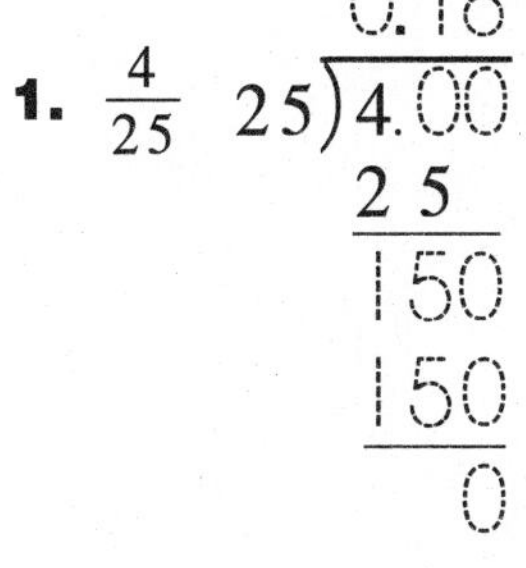

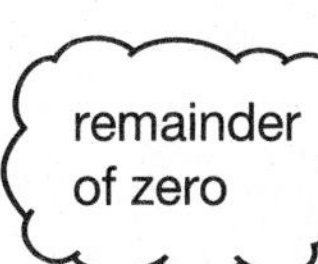

2. $\frac{8}{3}$ $3\overline{)8.000}$ $2.666 = 2.\overline{6}$

3. $\frac{2}{11}$

4. $\frac{3}{8}$

5. $\frac{5}{3}$

6. $\frac{2}{30}$

7. $\frac{7}{9}$

Name ____

Comparing and Ordering Fractions

Look at the denominators. → Write equivalent fractions with a common denominator. → Compare the numerators. → The fractions compare the same way the numerators compare.

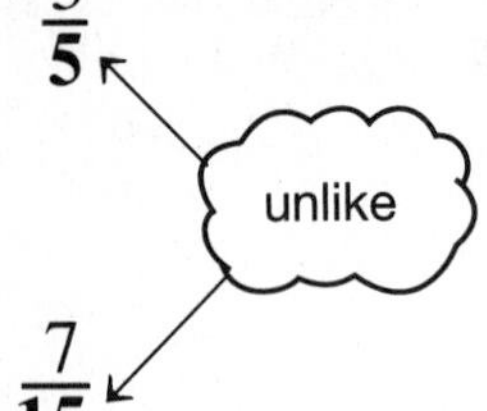

$\frac{3}{5} = \frac{9}{15}$

$\frac{7}{15}$

$9 > 7$

$\frac{9}{15} > \frac{7}{15}$

so $\frac{3}{5} > \frac{7}{15}$

Compare the fractions. Write > or < for each ◯.

1. $\frac{3}{4}$ (<) $\frac{5}{6}$ $\frac{9}{12}$ $\frac{10}{12}$

2. $\frac{2}{3}$ ◯ $\frac{3}{5}$ $\frac{10}{15}$ $\frac{9}{15}$

3. $\frac{7}{8}$ ◯ $\frac{9}{10}$ $\frac{\ }{40}$ $\frac{\ }{40}$

4. $\frac{5}{6}$ ◯ $\frac{7}{8}$ ____________

5. $\frac{2}{3}$ ◯ $\frac{4}{9}$ ____________

6. $\frac{4}{21}$ ◯ $\frac{2}{7}$ ____________

7. $\frac{3}{4}$ ◯ $\frac{3}{5}$ ____________

8. $\frac{5}{8}$ ◯ $\frac{1}{2}$ ____________

Compare the mixed numbers. Write > or < for each ◯.

9. $2\frac{3}{4}$ (>) $2\frac{5}{8}$ $2\frac{6}{8}$ $2\frac{5}{8}$

10. $4\frac{4}{9}$ ◯ $3\frac{7}{8}$ 4 is greater than 3.

11. $5\frac{2}{3}$ ◯ $5\frac{4}{9}$ ____________

12. $2\frac{5}{8}$ ◯ $2\frac{2}{3}$ ____________

Arrange in order from least to greatest.

13. $\frac{2}{3}$, $\frac{3}{7}$, $\frac{5}{6}$, $\frac{2}{5}$, $\frac{3}{4}$ ________________________________

14. $\frac{3}{4}$, $\frac{3}{8}$, $3\frac{1}{8}$, $4\frac{1}{3}$, $1\frac{3}{4}$ ________________________________

Name ______________________________

Using the Strategies

When you need to find how many different combinations are possible, drawing a picture or making an organized list are good strategies to use.

José has 5 sweaters—red, orange, yellow, green, blue—and 2 pairs of jeans—black, white. How many different combinations can he make?

Picture

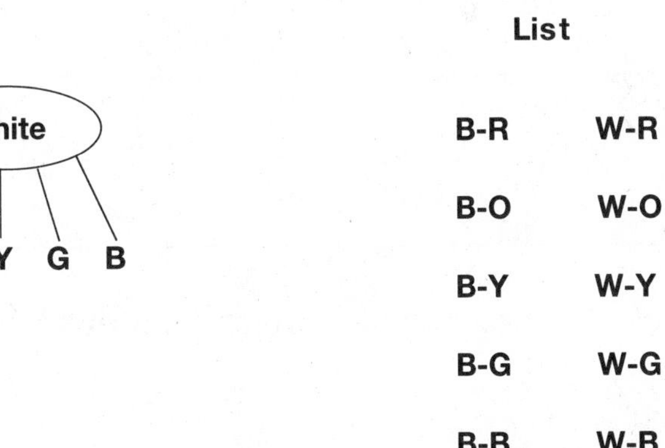

10 combinations

List

B-R	**W-R**
B-O	**W-O**
B-Y	**W-Y**
B-G	**W-G**
B-B	**W-B**

---

1. List all the ways you can make $30 using at least one of each of the following bills: $1 bill, $5 bill, $10 bill. How many combinations are there?

____

2. Dustin plans to take 3 jackets and 5 shirts on a trip. How many different outfits can he make from these choices?

____

3. Darren knows there are 18 black socks and 30 white socks in his drawer, but he does not want to turn on the light and wake his sleeping brother. What is the least number of socks he has to take out to be sure that he has a matching pair?

____

4. Alyssa, Ian, and Krystal will be appointed as officers of their school's Student Government Organization. The 3 positions are president, vice president, and secretary. How many different possibilities are there? Use the chart below.

______

	Students' Names					
President						
Vice President						
Secretary						

Name ____________________

Adding and Subtracting Fractions

Look at the denominators. → Find the LCD. → Write equivalent fractions using the LCD. → Add (or subtract) the numerators. Write the sum (or difference) over the LCD.

$$\begin{array}{r} \frac{2}{9} \\ +\ \frac{3}{6} \\ \hline \end{array}$$

They are not the same.

Look for multiples of 9 that are also multiples of 6:
$9 \times 1 = 9$ $6 \times ? = 9$ No.
$9 \times 2 = 18$ $6 \times 3 = 18$ Yes
The LCD is 18.

$$\begin{array}{rcl} \frac{2}{9} & = & \frac{4}{18} \\ +\ \frac{3}{6} & = & \frac{9}{18} \\ \hline \end{array}$$

$$\begin{array}{r} \frac{4}{18} \\ +\ \frac{9}{18} \\ \hline \frac{13}{18} \end{array}$$

Add or subtract. Write your answer in lowest terms.

1. $\begin{array}{rcl} \frac{5}{6} & = & \frac{\ }{6} \\ -\ \frac{2}{3} & = & \frac{\ }{6} \\ \hline & & \frac{\ }{6} \end{array}$

2. $\begin{array}{r} \frac{1}{5} \\ +\ \frac{3}{10} \\ \hline \end{array}$

3. $\begin{array}{r} \frac{2}{3} \\ -\ \frac{1}{6} \\ \hline \end{array}$

4. $\begin{array}{r} \frac{5}{8} \\ +\ \frac{1}{4} \\ \hline \end{array}$

5. $\begin{array}{r} \frac{11}{4} \\ -\ \frac{5}{6} \\ \hline \end{array}$

6. $\begin{array}{r} \frac{1}{2} \\ +\ \frac{5}{6} \\ \hline \end{array}$

7. $\begin{array}{r} \frac{3}{4} \\ +\ \frac{2}{5} \\ \hline \end{array}$

8. $\begin{array}{r} \frac{1}{6} \\ +\ \frac{5}{6} \\ \hline \end{array}$

9. $\begin{array}{r} \frac{3}{2} \\ +\ \frac{2}{3} \\ \hline \end{array}$

10. $\begin{array}{r} \frac{5}{6} \\ -\ \frac{0}{2} \\ \hline \end{array}$

11. $\begin{array}{r} \frac{2}{3} \\ -\ \frac{1}{4} \\ \hline \end{array}$

12. $\begin{array}{r} \frac{7}{9} \\ -\ \frac{2}{3} \\ \hline \end{array}$

Name ______________________

Estimating Sums and Differences

Write the expression. → Round the numbers. → Compute.

$6\frac{1}{3} - 2\frac{2}{3}$ (Round down for less than a half.) → $6\frac{1}{3} \to 6$; $2\frac{2}{3} \to 3$ (Round up for a half or more.) → $6 - 3 = 3$

Estimate each sum or difference. Use rounding.

1. $27 - 2\frac{1}{4}$ ______

2. $18\frac{3}{5} + 6\frac{1}{2}$ ______

3. $14\frac{1}{4} - 2\frac{2}{3}$ ______

4. $12\frac{3}{7} + 2\frac{1}{9}$ ______

5. $3\frac{1}{5} - 2\frac{2}{3}$ ______

6. $17\frac{1}{2} + 19\frac{9}{12}$ ______

7. $46 - 3\frac{7}{9}$ ______

8. $27\frac{3}{5} + 19\frac{2}{3}$ ______

9. $4\frac{1}{4} - 2\frac{2}{5}$ ______

10. $\frac{7}{9} + \frac{1}{4} + 2\frac{1}{3}$ ______

11. $12\frac{1}{2} - 2\frac{1}{3} - 3\frac{3}{5}$ ______

12. $5\frac{3}{10} + \frac{1}{8} + 2\frac{1}{3}$ ______

13. $27 - \frac{1}{2} - \frac{4}{5}$ ______

14. $\frac{1}{9} + \frac{2}{7} + \frac{3}{4}$ ______

15. $2\frac{1}{4} - \frac{1}{3} - 1\frac{1}{2}$ ______

16. $(35\frac{1}{2} + 12\frac{1}{4}) - 6\frac{6}{7}$ ______

17. $(52 - \frac{3}{7}) + 2\frac{1}{3}$ ______

18. $(15\frac{1}{4} + 2\frac{1}{2}) - 17\frac{1}{5}$ ______

19. $(24\frac{1}{9} - 2\frac{6}{7}) + 2\frac{3}{5}$ ______

20. $(\frac{17}{19} + \frac{1}{6}) - 1\frac{1}{3}$ ______

21. $(17 - \frac{2}{3}) - 6\frac{1}{2}$ ______

Name ______________________________

Adding Mixed Numbers

Find equivalent fractions with a common denominator. → Add the fractions. → Add the whole numbers.

$$\begin{array}{r} 4\frac{2}{3} = 4\frac{10}{15} \\ +\ 1\frac{3}{5} = 1\frac{9}{15} \\ \hline \end{array}$$

$$\begin{array}{r} 4\frac{2}{3} = 4\frac{\mathbf{10}}{\mathbf{15}} \\ +\ 1\frac{3}{5} = 1\frac{\mathbf{9}}{\mathbf{15}} \\ \hline \frac{\mathbf{19}}{\mathbf{15}} \end{array}$$

$$\begin{array}{r} 4\frac{2}{3} = \mathbf{4}\frac{10}{15} \\ +\ 1\frac{3}{5} = \mathbf{1}\frac{9}{15} \\ \hline \mathbf{5}\frac{19}{15} = 6\frac{4}{15} \end{array}$$

$1\frac{4}{15}$

Add. Write the answer in lowest terms.

1. $2\frac{3}{4} = 2\frac{6}{8}$
$+\ \frac{5}{8} = \frac{5}{8}$
$1\frac{3}{8}$
$2\frac{11}{8} =$

2. $5\frac{3}{5} = 5\frac{6}{10}$
$+2\frac{7}{10} = 2\frac{7}{10}$
$1\frac{3}{10}$
$7\frac{13}{10} =$

3. $1\frac{1}{3} = 1\frac{4}{12}$
$+3\frac{5}{6} = 3\frac{10}{12}$
$1\frac{?}{12}$
Lowest terms? $4\frac{14}{12} =$

4. $1\frac{3}{8} + 2\frac{1}{4}$

5. $3\frac{3}{5} + 2\frac{1}{2}$

6. $5\frac{2}{3} + 6\frac{1}{4}$

7. $5\frac{1}{4} + 7\frac{1}{3}$

8. $2\frac{1}{2} + 3\frac{1}{4}$

9. $4\frac{3}{4} + \frac{1}{2}$

10. $6\frac{1}{3} + 2\frac{5}{6}$

11. $1\frac{1}{8} + 7\frac{3}{4}$

Name ______________________________

Subtracting Mixed Numbers

Find equivalent fractions with a common denominator. → Rename the fractions if necessary. Subtract the fractions. → Subtract the whole numbers.

$$5\frac{1}{4} = 5\frac{2}{8} \qquad -\ 2\frac{3}{8} = 2\frac{3}{8}$$

Compare. $\frac{2}{8} < \frac{3}{8}$

$$5\frac{2}{8} = 4\frac{10}{8} \qquad -\ 2\frac{3}{8} = 2\frac{3}{8} \qquad \frac{7}{8}$$

Rename 5 as $4\frac{8}{8}$. Add $\frac{8}{8}$ to $\frac{2}{8}$.

$$4\frac{10}{8} \qquad -\ 2\frac{3}{8} \qquad 2\frac{7}{8}$$

Express in lowest terms.

Subtract.

1. $4\frac{1}{3} = 4\frac{4}{12} = 3\frac{16}{12}$ (4 − 1; $\frac{12}{12} + \frac{4}{12}$)
   $-\ 2\frac{5}{12} = 2\frac{5}{12} = 2\frac{5}{12}$
   $1\frac{11}{12}$

2. $6\frac{3}{5} = 6\frac{6}{10} = 5\frac{16}{10}$ (6 − 1; $\frac{10}{10} + \frac{6}{10}$)
   $-\ \frac{9}{10} = \frac{9}{10} = \frac{9}{10}$
   $5\frac{7}{10}$

3. $8 = 7\frac{5}{5}$ (8 − 1; $\frac{5}{5} + \frac{0}{5}$)
   $-\ 3\frac{3}{5} = 3\frac{3}{5}$

4. $5\frac{1}{2}$ $-\ 2\frac{2}{3}$

5. $9\frac{3}{5}$ $-\ 4\frac{3}{4}$

6. $5\frac{1}{6}$ $-\ 2\frac{1}{2}$

7. 8 $-\ 6\frac{2}{3}$

8. $3\frac{1}{4}$ $-\ \frac{5}{8}$

9. 12 $-\ 5\frac{2}{3}$

10. $7\frac{1}{5}$ $-\ 4\frac{2}{3}$

11. $6\frac{1}{16}$ $-\ \frac{3}{4}$

Name ______________________________

Using the Strategies

On the first of January, Dione has $75 in her bank account. On the last day of January she deposits $5 into her account. On the last day of each month, she plans to deposit twice as much as she deposited the previous month. If Dione does not withdraw any money, how much will be in her account on November 16 if she follows her plan?

Drawing a picture, making a table, or looking for a pattern can help in problem solving.

Making a table works here.

Month	Jan.	Feb.	Mar.	Apr.	May	June	July	Aug.	Sept.	Oct.
Deposit	$5	$10	$20	$40	$80	$160	$320	$640	$1,280	$2,560
Month-end Total	$80	$90	$110	$150	$230	$390	$710	$1,350	$2,630	$5,190

On November 1, Kelly will have $5,190 in her account.

Solve. Draw a picture, make a table, or look for a pattern.

1. During the matinee at Cinema 4 movie theater there was 1 person sitting in the first row, 2 people in the second row, 3 people in the third row, and so on. If the theater has 22 rows, how many people were at the matinee?

____

2. The Emerson Middle School Bowling League has 10 teams. If each team bowls against each other team 3 times, how many games will be bowled?

____

3. Piero grows tomatoes in his garden. Each day he picks 3 tomatoes. How many tomatoes did he pick after 3 weeks?

____

4. The debate club has 8 members. Each member will debate each of the other members. How many debates will they have?

____

Name ______________________________

Discovering Methods of Computing

ICON the robot has discovered a new way to add and subtract fractions. This is how ICON does it.

Subtract $\frac{2}{3} - \frac{1}{2}$.

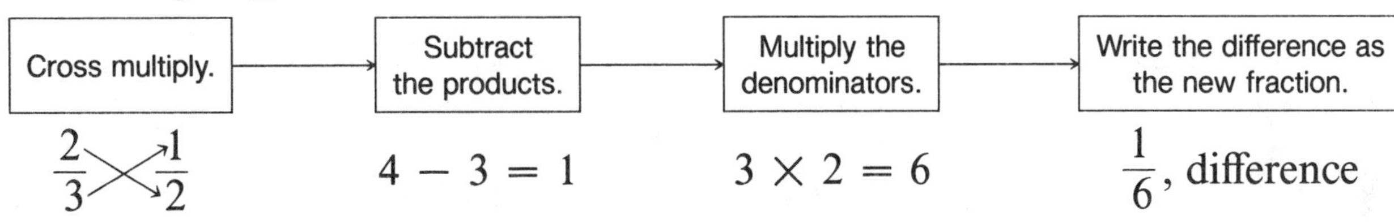

$\frac{2}{3} \times \frac{1}{2}$ $\quad 4 - 3 = 1 \quad 3 \times 2 = 6 \quad \frac{1}{6}$, difference

Use ICON's method to add or subtract. Write the number to show your thinking. The first one has been done for you.

1. $\frac{2}{3} + \frac{3}{4}$
2. $\frac{6}{5} - \frac{1}{2}$
3. $\frac{1}{2} + \frac{1}{4}$
4. $\frac{1}{3} + \frac{2}{5}$
5. $\frac{5}{8} - \frac{1}{4}$
6. $\frac{2}{3} + \frac{1}{6}$
7. $\frac{3}{5} - \frac{1}{7}$
8. $\frac{1}{2} + \frac{1}{3}$
9. $\frac{4}{3} - \frac{5}{6}$
10. $\frac{1}{5} + \frac{3}{4}$
11. $\frac{3}{7} - \frac{1}{3}$
12. $\frac{1}{5} + \frac{1}{8}$

Name ______________________________

Thinking About Functions

Function

baseball — 8
soccer — 6
tennis — 6
surfing — 7

Matched to more than 1 element. →

Not a Function

sports — o
helmet — e
bases — e, a
ball — a

Each word is matched to the number of letters it has.

Each word is matched to its vowels.

A **function** is a matching of one element of the first set to exactly one element of the second set.

Tell whether the relationship shown is a function.

1.

triangle — 3
square — 4
pentagon — 5

____

2.

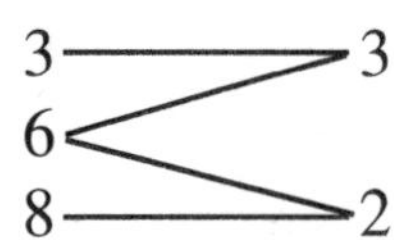

____

3.

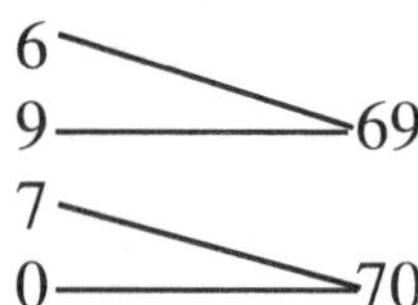

____

4.

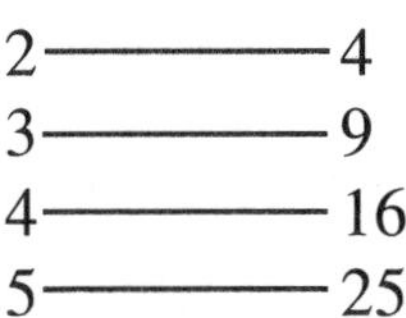

____

5.

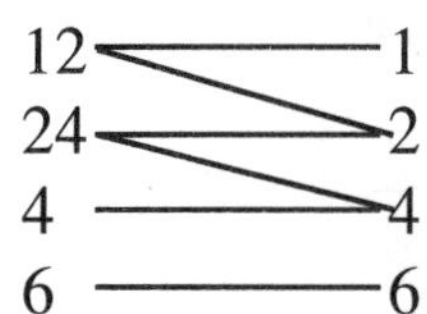

____

6.

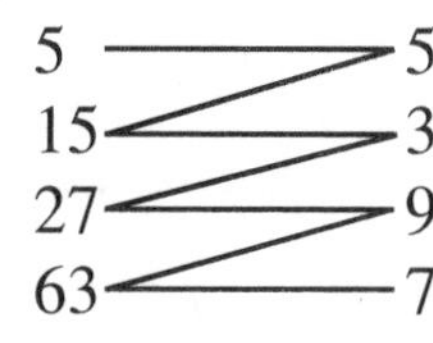

____

Tell whether the relationship that matches each first member of the ordered pair to the second number of the ordered pair is a function.

7. (0,1) (1,2) (2,3) ________

8. (0,1) (1,3) (0,5) (2,7) ________

9. (2,3) (2,6) (2,9) (2,12) ________

10. (3,2) (6,2) (9,2) (12,2) ________

11. (0,3) (3,0) (9,1) (1,9) (2,3) ________

12. (10,5) (8,4) (6,3) (4,2) (2,1) ________

13. (2,5) (3,6) (4,7) (5,9) (3,7) ________

14. (1,1) (2,2) (3,3) (4,4) (5,5) ________

Name ______________________________

Multiplying Fractions and Whole Numbers

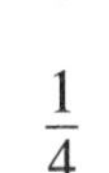

$\frac{1}{4}$	$\frac{1}{4}$	$\frac{1}{4}$	$\frac{1}{4}$

There are 12 coins in the set.

You think: $\frac{1}{4}$ of 12 is 3.

You write: $\frac{1}{4} \times 12 = 3$.

To find $\frac{1}{4}$ of a number, divide the number by 4.

You think: $\frac{3}{4}$ of 12 is 9.

You write: $\frac{3}{4} \times 12 = 9$.

To find $\frac{3}{4}$ of a number find $\frac{1}{4}$ of the number, then multiply by 3.

Ring the dots. Find the fraction of the number.

1. $\frac{1}{3}$ $\frac{1}{3}$ $\frac{1}{3}$

$\frac{1}{3}$ of 6 is 2.

$\frac{2}{3}$ of 6 is 4. (2 × 2)

2. $\frac{1}{8}$

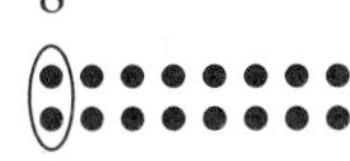

$\frac{1}{8}$ of 16 is ______.

$\frac{3}{8}$ of 16 is ______. (2 × 3)

3.

$\frac{1}{3}$ of 12 is ______.

$\frac{2}{3}$ of 12 is ______.

4.

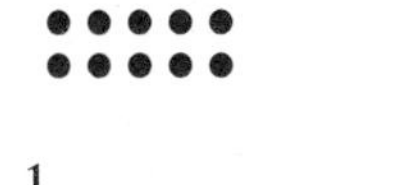

$\frac{1}{5}$ of 20 is ______.

$\frac{2}{5}$ of 20 is ______.

5.

$\frac{1}{6}$ of 18 is ______.

$\frac{5}{6}$ of 18 is ______.

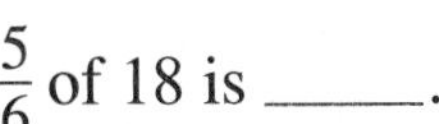

6.

$\frac{1}{10}$ of 30 is ______.

$\frac{3}{10}$ of 30 is ______.

7.

$\frac{1}{8}$ of 16 is ______.

$\frac{5}{8}$ of 16 is ______.

8. $\frac{2}{7} \times 21 =$ ______ **9.** $\frac{5}{6} \times 18 =$ ______ **10.** $\frac{4}{5} \times 40 =$ ______ **11.** $\frac{2}{3} \times 12 =$ ______

12. $\frac{3}{4} \times 28 =$ ______ **13.** $\frac{2}{4} \times 12 =$ ______ **14.** $\frac{1}{2} \times 42 =$ ______ **15.** $\frac{5}{8} \times 16 =$ ______

16. $\frac{9}{10} \times 50 =$ ______ **17.** $\frac{5}{7} \times 14 =$ ______ **18.** $\frac{2}{5} \times 20 =$ ______ **19.** $\frac{3}{4} \times 36 =$ ______

20. $\frac{2}{6} \times 18 =$ ______ **21.** $\frac{7}{8} \times 64 =$ ______ **22.** $\frac{1}{2} \times 46 =$ ______ **23.** $\frac{4}{5} \times 95 =$ ______

Name ______________________________

Multiplying Fractions

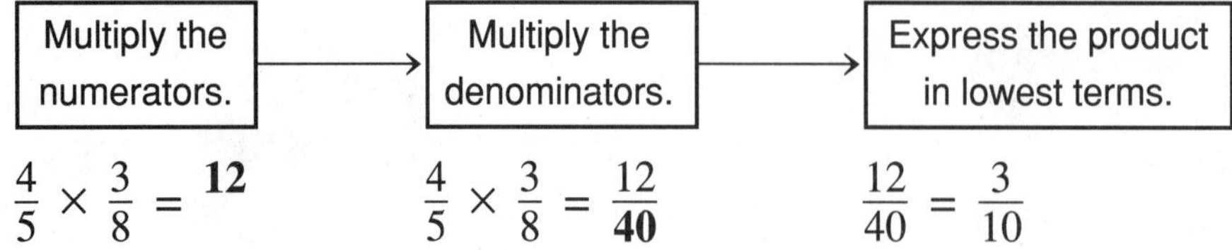

$\frac{4}{5} \times \frac{3}{8} = \mathbf{12}$ $\quad \frac{4}{5} \times \frac{3}{8} = \frac{12}{\mathbf{40}}$ $\quad \frac{12}{40} = \frac{3}{10}$

Here is a shortcut. $\frac{\overset{1}{\cancel{4}}}{5} \times \frac{3}{\underset{2}{\cancel{8}}} = \frac{3}{10}$ Divide a numerator and denominator by then same number, then multiply.

Multiply. Express the product in lowest terms.

1. $\frac{5}{6} \times \frac{1}{4} = \frac{5}{24}$ (5 × 1) (6 × 4)

2. $\frac{6}{1} \times \frac{2}{3} = \frac{12}{3} =$ ______ (Place whole numbers over 1.)

3. $\frac{7}{8} \times \frac{5}{9} = \frac{35}{}$ ______ (8 × 9)

4. $\frac{1}{2} \times \frac{7}{10} =$ ______

5. $\frac{1}{4} \times \frac{2}{3} =$ ______

6. $\frac{1}{2} \times \frac{3}{4} =$ ______

7. $\frac{1}{3} \times \frac{3}{8} =$ ______

8. $\frac{1}{4} \times \frac{1}{4} =$ ______

9. $\frac{4}{5} \times \frac{1}{2} =$ ______

10. $\frac{3}{5} \times \frac{5}{6} =$ ______

11. $\frac{2}{3} \times \frac{7}{8} =$ ______

12. $\frac{9}{10} \times \frac{2}{3} =$ ______

13. $\frac{3}{4} \times \frac{8}{9} =$ ______

14. $\frac{4}{5} \times \frac{5}{8} =$ ______

15. $\frac{3}{16} \times \frac{2}{3} =$ ______

16. $\frac{2}{5} \times \frac{1}{4} =$ ______

17. $\frac{3}{10} \times \frac{5}{6} =$ ______

18. $\frac{3}{5} \times \frac{5}{12} =$ ______

19. $\frac{3}{7} \times \frac{7}{12} =$ ______

20. $\frac{1}{8} \times \frac{4}{5} =$ ______

21. $\frac{4}{5} \times \frac{9}{16} =$ ______

Name ______________________________

Multiplying Mixed Numbers

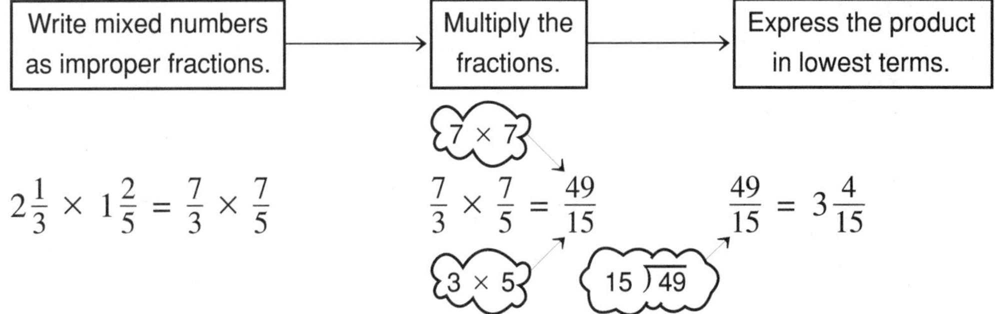

Multiply. Express the product in lowest terms.

1. $1\frac{3}{4} \times \frac{1}{2}$ = $\frac{7}{4} \times \frac{1}{2} = \frac{7}{8}$

$\frac{4 \times 1 + 3}{4}$

2. $2\frac{1}{3} \times 5$ = $\frac{7}{3} \times \frac{5}{1}$ = ______

Place whole numbers over 1.

3. $3 \times 2\frac{2}{3}$ = ______

4. $2\frac{1}{5} \times 2\frac{1}{5}$ = ______

5. $7\frac{3}{4} \times 9$ = ______

6. $\frac{2}{5} \times 2\frac{3}{8}$ = ______

7. $1\frac{1}{4} \times 2\frac{1}{2}$ = ______

8. $4\frac{2}{12} \times 3$ = ______

9. $3\frac{3}{4} \times 5\frac{1}{10}$ = ______

10. $4\frac{3}{12} \times 2$ = ______

Estimate each product.

11. $\frac{2}{3} \times 3\frac{1}{3} \times 2\frac{1}{4}$ = ______

12. $4 \times 4\frac{5}{15} \times \frac{3}{4}$ = ______

13. $5\frac{1}{2} \times \frac{3}{4}$ = ______

14. $9\frac{1}{3} \times 2\frac{5}{8}$ = ______

15. $5\frac{7}{8} \times 1\frac{1}{10} \times 1\frac{1}{9}$ = ______

16. $7\frac{2}{3} \times 5\frac{4}{10} \times \frac{9}{10}$ = ______

Name ______________________________

Dividing Fractions

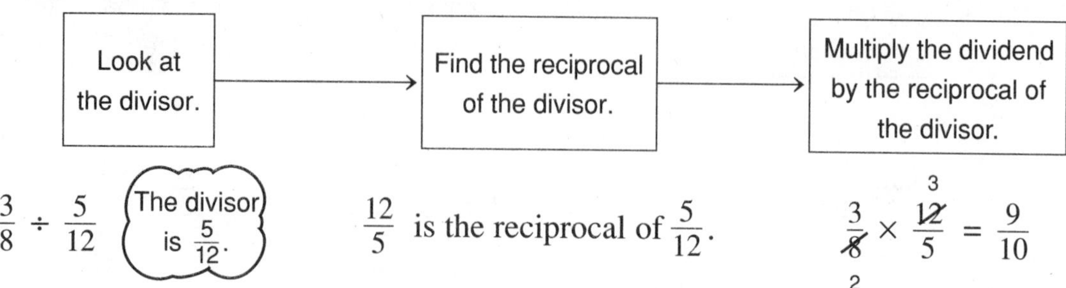

Divide. Express the quotient in lowest terms.

1. $\frac{3}{4} \div \frac{2}{3}$ $\frac{3}{4} \times \frac{3}{2} = \frac{9}{8} = 1\frac{1}{8}$ (reciprocal)

2. $\frac{3}{8} \div 2$ $\frac{3}{8} \times \frac{1}{2} =$ (Use the reciprocal of $\frac{2}{1}$.)

3. $\frac{6}{9} \div \frac{1}{3}$ ________

4. $\frac{4}{5} \div \frac{3}{9}$ ________

5. $\frac{3}{8} \div \frac{5}{6}$ ________

6. $\frac{4}{5} \div 6$ ________

7. $\frac{2}{8} \div \frac{3}{7}$ ________

8. $\frac{1}{5} \div 4$ ________

9. $\frac{4}{10} \div \frac{2}{5}$ ________

10. $8 \div \frac{3}{9}$ ________

11. $\frac{5}{12} \div \frac{4}{8}$ ________

12. $7 \div \frac{5}{6}$ ________

13. $\frac{2}{3} \div 4$ ________

14. $\frac{1}{5} \div 10$ ________

15. $\frac{5}{16} \div \frac{7}{10}$ ________

16. $\frac{3}{5} \div \frac{7}{8}$ ________

17. $1 \div \frac{2}{9}$ ________

18. $\frac{4}{11} \div \frac{3}{8}$ ________

Name ______________________________

Dividing Mixed Numbers

Write mixed numbers or whole numbers as improper fractions. → Multiply by the reciprocal of the divisor. → Complete the operations.

$6\frac{7}{8} \div 2\frac{1}{16} = \frac{55}{8} \div \frac{33}{16}$ $\qquad \frac{55}{8} \times \frac{16}{33}$ $\qquad \frac{\overset{5}{\cancel{55}}}{\underset{1}{\cancel{8}}} \times \frac{\overset{2}{\cancel{16}}}{\underset{3}{\cancel{33}}} = \frac{10}{3} = 3\frac{1}{3}$

Simplify where possible.

Find the quotient. Reduce to lowest terms.

1. $1\frac{5}{6} \div \frac{3}{8} = \frac{11}{6} \div \frac{3}{8} = \frac{11}{6} \times \frac{8}{3} = \frac{44}{9} = 4\frac{8}{9}$ (Use the reciprocal.)

2. $2\frac{3}{10} \div 15 = \frac{23}{10} \div \frac{15}{1} = \frac{23}{10} \times \frac{1}{15} =$ ______

3. $5\frac{5}{6} \div 1\frac{1}{2} =$ ______

4. $4\frac{3}{4} \div 2\frac{1}{5} =$ ______

5. $2 \div 3\frac{6}{7} =$ ______

6. $4\frac{1}{2} \div 3 =$ ______

7. $\frac{3}{11} \div 2\frac{2}{3} =$ ______

8. $4\frac{5}{8} \div 3\frac{2}{9} =$ ______

9. $7\frac{4}{5} \div 2\frac{1}{3} =$ ______

10. $6 \div 2\frac{1}{2} =$ ______

11. $\frac{9}{10} \div 4\frac{2}{3} =$ ______

12. $\frac{6}{7} \div 5\frac{1}{6} =$ ______

13. $8\frac{2}{5} \div 4\frac{3}{8} =$ ______

14. $3\frac{1}{2} \div 3\frac{1}{2} =$ ______

Estimate each quotient.

15. $6\frac{2}{7} \div 1\frac{9}{10}$ ______

16. $2\frac{1}{6} \div \frac{1}{3}$ ______

17. $21\frac{1}{9} \div 2\frac{7}{8}$ ______

18. $9\frac{1}{8} \div 3\frac{1}{9}$ ______

19. $\frac{13}{15} \div \frac{4}{15}$ ______

20. $29\frac{8}{9} \div 5\frac{9}{10}$ ______

Name ____________________

Determining Reasonable Answers

Do not solve the problem. Decide if the answer given is reasonable. If it is not reasonable, explain why.

Estimate using rounded or compatible numbers.

Example:

There are 2,436 seats in the football stadium. The seats are arrange in rows. Each row has 42 seats. How many rows are in the stadium?

Answer: There are 582 rows.

Check: 582 may not be reasonable.
Divide to find how many 42's are in 2,436.
2,436 ÷ 42 is about 2,400 ÷ 40 or 60.
So, 582 is not reasonable.

The answer should be close to 60.

---

1. As coach of the football team, Mr. Clark ordered 17 footballs at $28.79 each. How much did he spend?

   Answer: Mr. Clark spent $894.30.

   ____

   ____

   ____

2. The team played 57 games last year and 87 games this year. How many games were played in these 2 years?

   Answer: The team played 194 games.

   ____

   ____

   ____

3. During yesterday's game, Mr. Clark's team scored 45 points. Of these points, $\frac{5}{9}$ of them were scored by Mario, the team's best wide receiver. How many points did Mario score?

   Answer: Mario scored 20 points.

   ____

   ____

   ____

4. Mario scored 36 points in the first game, 18 points in the second game, and 31 points in the thired game. How many points does he need to score in the last game to score 100 points?

   Answer: Mario needs 15 points.

   ____

   ____

   ____

5. Out of 70 games, 25 were home games. Of the remaining games, $\frac{1}{5}$ were played out of state. How many games were played out of state?

   Answer: 45 games played out of state.

   ____

   ____

   ____

6. The football team traveled 603 miles by bus for 9 games. What was the average number of miles traveled for each game?

   Answer: 67 miles per game.

   ____

   ____

   ____

Name ______________________________

Algebraic Expressions: Addition and Subtraction

Diagrams can help you understand algebraic expressions.

Word Phrase	Diagram	Expression
cost increased by $3	c, 3	$c + 3$
age decreased by 2	a ?, 2	$a - 2$
weight plus 4	w	$w + 4$

Draw a line from the expression to the correct diagram.

1. $x + 5$ **2.** $x - 5$ **3.** $5 - x$

5
?, x

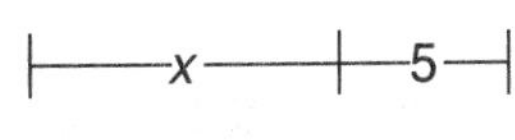

x
?, 5

Write an algebraic expression for each word phrase.

4. n feet increase by 3.5 feet

____

5. n months less than 6 months

____

6. the sum of n boxes and 24 boxes

____

7. $45 decreased by n dollars

____

8. 1.4 inches less than n inches

____

9. n chairs more than 67

____

10. n books minus 189 books

____

11. n roses decreased by 5 roses

____

12. 6.89 yards plus n yards

____

13. n dresses increased by 23 dresses

____

Name ______________________________

Algebraic Expressions: Multiplication and Division

Diagrams can help you understand algebraic expression.

Word Phrase	Diagram	Expression
length m divided by 4	m	$\frac{m}{4}$
3 times weight t	t t t	$3t$
the product of 4 and a cost c	c c c c	$4c$
feet divided by 3	f	$\frac{f}{3}$

Draw a line from the expression to the correct diagram.

1. $2r$ **2.** $\frac{r}{2}$ **3.** $3r$

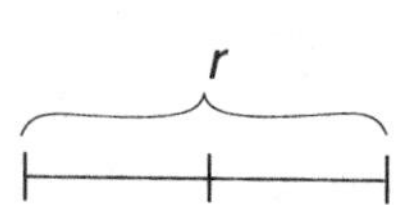

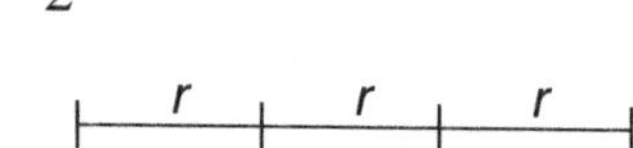

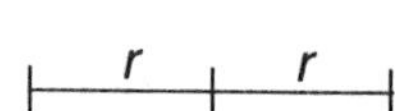

Write an algebraic expression for each word phrase.

4. a cost 7 times as much as c ________

5. an area a divided into 3 equal parts ________

6. 5 times a perimeter p ________

7. 8 pounds divided by n parts ________

8. the product of 6 and x ________

9. n inches divided by 12 inches ________

Write an algebraic expression that tells you how many:

10. inches are in x yards ________

11. hours in x days ________

12. ounces are in x pounds ________

13. dimes are in x dollars ________

14. centimeters are in x meters ________

15. candles are in x dozen ________

Write an algebraic expression that tells how to change:

16. n days into years ________

17. n ounces into pounds ________

18. n feet into yards ________

19. n nickels into dollars ________

20. n centimeters into meters ________

21. n inches into yards ________

Draw diagrams for these expression.

22. $3d$ **23.** $4y$ **24.** $\frac{r}{3}$

Name ____________________

Translating Phrases into Algebraic Expressions

Algebraic expressions can be used to solve many types of problems. The variable represents the number that is missing.

Examples: **A** 12 seats were added to the orchestra pit.

$12 \quad + \quad x$

Use x to represent the number of seats that were in the orchestra pit.

B He sold 3 times as many violins as John did.

$3 \quad \cdot \quad v \quad$ or $3v$

Use v to represent the number of violins that John sold.

Translate each situation into an algebraic expression.

1. Each music book costs c dollars. The school bought 16 books. Write an expression that tells the total cost of the books.

____

2. Jan paid g dollars for all 15 guitar lessons. Write an expression that tells the cost for one guitar lesson.

____

3. The music shop ordered d sets of drums. Only 6 sets were delivered. Write an expression that tells the number of sets left to be delivered.

____

4. Drumsticks are sold in pairs. Dan sold s drumsticks. Write an expression that tells the number of pairs he sold.

____

5. Last year r records were sold. This year twice that number has been sold. Write an expression that tells the number of records sold this year.

____

6. Last week m cassettes were sold. This week that number has been increased by 11. Write an expression that tells the number of cassettes that were sold this week.

____

7. One new instrument was rented by each of 16 customers. Of those customers, n instruments were returned. Write an expression that tells how many new instruments were still rented.

____

8. Last year x compact discs were sold. This year compact disc sales have tripled. Write an expression that tells the number of compact discs sold this year.

____

Name ______________________________

Solving Equations

Let [X] be the unknown number. ○ means subtract 1, and ● means add 1. Then the picture for 2x – 1 = 3 is:

[X] [X] ○	● ● ●

To solve for the value of [X], isolate [X] on one side. Fill in the missing black or white chips in Steps 1 to 3.

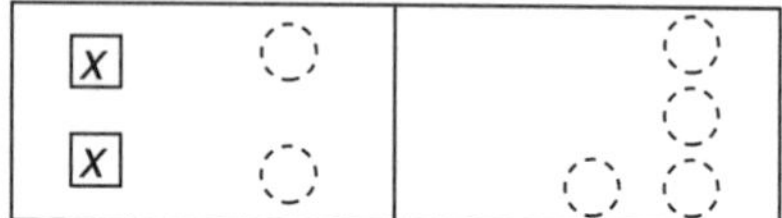

Step 1: Add 1 to each side.

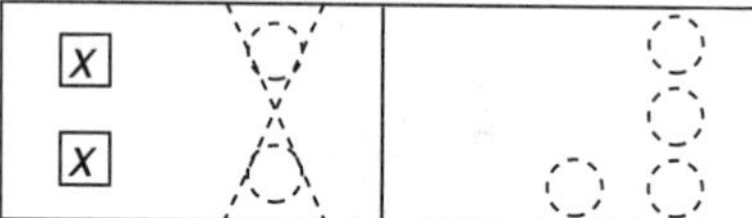

Step 2: The 2 chips on the left side "cancel" each other.

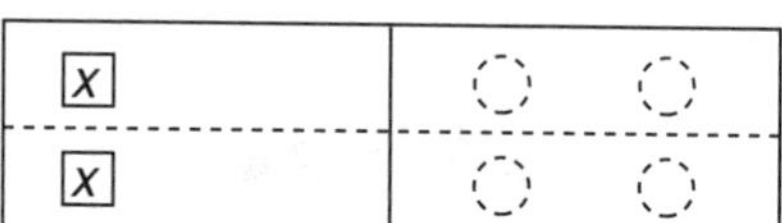

Step 3: Separate into 2 equal groups so $x =$ ________ .

Use objects to find what [X] stands for in terms of chips.

1. 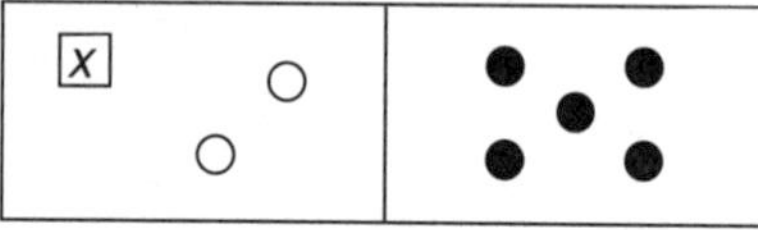

____

2. 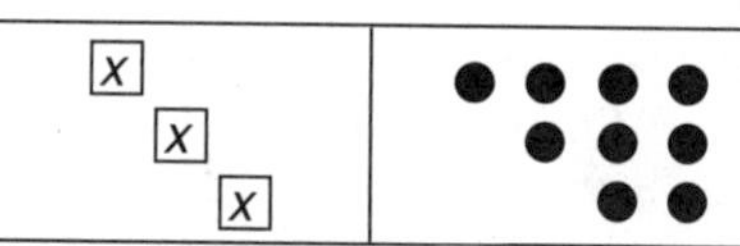

____

3. 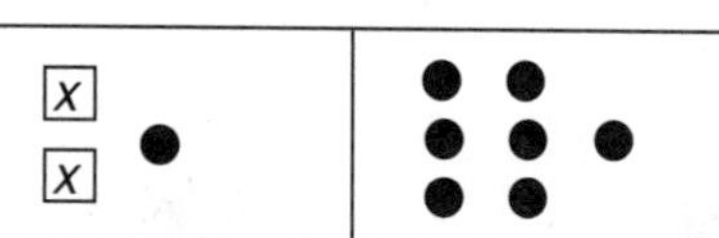

____

4. 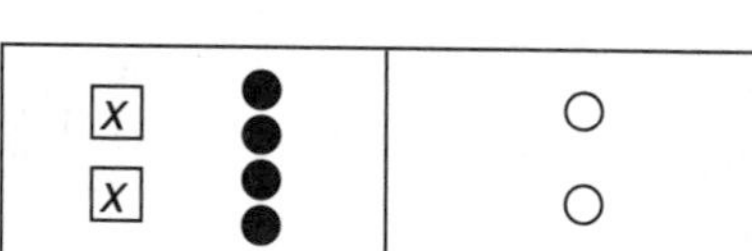

____

5. 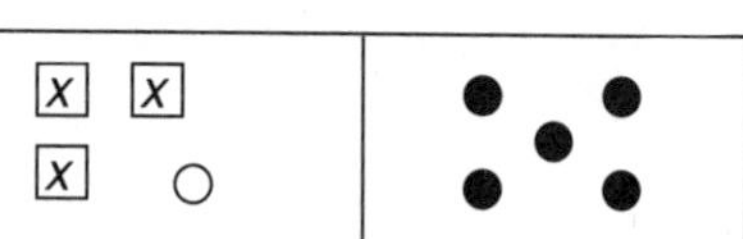

____

6. 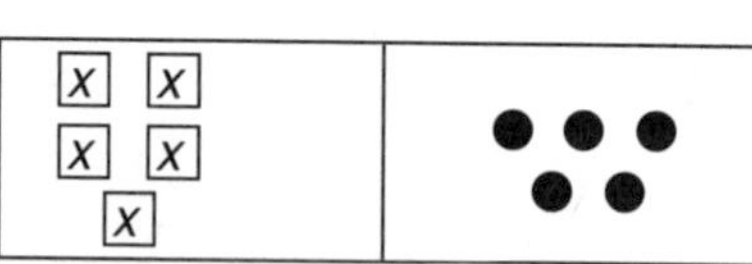

____

7. 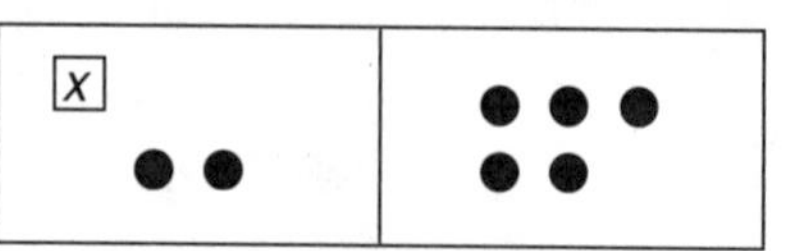

____

8. 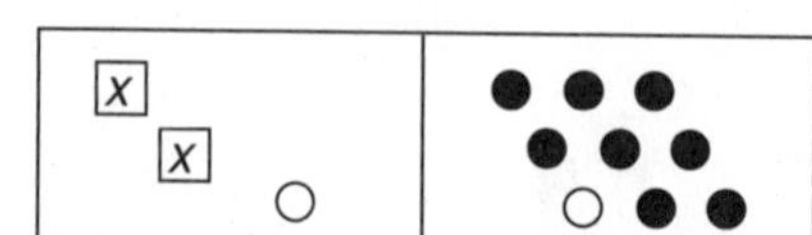

____

Name ______________________________

Analyzing Data to Discover a Pattern

Patterns can be used to solve many problems. Be sure to analyze enough data when you look for a pattern.

The new plant had 2 blossoms on Monday, 4 on Tuesday, and 8 on Wednesday. Predict the number of blossoms for Thursday

The same patterns can lead to different predictions.

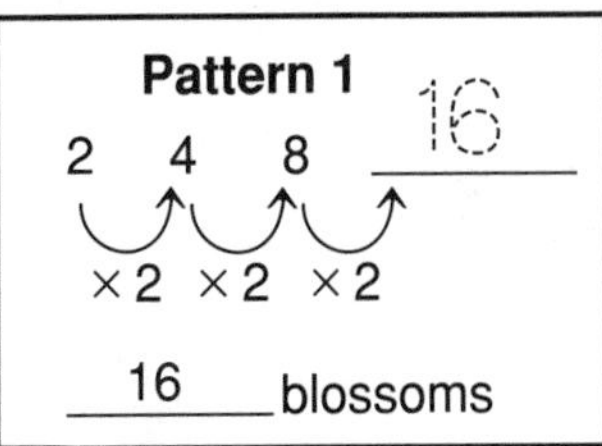

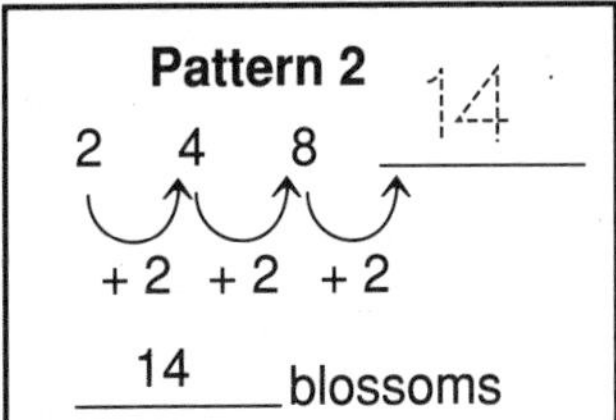

Look for a pattern. Find the missing numbers.
Then explain your pattern.

1.

Inches	Cost
10	$90
20	$180
30	$270
40	
50	

____

2.

Months	Number of Books
June	5
July	10
August	5
September	
October	

____

3.

Days	Number Sold
5	35
6	
7	49
8	
9	63

____

4.

Minutes	Number Made
15	5
30	20
36	
42	32
	54

____

5.

Feet	Time
2	4:00
3	4:30
5	5:00
8	5:30
	6:00

____

6.

Cost	Number of Pens
$2.40	10
$3.12	13
$1.92	
	7
$4.56	

____

Name ______________________________

Solving Equations and Mental Math

Use mental math to solve each equation.

Look at the equation. → Isolate the variable. → Use mental math if possible. → Check.

Examples:

$a + 8 = 72$ $a + 8 - 8 = 72 - 8$ $a = 72 - 8$ $64 + 8 = 72$ ✓
$a = 64$

The equation remains balanced.

$\frac{r}{15} = 6$ $\frac{15}{1} \bullet \frac{r}{15} = 6 \bullet 15$ $r = 6 \bullet 15$ $\frac{90}{15} = 6$ ✓
$r = 90$

---

1. $2v = 36$, $v =$ ______

2. $\frac{1}{2}y = 36$, $y =$ ______

3. $b - 42 = 24$, $b =$ ______

4. $11 + c = 84$, $c =$ ______

5. $181 + x = 200$, $x =$ ______

6. $\frac{t}{4} = 8$, $t =$ ______

7. $18a = 9$, $a =$ ______

8. $64 - c = 12$, $c =$ ______

Decide which equations can be solved using mental math.
Solve only those equations.

9. $23q = 69$

____

10. $\frac{2}{3}b = 44$

____

11. $5{,}836 - b = 725$

____

12. $\frac{486}{m} = 27$

____

Check the answers. Correct those that are wrong.

13. $16r = 4$, $r = \frac{1}{4}$ ______

14. $96 - s = 80$, $s = 16$ ______

15. $b + 18 = 30$, $b = 12$ ______

16. $\frac{x}{6} = 12$, $x = 64$ ______

17. $\frac{1}{2}m = 54$, $m = 27$ ______

18. $p - 11 = 87$, $p = 98$ ______

Name ______________________________

Problem Solving: Using Guess and Check to Solve Equations

Solve the equations using the strategy Guess and Check. Use a complete sentence to answer the question.

Example:
Sylvie saved \$336 from her summer earnings. Her average savings were \$42 per week. How many weeks did she work?

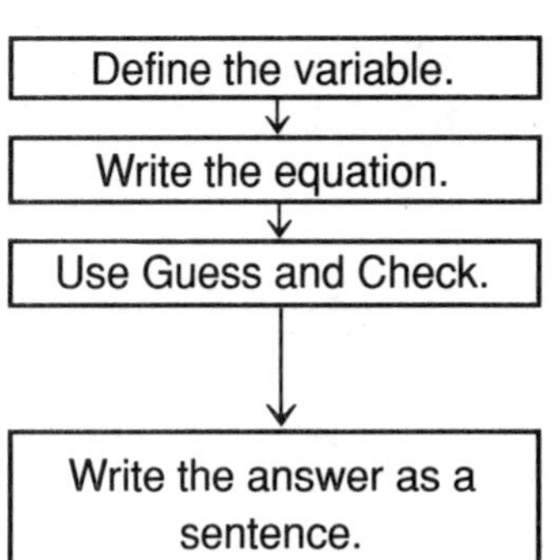

Let w be the number of weeks.

Solve $\frac{336}{w} = 42$ to find the number of weeks.

Try $c = 7$: $\frac{336}{7} = 48$—too low

Try $c = 8$: $\frac{336}{8} = 42$—correct

She worked 8 weeks.

---

1. Joe, Laura, and Penny ate take-out Chinese food. Laura ordered all the food and paid the \$10.15 bill. Laura's share was \$2.50, Joe's was \$3.90. How much does Penny owe Laura?

Let p be Penny's share.
Solve $2.50 + 3.90 + p = 10.15$ to find Penny's share.

$p =$ ______ ______________________________

2. Jack saved \$10.60 when he bought a new catcher's mitt during a 20% off sale. What was the original price of the mitt?

Let g be the original price of the mitt.
Solve $0.20\,g = 10.60$ to find the original price.

$g =$ ______ ______________________________

Solve. Use Guess and Check.

3. $7q = 392$ $q =$ ______

4. $b + 172 = 321$ $b =$ ______

5. $\frac{z}{12} = 13$ $z =$ ______

Name ______________________________

Inverse Operations

Find the answers. Look for a pattern.

$5 + 3 - 3$ ______ $6 + 4 - 4$ ______ $78 + 45 - 45$ ______

$28 - 7 + 7$ ______ $176 - 89 + 89$ ______ $123 - 78 + 78$ ______

The same pattern is used below.

$y + 13 - 13$ ______ $w + 45 - 45$ ______ $m + 167 - 167$ ______

$b - 90 + 90$ ______ $i - 166 + 166$ ______ $p - 234 + 234$ ______

An inverse operation can undo another operation. Inverse operations are used to get the variable alone.

The picture shows $x + 4.7$.
To find x, use the inverse operation:

$x + 4.7 - 4.7$

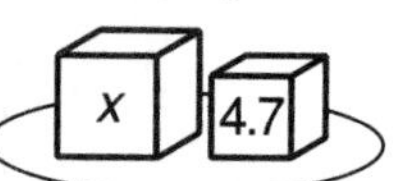

Give the inverse operation.

1. adding 65.9 ______

2. subtracting 7.98 ______

3. adding 14.14 ______

Give the inverse operation that would get the variable alone.

4. $x - 3$ ______

5. $n + 3.4$ ______

6. $a - 6.72$ ______

Write an algebraic expression for each picture. Then give the inverserse operation that would get the variable alone.

7.

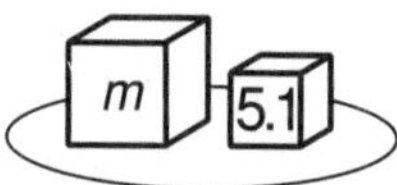

______

8.

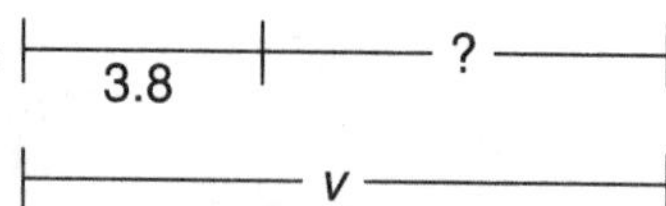

______

9.

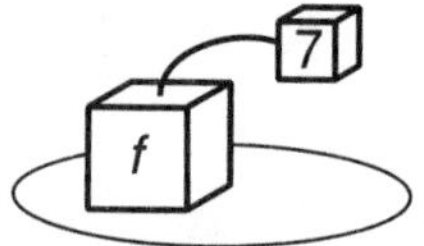

______

Write an algebraic expression for each phrase. Then give the inverse operation.

10. 7 increased by t ______

11. 7.8 less than f ______

12. 12.3 plus r ______

13. h less 54 ______

14. $6\frac{1}{4}$ older than k ______

15. the sum of t and 98 ______

Name ______________________________

Solve Addition and Subraction Equations

Find x by using inverse operations.

Decide which inverse operation to use. | $x - 12 = 33$ (12 is subtracted. The inverse operation is adding 12.)

Use the inverse operation on both sides of the equation. | $x - 12 + 12 = 33 + 12$

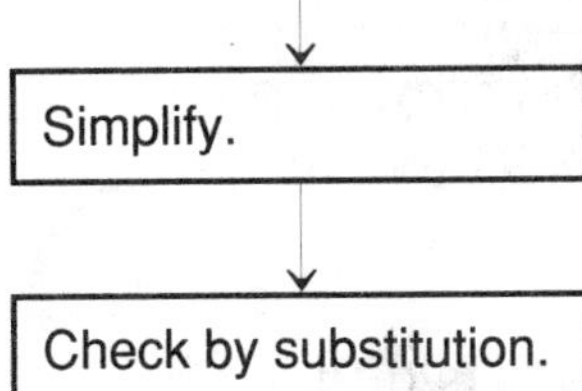

Simplify: $x - \cancel{12 + 12} = 33 + 12$

$x = 45$

Check by substitution:

$x - 12 = 33$

$45 - 12 = 33$

$33 = 33$ (Both sides are equal.)

Solve and check.

1. $h + 13 = 479$

$h + 13$ ______ $= 479$ ______

$h =$ ______

2. $13.4 = g + 7.8$

13.4 ______ $= g + 7.8$ ______

______ $= g$

3. $t + 8 = 19$

$t + 8$ ______ $= 19$ ______

$t =$ ______

4. $m - 7 = 32$

$m =$ ______

5. $67.5 = v - 4.56$

______ $= v$

6. $s - 123 = 21$

$s =$ ______

7. $w - 12.89 = 5.76$

$w =$ ______

8. $r + 45 = 62$

$r =$ ______

9. $41.7 = b + 9.9$

______ $= b$

10. $38 = j + 12.6$

______ $= j$

11. $89 = y - 54$

______ $= y$

12. $p - 90 = 34$

$p =$ ______

13. $k - 1\frac{1}{2} = 3$

$k =$ ______

14. $q + 2\frac{1}{4} = 6$

$q =$ ______

15. $n - 2 = 5\frac{1}{2}$

$n =$ ______

16. $h - 3\frac{1}{2} = 1\frac{1}{4}$

$h =$ ______

17. $12\frac{3}{5} + x = 16\frac{4}{5}$

$x =$ ______

18. $5\frac{1}{3} = z - 2\frac{1}{2}$

______ $= z$

Name ____________________

More Inverse Operations

An inverse operation will undo another operation.

____________ is the inverse operation of division.

____________ is the inverse operation of multiplication.

Use inverse operations to get the variable alone.

Examples:

A The cost of 7 tennis ractets is $7t$.

What is the cost of one racket?

$\frac{7t}{7}$

t is multiplied by 7. The inverse operation is dividing by 7.

B There are 3 tennis balls in each can. The cost of 1 tennis ball is $\frac{x}{3}$.

What is the cost of a can of tennis balls?

$\frac{x}{3} \bullet 3$

x is divided by 3. The inverse operation is muliplying by 3.

Give the inverse operation that would get the variable alone.

1. $\frac{n}{52}$ ____________

2. $5.8m$ ____________

3. $\frac{y}{9.1}$ ____________

4. $67g$ ____________

5. $t \div 61$ ____________

6. $9.74e$ ____________

7. $c \div 5.4$ ____________

8. $32.5k$ ____________

9. $\frac{i}{7.8}$ ____________

Write an algebraic expression for each. Then give the inverse oepration that would get the variable alone.

10. Three time m miniutes ____________

11. half of p pounds ____________

12. six times length x ____________

13. y yards cut in 9 equal lengths ____________

14. 7.5 times higher than r ____________

15. twice Tom's age (t) ____________

16. area n divided by 5.3 ____________

17. a third of d dollars ____________

18. five times m meters ____________

Name ______________________________

Solving Multiplication and Division Equations

Find x by using inverse operations.

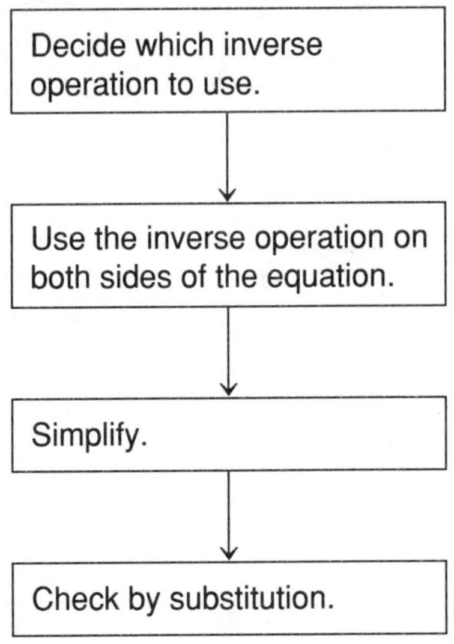

$\frac{x}{7} = 6.3$

x is divided by 7. The inverse operation is multiplying by 7.

$\frac{x}{7} \cdot 7 = 6.3 \cdot 7$

$x = 44.1$

$\frac{x}{7} = 6.3$

$\frac{44.1}{7} = 6.3$

$6.3 = 6.3$

Both sides are equal.

Solve and check using a calculator.

1. $12d = 276$

$\frac{12d}{\square} = \frac{276}{\square}$

$d =$ ______

2. $\frac{i}{3} = 29$

$\frac{i}{3} \cdot$ ____ $= 29 \cdot$ ____

$i =$ ______

3. $3.5g = 32.2$

$\frac{3.5g}{\square} = \frac{32.2}{\square}$

$g =$ ______

4. $450 = \frac{k}{15}$

______ $= k$

5. $67.8 = 22.6h$

______ $= h$

6. $8.9 = 5r$

______ $= r$

7. $8t = 504$

$t =$ ______

8. $\frac{i}{8} = 17$

$i =$ ______

9. $8.9 = \frac{y}{12}$

______ $= y$

10. $5.6p = 28$

$p =$ ______

11. $78 = \frac{w}{2}$

$w =$ ______

12. $1{,}110 = 37m$

______ $= m$

Name ______________________________

Ratio

A ratio is a comparison of two numbers.

The ratio of the number of apples to the number of oranges is $\frac{12}{6}$.

Write the ratio in lowest terms.

$$\frac{12}{6} = \frac{2}{1}$$

Use the drawing above to help you. Write the ratio as a fraction in lowest terms.

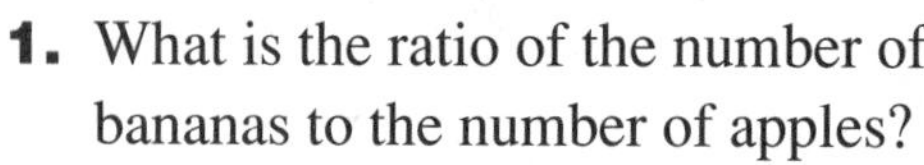

1. What is the ratio of the number of bananas to the number of apples?

____

2. What is the ratio of the number of watermelons to the number of bananas?

____

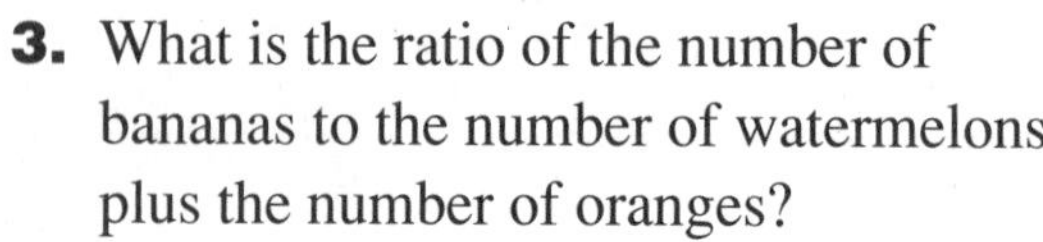

3. What is the ratio of the number of bananas to the number of watermelons plus the number of oranges?

____

4. What is the ratio of the number of apples to the number of oranges plus the number of bananas?

____

5. What is the ratio of the number of apples to all the fruit shown?

____

6. What is the ratio of the number of bananas plus the number of oranges to all the fruit shown?

____

Write the ratio as a fraction in lowest terms.

7. 30 to 36 ______

8. $\frac{60}{42}$ ______

9. 18:2 ______

10. $\frac{24}{16}$ ______

11. 24:15 ______

12. 4 to 24 ______

13. 45:60 ______

14. 36 to 15 ______

15. $\frac{36}{28}$ ______

Name ______________________________

Proportions

Ratios are equal if their cross product equal.

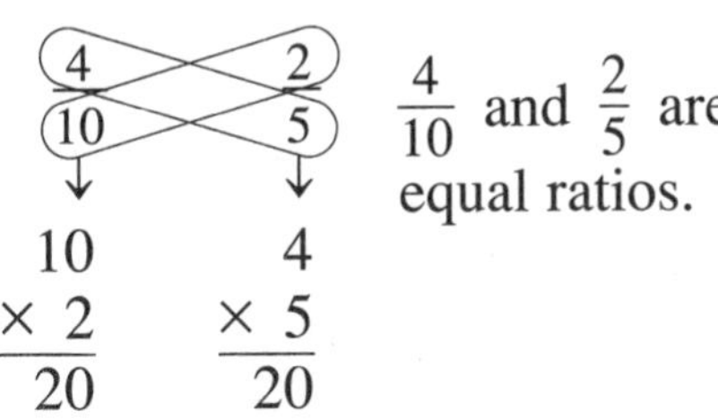

$\frac{4}{10}$ and $\frac{2}{5}$ are equal ratios.

Equal ratios can be written as a proportion.

A proportion: $\frac{4}{10} = \frac{2}{5}$

Write = (equal) or ≠ (not equal) for each ◯.
Use cross products to decide.

1. $\frac{3}{8}$ (=) $\frac{27}{72}$

$$\begin{array}{r} 27 \\ \times\ 8 \\ \hline 216 \end{array} \quad \begin{array}{r} 72 \\ \times\ 3 \\ \hline 216 \end{array}$$

equal

2. $\frac{4}{25}$ (≠) $\frac{12}{85}$

$$\begin{array}{r} 85 \\ \times\ 4 \\ \hline \_\_\_ \end{array} \quad \begin{array}{r} 12 \\ \times\ 25 \\ \hline \_\_\_ \end{array}$$

3. $\frac{8}{15}$ (=) $\frac{40}{75}$

$$\begin{array}{r} 15 \\ \times\ \_\_ \\ \hline \_\_\_ \end{array} \quad \begin{array}{r} 75 \\ \times\ \_ \\ \hline \_\_\_ \end{array}$$

4. $\frac{4}{5}$ ◯ $\frac{8}{10}$ **5.** $\frac{3}{6}$ ◯ $\frac{6}{12}$ **6.** $\frac{3}{4}$ ◯ $\frac{7}{8}$ **7.** $\frac{2}{5}$ ◯ $\frac{8}{11}$

8. $\frac{6}{8}$ ◯ $\frac{9}{12}$ **9.** $\frac{2}{15}$ ◯ $\frac{5}{36}$ **10.** $\frac{14}{15}$ ◯ $\frac{42}{45}$ **11.** $\frac{8}{12}$ ◯ $\frac{16}{24}$

12. $\frac{13}{29}$ ◯ $\frac{8}{17}$ **13.** $\frac{18}{24}$ ◯ $\frac{45}{60}$ **14.** $\frac{9}{12}$ ◯ $\frac{10}{15}$ **15.** $\frac{8}{13}$ ◯ $\frac{16}{24}$

16. $\frac{3}{8}$ ◯ $\frac{15}{40}$ **17.** $\frac{8}{45}$ ◯ $\frac{24}{135}$ **18.** $\frac{17}{21}$ ◯ $\frac{51}{63}$ **19.** $\frac{7}{9}$ ◯ $\frac{15}{27}$

Name ______________________________

Solving Proportions

The animal shelter has 5 cats for every 2 dogs.

The shelter has 6 dogs. How many cats are in the shelter?

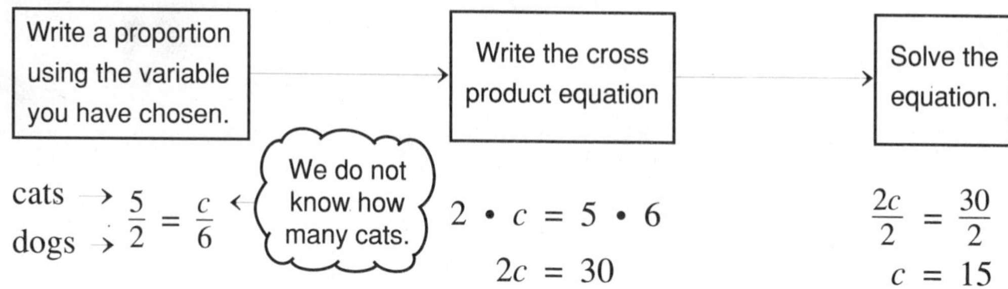

Read the problem. Complete and solve the proportion for the problem.

1. $\frac{3}{5} = \frac{12}{n}$

$3 \cdot n = 5 \cdot 12$

$\frac{3n}{3} = \frac{60}{3}$

$n =$ 20

2. $\frac{x}{24} = \frac{5}{8}$

$8 \cdot x = 24 \cdot 5$

$\frac{8x}{8} = \frac{120}{8}$

$x =$ 15

3. $\frac{3}{r} = \frac{18}{20}$

$r =$ ______

4. $\frac{2}{3} = \frac{14}{t}$

$t =$ ______

Read the problem. Then solve the proportion.

5. The zoo has 3 elephants for every 7 monkeys. It has 21 monkeys. How many elephants are in the zoo?

elephants → $\frac{3}{7} = \frac{e}{21}$ ______
monkeys →

Use a letter for the number of elephants.

6. The lions in the zoo eat 40 kilograms of food every 7 days. How many kilograms do they eat in 28 days?

kilograms → $\frac{40}{7} = \frac{\_\_}{\_\_}$ ______
days →

7. In the fish tank, 4 out of 5 fish are guppies. There are 25 fish in the tank. How many are guppies?

guppies →
fish → ______

8. The shelter has 3 baby animals for every 8 adults. It has 12 baby animals. How many adults are there?

babies →
adults → ______

Name ______________________________

Rate

A **rate** is a ratio that involves two different units.

A rate is usually given as a quantity per unit, such as dollars per hour. This is called a **unit rate**.

Example:

Marty earns $570 in 38 hours. How much does he earn an hour?

$ → 570; hours → 38

$$\frac{570}{38} = \frac{x}{1}$$ Set up a proportion.

$$38x = 570 \cdot 1$$ Cross multiply.

$$\frac{x}{38} = \frac{570}{38}$$ Isolate the variable.

$$x = 15$$ Divide to get the answer.

Find the unit rate.

1. $\frac{\text{16 degrees}}{\text{2 hr}}$ ________

2. $\frac{\text{1,584 computers}}{\text{88 schools}}$ ________

3. $\frac{\text{135 students}}{\text{5 classes}}$ ________

4. $\frac{\text{60 min}}{\text{10 km}}$ ________

5. $\frac{\$588}{\text{42 hr}}$ ________

6. $\frac{\text{7,084 cars}}{\text{88 days}}$ ________

7. $\frac{\$8.72}{\text{4 cheeses}}$ ________

8. $\frac{\$0.99}{\text{3 apples}}$ ________

9. $\frac{\$475}{\text{100 tickets}}$ ________

Solve.

10. Chung made $13.75 for babysitting 5 hours. How much does Chung make an hour babysitting?

____

11. Donna drove 468 miles in 9 hours. How many miles did she drive in 1 hour?

____

12. Lara did 80 sit-ups in 40 seconds. How many sit-ups did she do in 1 second?

____

13. Pat swam 40 laps in 2 hours. How many laps did Pat swim in a half hour?

____

Name ______________________

Unit Pricing

Find the better buy.

Example:

16 oz of butter for $2.20

Let b equal the cost of 1 oz of butter.

$$\frac{2.20}{16} = \frac{b}{1}$$
$$2.20 = 16b$$
$$0.1375 = b$$

OR

10 oz of butter for $1.29

Let m equal the cost of 1 oz of butter.

$$\frac{1.29}{10} = \frac{m}{1}$$
$$1.29 = 10m$$
$$0.129 = m$$

The 10 oz of butter is the better buy.

Solve.

1. At Boudine's Department Store, 3 pairs of earrings cost $5. You can also buy 1 pair for $1.75. Which is the better buy?

   ____

2. At Michael's Sports Store, a 10-pack of socks costs $6 and a 3-pack of socks costs $1.50. Which is the better buy?

   ____

3. Savemart has two different-size apple juice containers: 36 oz of apple juice cost $1.99 and 24 oz of apple juice cost $1.19. Which is the better buy?

   ____

4. A 10-oz can of soup costs $0.59. The same kind of soup in a 19-oz can costs $1.59. Which size can is a better buy?

   ____

5. T-shirts at Murray's are on sale at 3 for $10. Next door at Annie's, they are on sale at 4 for $12. Which store has the better buy?

   ____

6. At Homevideo, you can rent 3 tapes for $6.75. At Movieland, you can rent 1 tape for $2.15. At which store will you get more for your money?

   ____

7. At Parkway Sports Shop, golf balls are 10 for $8.99 or 12 for $10.99. Which package of golf balls is a better buy?

   ____

8. At Music City, 1 album costs $8.99, or you can buy 3 for $25. Which is the better buy?

   ____

Name ______________________________

Using Critical Thinking: Making Judgments

The ancient Greeks considered a rectangle in this shape to be the most pleasant to look at. They named it the Golden Rectangle. The ratio of its length to its width is 1.618:1.

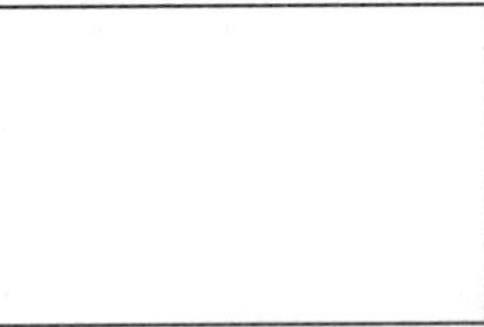

Golden Rectangle

Look at the rectangles below. Judge which rectangles are close in proportion to the Golden Rectangle. Then use your calculator to find each ratio. Round answers to the nearest thousandth.

1. 3, 4 ____________

2. 6, 10 ____________

3.

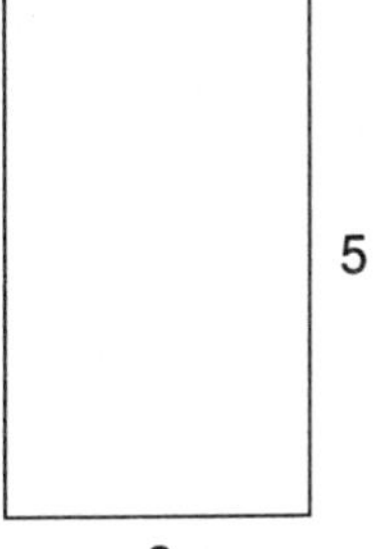

____

4.

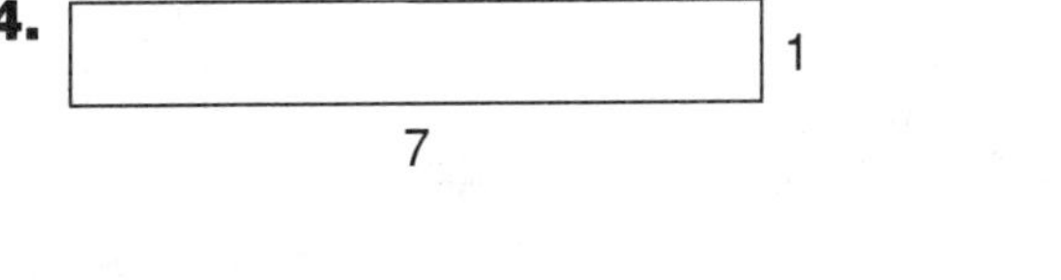

____

5.

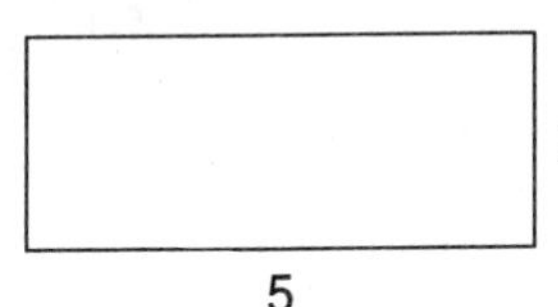

____

6.

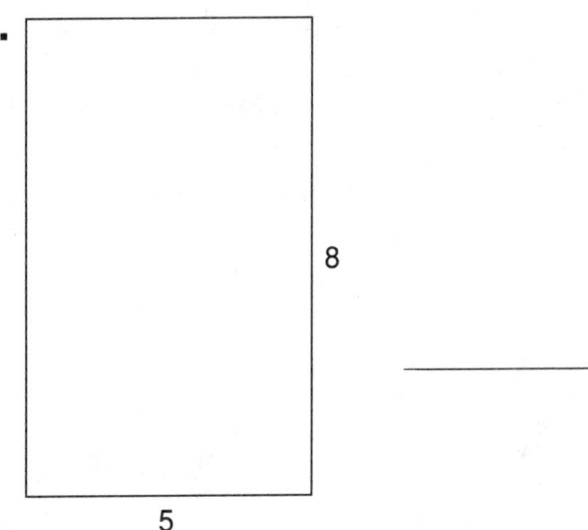

____

Name ______________________________

Scale Drawings

What is the actual length of the rectangle at the right?

$\frac{1}{2}$ in.

$\frac{3}{16}$ in.

Scale: $\frac{1}{8}$ in. = 2 ft

The scale of $\frac{1}{8}$ in. to 2 ft means that $\frac{1}{8}$ in. in the drawing is equivalent to 2 ft of actual length. Make a proportion:

$$\frac{\frac{1}{8}}{2} = \frac{\text{length in drawing}}{\text{actual length}}$$

Solve:

$$\frac{\frac{1}{8}}{2} = \frac{\frac{1}{2}}{a}$$

$$\frac{1}{8} \bullet \frac{a}{1} = \frac{2}{1} \bullet \frac{1}{2}$$

$$\frac{a}{8} = 1$$

$$a = 8$$

The actual length of the rectangle is 8 ft.

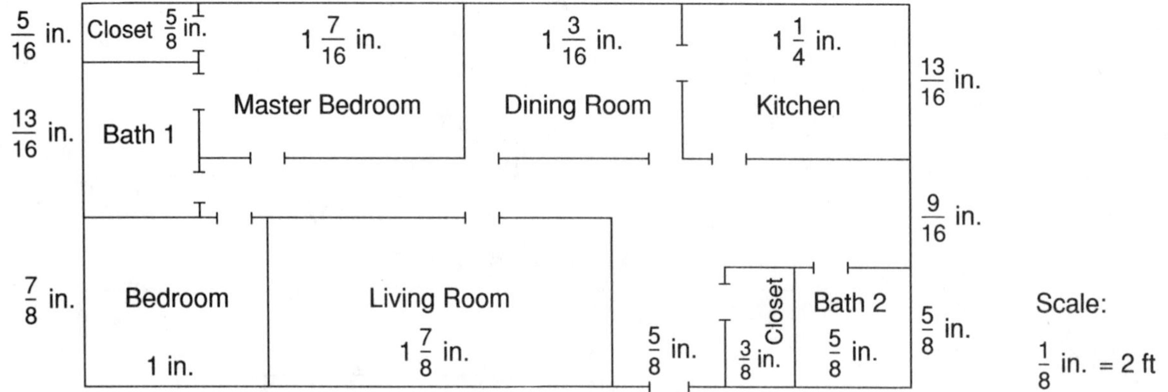

Refer to the scale drawing above to fill in the blanks.

1. Actual length of the master bedroom ____________

2. Actual width of the living room ____________

3. Actual length of the entire apartment ____________

4. Actual width of the entire apartment ____________

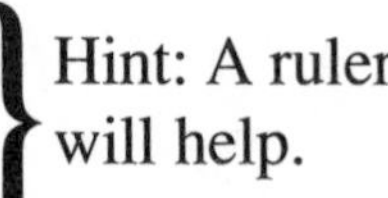

Name ______________________________

Using Variables

Write an algebraic expression to find the number of pages typed in different numbers of hours.

Let h = the number of hours worked.

hours worked	1	2	3	4	5
pages typed	1	4	7	10	13

The rule in words: The number of pages typed is 3 times the number of hours worked minus 2.

$3 \quad \bullet \quad h \quad - \quad 2$

As an algebraic expression: $3h - 2$

Write the rule in words and as an algebraic expression.

Let n = the input number.

1.

input	1	2	3	4	5
output	8	16	24	32	40

____

____

2.

input	1	2	3	4	5
output	4	5	6	7	8

____

____

3.

input	1	2	3	4	5
output	2	7	12	17	22

____

____

4.

input	1	2	3	4	5
output	5	9	13	17	21

____

____

Name ______________________________

Similar Figures

Similar figures have the **same shape.**

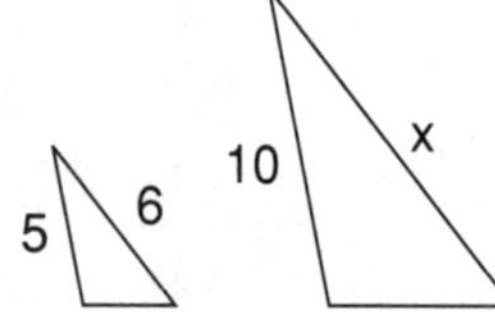

The lengths of the corresponding sides of similar figures have equal ratios.

You can find the length x by writing and solving a proportion.

$$\begin{matrix}\text{small } \triangle \rightarrow \\ \text{large } \triangle \rightarrow\end{matrix} \frac{5}{10} = \frac{6}{x} \begin{matrix}\leftarrow \text{small } \triangle \\ \leftarrow \text{large } \triangle\end{matrix}$$

$$5 \bullet x = 10 \bullet 6$$

$$\frac{5}{5}x = \frac{60}{5}$$

$$x = 12$$

Find the length of x for each pair of similar figures

1.

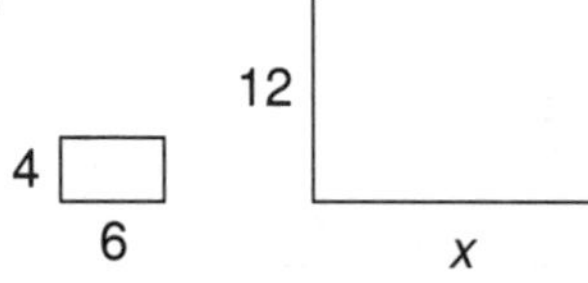

small → $\frac{4}{12} = \frac{6}{x}$ ← large

$4 \bullet x = 6 \bullet 12$

$\frac{4 \bullet x}{4} = \frac{72}{4}$

$x =$ 18

2.

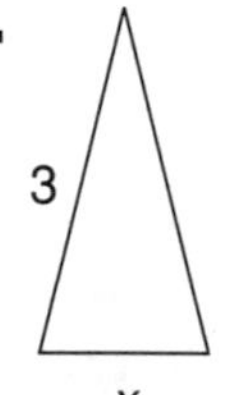

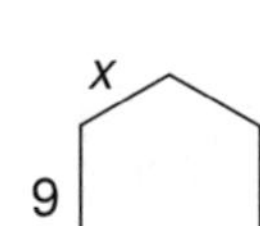

small → $\frac{2}{3} = \frac{1}{x}$ ← large

$x =$ ______

3.

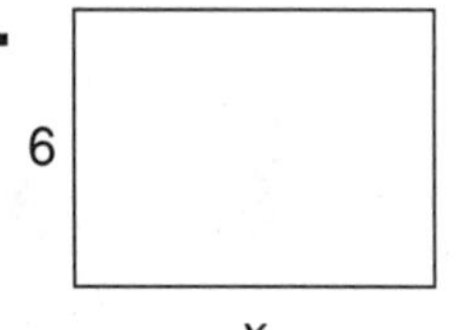

$x =$ ______

4.

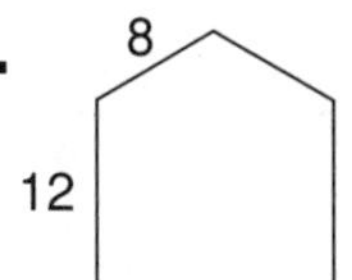

$x =$ ______

5.

$x =$ ______

6.

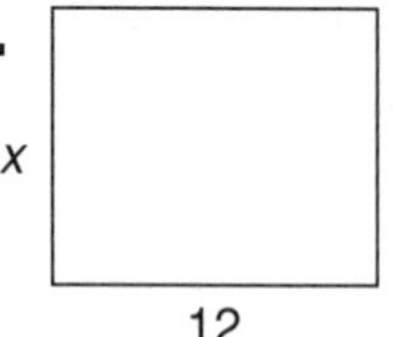

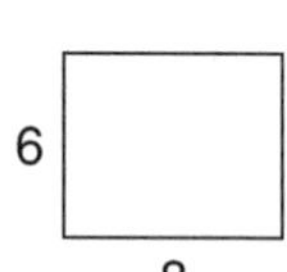

$x =$ ______

7.

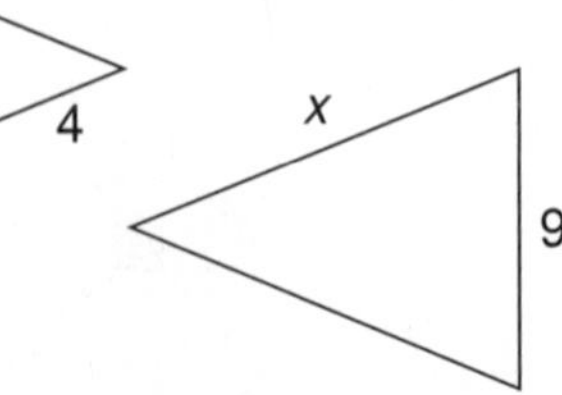

$x =$ ______

8.

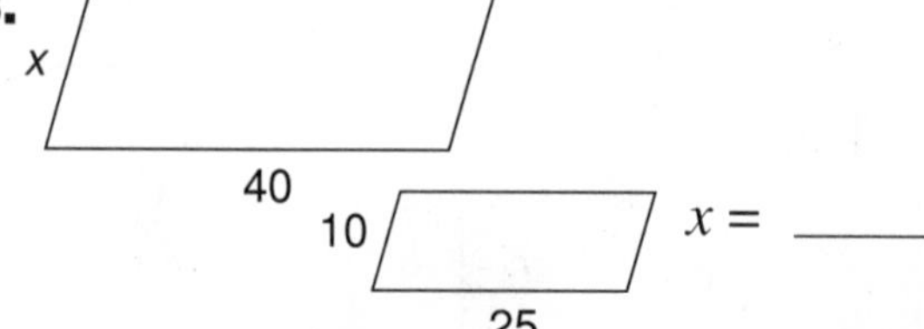

$x =$ ______

Name ____________________

The Special Ratio π

The Greek letter π (pi) is used to represent the ratio of the circumference of a circle to its diameter. ($\pi = \frac{C}{d}$). We commonly use 3.14 or $\frac{22}{7}$ as an approximation for π.

Find the circumference of a circle with a *diameter* of 12 cm.

$C = \pi d$

$C = 3.14(12)$

$C = 37.68$

The circumference is 37.68

Find the circumference of a circle with a *radius* of 8 cm.

$C = 2\pi r$

$C = 2(3.14)(8)$

$C = 50.24$

The circumference is 50.24 cm.

Find the circumference for each diameter or radius. Use 3.14 for π.

1. $d = 10$ cm ________

2. $r = 4$ ft ________

3. $r = 5$ yd ________

4. $d = 7$ in. ________

5. $d = 15$ mm ________

6. $r = 14$ m ________

7. $r = 0.14$ km ________

8. $d = 21$ yd ________

9. $r = 0.14$ cm ________

10. $d = 4$ mm ________

Find the circumference for each diameter or radius. Use $\frac{22}{7}$ for π.

11. $d = 7$ mm ________

12. $d = \frac{1}{2}$ in. ________

13. $r = 7$ ft ________

14. $r = \frac{3}{4}$ yd ________

Name ________________________________

Using the Strategies

Marymount State Park has 4 main hiking trails, each with subtrails. Bluebird trail has half as many subtrails as Overlook trail. Cardinal trail has 6 more subtrails than Bluebird trail. Mountain trail has 7 fewer subtrails than Cardinal. Mountain trail has 8 subtrails. How many subtrails are on Overlook trail?

This problem can be solved using either of these strategies:

Guess and check

$20 \div 2 = 10$	$16 \div 2 = 8$	$18 \div 2 = 9$
$10 + 6 = 16$	$8 + 6 = 14$	$9 + 6 = 15$
$16 - 7 = 9$ too big	$14 - 7 = 7$ too small	$15 - 7 = 8$ correct

Work Backward

Overlook $\xrightarrow{\times 2}$ Bluebird $\xrightarrow{+6}$ Cardinal $\xrightarrow{-7}$ Mountain $\overset{=8}{}$

Working backward: 18 $\xleftarrow{\div 2}$ 9 $\xleftarrow{-6}$ 15 $\xleftarrow{+7}$ 8

Overlook has 18 subtrails.

Solve. Use Guess and Check or Work Backward.

1. Manny went to the school supply store. He spent half of his money on books, half of what was left on paper, $2 less than what he spent on paper on computer disks, and half of what he spent on computer disks on pens. He spent $2 on pens. How much did he spend on supplies?

____

2. In the classroom library there are twice as many biography books as autobiography. There are 3 times more nonfiction than autobiography books. If there are 99 nonfiction books, how many books are in the class library?

____

3. Barry bought a super-big pack of baseball cards. He gave Susan 8. Lara took $1\frac{1}{2}$ times as many as Susan. He gave Kelly 2 fewer than Lara. Barry had $\frac{1}{3}$ of the original total left. How many baseball cards were in the pack?

____

4. On Saturday, Artie sold $\frac{1}{3}$ as many glasses of lemonade as Cori. Dan sold 12 more than Artie. Sue sold 7 fewer than Dan. Sue sold 26 glasses. How many did Cori sell?

____

Name ______________________________

Percent

Percent means *per hundred*. Any ratio with 100 as the second number can be expressed in three ways.

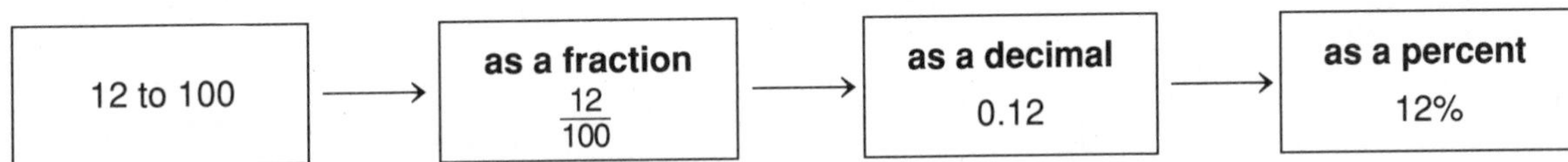

Write each ratio as a fraction.

1. 17 to 100 ______ **2.** 50 to 100 ______ **3.** 38 to 100 ______

4. 83 to 100 ______ **5.** 97 to 100 ______ **6.** 64 to 100 ______

Write each ratio as a decimal.

7. 17 to 100 ______ **8.** 50 to 100 ______ **9.** 38 to 100 ______

10. 83 to 100 ______ **11.** 97 to 100 ______ **12.** 64 to 100 ______

Write each ratio as a percent.

13. 17 to 100 ______ **14.** 50 to 100 ______ **15.** 38 to 100 ______

16. 83 to 100 ______ **17.** 97 to 100 ______ **18.** 64 to 100 ______

Give a fraction, decimal, and a percent for each shaded region.

19. 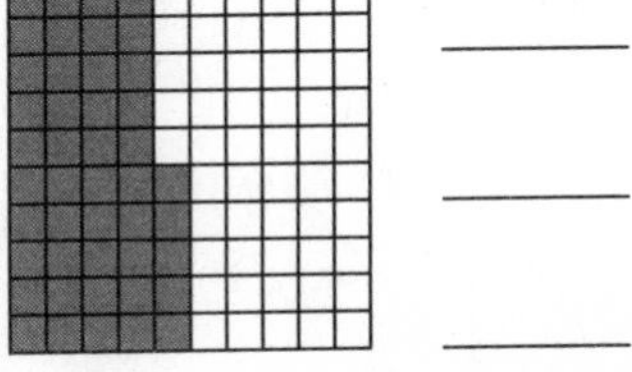 ______ ______ ______

20. 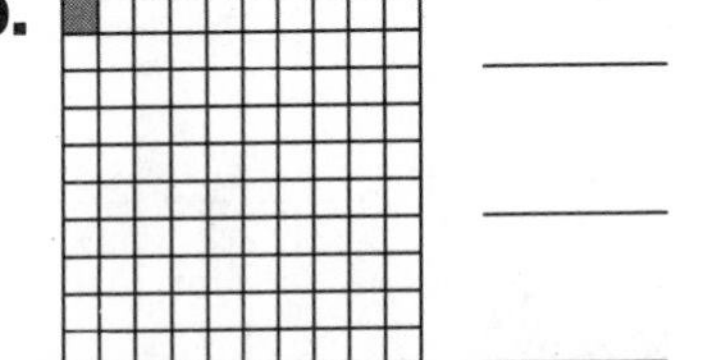 ______ ______ ______

21. 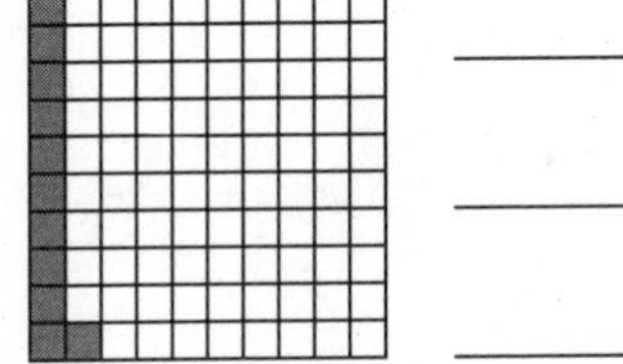 ______ ______ ______

 Use with text pages 256–257.

Name ______________________________

Percents and Fractions

Percents to fractions

$75\% = \frac{75}{100} = \frac{3}{4}$

Write in lowest terms.

Fractions to percents

$\frac{1}{10} \rightarrow$ Think $\frac{1}{10} = \frac{?}{100}$ $\rightarrow \frac{10}{100} = 10\%$

Find the lowest-terms fraction for each percent.

1. 48% = $\frac{48}{100} = \frac{12}{25}$ (÷ 4)
2. 18% = $\frac{18}{100} =$ ______
3. 52% = $\frac{}{100} =$ ______
4. 50% = ______
5. 28% = ______
6. 8% = ______
7. 20% = ______
8. 56% = ______
9. 15% = ______
10. 4% = ______
11. 64% = ______
12. 36% = ______
13. 90% = ______
14. 44% = ______
15. 1% = ______

Find the percent for each fraction.

16. $\frac{7}{10} = \frac{70}{100} = 70$% (× 10)
17. $\frac{3}{5} = \frac{}{100} = 60$% (× 20)
18. $\frac{1}{20} = \frac{}{100} =$ ______%
19. $\frac{3}{4} =$ ______
20. $\frac{9}{20} =$ ______
21. $\frac{6}{25} =$ ______
22. $\frac{6}{100} =$ ______
23. $\frac{1}{50} =$ ______
24. $\frac{3}{25} =$ ______
25. $\frac{9}{10} =$ ______
26. $\frac{83}{100} =$ ______
27. $\frac{9}{50} =$ ______

Name ______

Percents and Decimals

Percents to Decimals

54.9% = 0.549 — Decimal shifts 2 places left.

Decimals to Percents

0.035 = 3.5% — Decimal shifts 2 places right.

Write each percent as a decimal.

1. 5% 0.05 (Think 05.)
2. 250% 2.__
3. 16% 0.__
4. 17% ______
5. 46% ______
6. 57% ______
7. 99% ______
8. 39% ______
9. 63% ______
10. 12.5 ______
11. 5% ______
12. 10% ______
13. 350% ______
14. 82% ______
15. 18.25% ______
16. 25% ______
17. 1% ______
18. 275% ______

Write the percent for each decimal.

0.06

19. 0.21 ______
20. 0.06 ______
21. 0.52 ______
22. 0.19 ______
23. 0.20 ______
24. 0.64 ______
25. 0.97 ______
26. 0.37 ______
27. 0.003 ______
28. 0.46 ______
29. 0.014 ______
30. 0.75 ______
31. 0.59 ______
32. 0.265 ______
33. 0.732 ______

Name ____________________

Fractions, Decimals, and Percents

To compare fractions and percents:

Compare 88% to $\frac{7}{8}$.

Express the percent as a decimal.	Express the fraction as a decimal.	Compare the two decimals.	Write the answer.
$88\% = 0.88$	$\frac{7}{8} = 0.875$	$0.88 > 0.875$	$88\% > \frac{7}{8}$

Use a calculator or mental math to find which is greater.

1. $\frac{1}{2}$ or 48% ________

2. 53% or $\frac{1}{2}$ ________

3. $\frac{6}{7}$ or 86% ________

4. 66% or $\frac{2}{3}$ ________

5. $\frac{3}{12}$ or 30% ________

6. 26% or $\frac{5}{20}$ ________

7. $\frac{10}{14}$ or 70% ________

8. 20% or $\frac{1}{4}$ ________

9. $\frac{3}{4}$ or 80% ________

10. 23% or $\frac{2}{9}$ ________

11. $\frac{1}{8}$ or 12% ________

12. 30% or $\frac{5}{18}$ ________

13. $\frac{4}{9}$ or 45% ________

14. 63.5% or $\frac{7}{11}$ ________

15. $\frac{2}{15}$ or 13% ________

16. 8% or $\frac{1}{14}$ ________

17. $\frac{13}{15}$ or 86.5% ________

18. 90% or $\frac{19}{20}$ ________

19. $\frac{8}{12}$ or 67% ________

20. 72% or $\frac{21}{30}$ ________

Use with text pages 262–263.

Name ______________________________

Functions and Function Notation

To evaluate a function f(x) for a given value of x:

Given: a function of x and x = a	→	Substitute the given value, *a*, for the variable x in the function.	→	Simplify.

Example: $f(x) = 7x - 5$, $x = 4$ $\quad$ $f(4) = 7(4) - 5$ $\quad$ $f(4) = 28 - 5$, $f(4) = 23$

Evaluate each function for the value given.

	Given	Substitute	Answer
1.	Find f(3) for $f(h) = 4h - 1$	$f(3) = 4(3) - 1$	11
2.	Find f(7) for $f(j) = 32 - 2j$	______	______
3.	Find f(22) for $f(y) = 8y$	______	______
4.	Find f(6) for $f(d) = \frac{d}{2} + 5$	______	______
5.	Find f(5) for $f(g) = 3g^2$	______	______
6.	Find f(18) for $f(w) = \frac{w}{2} - 8$	______	______
7.	Find f(0) for $f(x) = 2x + 3$	______	______
8.	Find $f(\frac{1}{2})$ for $f(r) = 4r - 1$	______	______
9.	Find f(16) for $f(t) = (t - 12) \bullet (t + 4)$	______	______
10.	Find f(18) for $f(n) = 4(n - 10)$	______	______
11.	Find f(11) for $f(v) = 130 - v^2$	______	______

Name ______________________________

Percents Greater Than 100 and Less Than 1

To express a fraction as a percent:

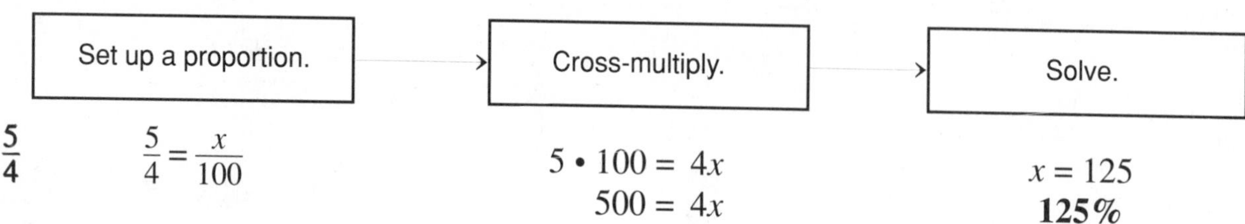

$\frac{5}{4}$ $\quad \frac{5}{4} = \frac{x}{100}$ $\quad 5 \cdot 100 = 4x$ $\quad 500 = 4x$ $\quad x = 125$ **125%**

Express the fractions as percents.

1. $\frac{7}{5} =$ ______ **2.** $\frac{1}{400} =$ ______

3. $\frac{12}{3} =$ ______ **4.** $\frac{2}{500} =$ ______

5. $\frac{4}{1000} =$ ______ **6.** $\frac{35}{8} =$ ______

To express a percent as a fraction or a decimal:

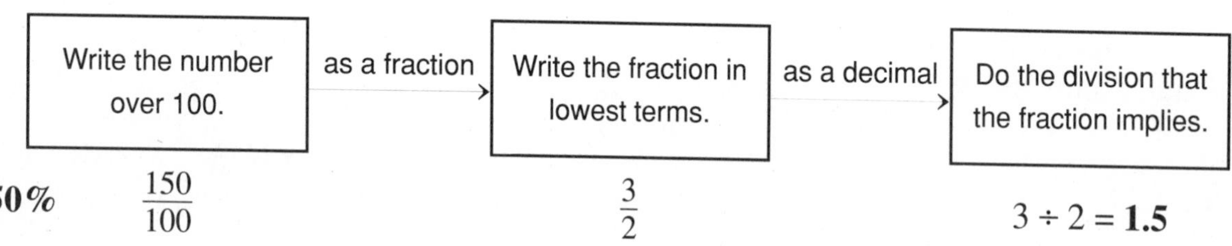

150% $\quad \frac{150}{100}$ $\quad \frac{3}{2}$ $\quad 3 \div 2 =$ **1.5**

Express each percent as a fraction in lowest terms and as a decimal.

7. 250% ______ ______ **8.** $\frac{3}{10}\%$ ______ ______

9. 375% ______ ______ **10.** $\frac{1}{8}\%$ ______ ______

11. $\frac{1}{4}\%$ ______ ______ **12.** 130% ______ ______

Name ______________________________

Finding Percent Patterns

Look at all of the conditions present. → Try to find patterns. → Use the patterns to make predictions.

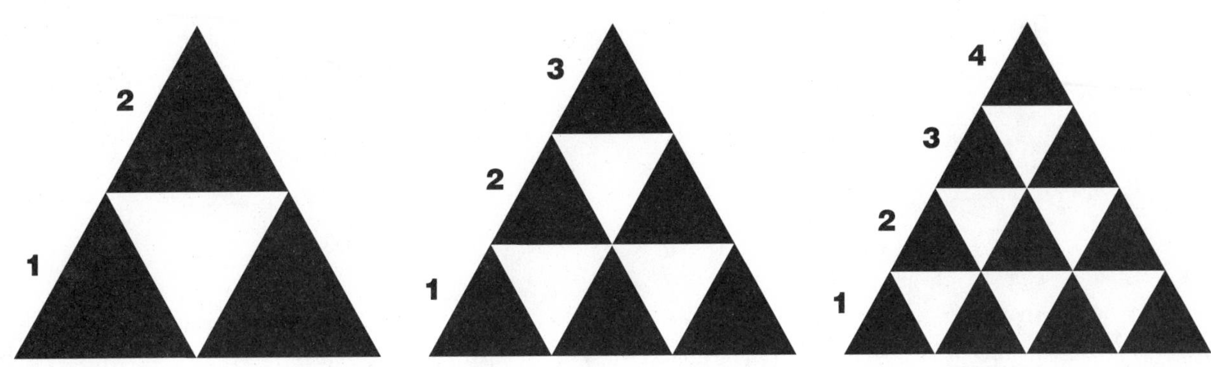

Look at the triangles above. See how each condition changes as the number of segments changes. Use the relationship patterns to complete the table.

Number of Segments	Shaded Triangles	White Triangles	Total Triangles	Percent Shaded	Percent White
2	3	1	4 $(= 2^2)$	75	25
	+ 3	+ 2			
3	6	3	9 $(= 3^2)$	67	33
	+ 4	+ 3			
4	10	6	16 $(= 4^2)$	62	38
	+ ______	+ ______			
5	______	______	______	______	______
	+ ______	+ ______			
6	______	______	______	______	______
	______	______			
7	______	______	______	______	______

Name ______________________________

Fractional Percents

Express $4\frac{3}{5}\%$ as a decimal.
To express a mixed number percent as a decimal:

Express the fractional part of the percent as a decimal.	→	Rewrite the percent using the decimal in place of the fraction.	→	Express the percent as a decimal.
$\frac{3}{5} = 0.6$		4.6%		0.046

Express each percent as a decimal.

1. $10\frac{1}{2}\% =$ ______ **2.** $7\frac{4}{5}\% =$ ______ **3.** $13\frac{3}{4}\% =$ ______

4. $20\frac{3}{8}\% =$ ______ **5.** $100\frac{1}{10}\% =$ ______ **6.** $6\frac{1}{25}\% =$ ______

7. $2\frac{2}{5}\% =$ ______ **8.** $10\frac{1}{100}\% =$ ______ **9.** $1\frac{3}{8}\% =$ ______

Express 0.3485 as a percent.
To express a decimal as a percent with a fraction:

Move the decimal two places to the right to get a percent.	→	Change the decimal part of the percent to a fraction.	→	Rewrite the percent using the fraction in place of the decimal.
0.34.85%		$0.85 = \frac{85}{100} = \frac{17}{20}$		$34\frac{17}{20}\%$

Express each decimal as a percent with a fraction.

10. 0.8225 = ______ **11.** 0.02125 = ______ **12.** 0.1348 = ______

13. 1.225 = ______ **14.** 0.0675 = ______ **15.** 0.5395 = ______

16. 0.011 = ______ **17.** 0.2001 = ______ **18.** 5.555 = ______

Name ______________________________

Estimating Percents

To estimate a percent for a given ratio:

Write the ratio in the form of a fraction.	→	Substitute compatible numbers for the numerator and/or the denominator.	→	Change that fraction to a percent.
28 to 59 $\frac{28}{59}$		$\frac{30}{60} = \frac{1}{2}$		**50%**

Estimate the percents for the ratios.

1. 22 to 79 ____________

2. 7 to 68 ____________

3. 92 to 123 ____________

4. 119 to 353 ____________

5. 148 to 743 ____________

6. 76 to 318 ____________

7. 12 to 220 ____________

8. 98 to 199 ____________

9. 79 to 97 ____________

10. 42 to 59 ____________

Solve. Use estimation.

11. One day Jennifer noticed that of the 20 people in her class, 9 were wearing blue and 6 were wearing red.

About what percent of the people in her class were wearing blue? ____________

About what percent of the people in her class were wearing red? ____________

Name

Using the Strategies

To solve some problems, **Use Objects** or **Act Out** the problem. Fill in the blanks in the detailed solution to the problem below.

1. Alyssa, Nils, and Jeff are handing out a 3-part worksheet to the class. Alyssa distributes Part 1, Nils follows with Part 2, then Jeff hands out Part 3 to each row. It takes each one of them 5 seconds to pass out the papers to one row. There are 4 rows. How long will it take all three of them to pass out the papers?

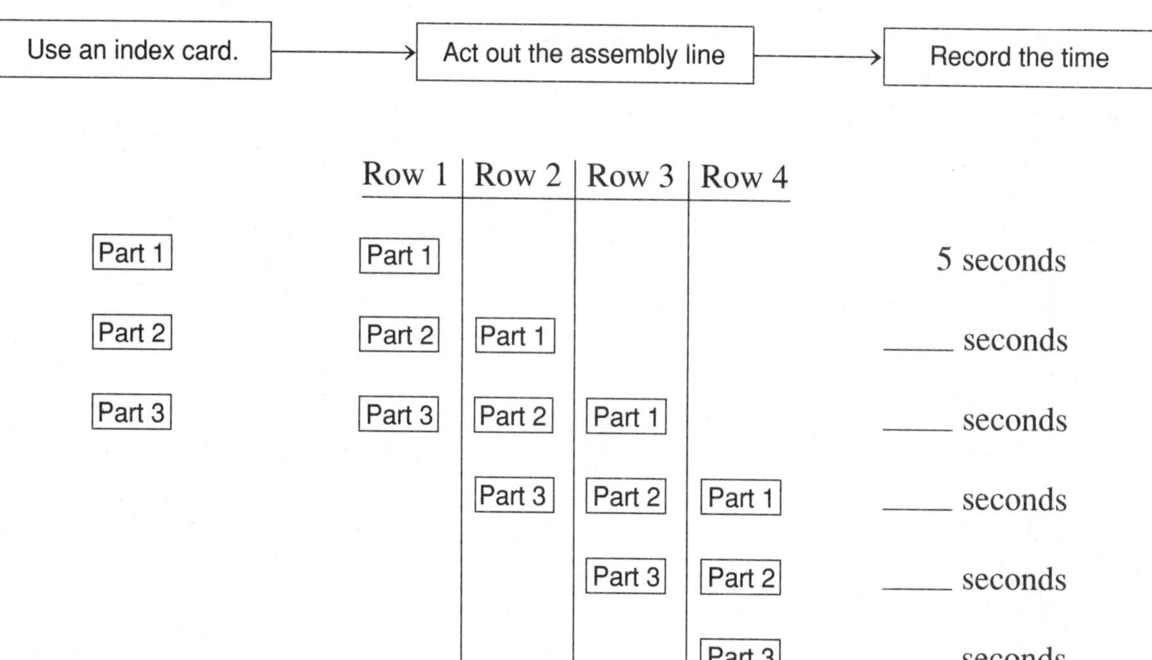

It will take ______ seconds.

Solve using the Act Out or Use Objects strategy.

2. At camp, each group spends 20 minutes at the basketball court and the goes direct to the pool for 20 minutes. How long will it take 3 groups to go through the basketball activity and the pool?

____

Name ______________________________

Finding a Percent of a Number

What is 80% of 35?
80% of 35 means 80% × 35.
80% = 0.80
0.80 × 35 = 28

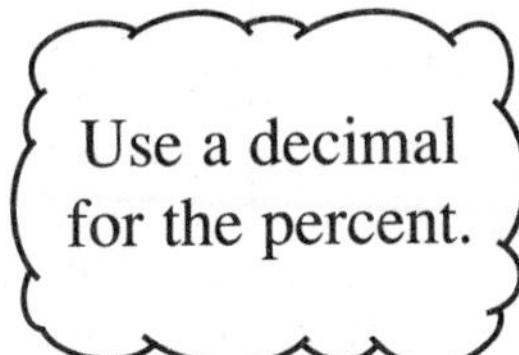

Find the percent of each number.

1. 38% of 64

38% = 0.38

0.38 × 64 = 24.32

2. 2% of 18

2% = 0.02

______

3. 130% of 25

130% = ______

______

4. 20% of 35 ______

5. 50% of 160 ______

6. 2% of 50 ______

7. 40% of 300 ______

8. 25% of 60 ______

9. 27% of 90 ______

10. 42% of 700 ______

11. 38% of 96.4 ______

12. 46% of 72 ______

13. 20% of 82 ______

14. 125% of 34 ______

15. 70% of 91 ______

16. 75% of 59 ______

17. 150% of 95 ______

18. 4% of 16.3 ______

19. 16% of 20.5 ______

20. 18% of 400 ______

21. 15% of 180 ______

22. 75% of 640 ______

23. 9% of 70 ______

Name ______________________________

Estimating a Percent of a Number

The table to the right can help you estimate the percent of a number.

$\frac{1}{2} = 50\%$	$\frac{1}{8} = 12\frac{1}{2}\%$
$\frac{1}{3} = 33\frac{1}{3}\%$	$\frac{1}{10} = 10\%$
$\frac{1}{4} = 25\%$	$\frac{2}{3} = 66\frac{2}{3}\%$
$\frac{1}{5} = 20\%$	$\frac{3}{4} = 75\%$

Example:

Estimate $48\frac{1}{2}\%$ of 69.

Think: $48\frac{1}{2}\%$ is about 50% or $\frac{1}{2}$.

69 is about 70.

$\frac{1}{2}$ of 70 = 35.

$48\frac{1}{2}\%$ of 69 is about 35.

Use compatible numbers to estimate.

1. 22.5% of 60 ______

2. 10.2% of 40 ______

3. 67% of 150 ______

4. 23% of 70 ______

5. 77% of 128 ______

6. 49% of 147 ______

7. 17% of 226 ______

8. 27% of 54 ______

9. 9% of 4,710 ______

10. 51% of 77 ______

11. 35% of 6 ______

12. 67% of 99 ______

13. $11\frac{1}{2}\%$ of 68 ______

14. 48% of 172 ______

15. 51% of 171 ______

16. 32% of 89 ______

17. 13% of 67 ______

18. 11% of 26 ______

19. About how much is 76.5% of 48? ______

20. About how much is 16% of 108? ______

Name ______________________________

Finding Simple Interest

Interest
Interest = Principal x Rate x Time

I = PRT

Principal = $250
Rate = 15% per year
Time = 6 years

$250 ← P
x 0.15 ← R
$37.50 ← Interest for 1 year
x 6
$225.00 ← Interest for 6 years

Amount
Amount = Principal + Interest

A = P + I

$250 ← P
+ 225 ← I
$475 ← Amount

Find the interest. Use a calculator.

1. P = $3,000
R = 16% per year
T = 3 years

3000
× 0.16
480.00
× 3
1,440.00

I = ____________
Interest
for 3 years

2. P = $25,000
R = 15% per year
T = 4 years

I = ____________

3. P = $6,000
R = 12% per year
T = 6 months

I = ____________

4. P = $1,900
R = 18% per year
T = 5 years

I = ____________

Find the amount. Use a calculator.

5. P = $6,500
R = 14% per year
T = 3 years

A = ____________

6. P = $7,000
R = 10% per year
T = 8 years

A = ____________

Name ______________________________

Applying Percent: Finding the Percent One Number Is of the Other

Only 14 out of 70 dogs liked new Fido Treats.
14 is what percent of 70?

Method 1: Use proportions.

Write the ratio. → $\frac{14}{70} = \frac{n}{100}$ ← Write the unknown percent as a ratio.

$70n = 1{,}400$

$n = 20$

14 is 20% of 70.

Method 2: Write an equation using the question.

14 is what percent of 70?

$14 = n \times 70$

$\frac{14}{70} = n$

$0.2 = n$ ← Multiply the decimal by 100 to make a percent.

$20\% = n$

Solve. Round to nearest whole percent. Show your work for Exercises 1 to 4.

1. What percent of 24 is 12? ______

____

2. 24 is what percent of 96? ______

____

3. 18 is what percent of 90? ______

____

4. What percent of 45 is 27? ______

____

5. What percent of 115 is 46? ______

6. 42 is what percent of 56? ______

7. What percent of 1,600 is 80? ______

8. What percent of 450 is 45? ______

9. 56 is what percent of 100? ______

10. 2 is what percent of 25? ______

11. What percent of 50 is 15? ______

12. 18 is what percent of 25? ______

13. 72 is what percent of 72? ______

14. What percent is 60 of 96? ______

15. What percent of 300 is 45? ______

16. What percent of 23 is 23? ______

17. 12 is what percent of 25? ______

18. What percent of 23 is 23? ______

19. 11 is what percent of 44? ______

20. 135 is what percent of 180? ______

Name ______________________________

Percent of Increase or Decrease

A restaurant served 120 meals on Friday and 138 meals on Saturday. What was the percent of increase?

First amount = 120
Second amount = 138
Increase: 138 – 120 = 18

$$\frac{\text{Increase}}{\text{First amount}} = \frac{18}{120} = 15\%$$

A shipment of seafood cost a restaurant \$850. The next shipment of the same quantity of seafood cost only \$782. What was the percent of decrease?

First amount = \$850
Second amount = \$782
Decrease: \$850 – \$782 = \$68

$$\frac{\text{Decrease}}{\text{First amount}} = \frac{\$68}{\$850} = 8\%$$

Use a calculator to find the percent of increase or decrease to the nearest percent.

1. 57 to 12 __________ **2.** 6 to 10 __________

3. 143 to 142 __________ **4.** 123 to 110 __________

5. 99 to 102 __________ **6.** 12 to 18 __________

7. 21 to 31 __________ **8.** 58 to 22 __________

The chart shows the total sales for each person for two months. Complete the chart. Find the percent increase or decrease in sales for each person.

Name	June Sales	July Sales	Increase or Decrease	Amount	Percent
9. Cain	\$3,000	\$5,000	______	______	______
10. Arvola	7,500	6,000	______	______	______
11. Peters	8,550	10,260	______	______	______
12. Logan	7,000	6,300	______	______	______
13. Kramer	5,000	8,500	______	______	______
14. Grier	3,630	7,260	______	______	______
15. Healy	2,840	2,130	______	______	______

Name ______________________________

Using Critical Thinking

The advertisement shown may be misleading. Do you pay the same amount per ounce?

Now 25% OFF
Usually 16 oz for $2.20

crackers

The small box sells for $1.65. If 16 oz cost $1.65, then 1 oz costs $0.10.

The large box sells for $2.20, but it contains 25% more crackers than the small box. The large box contains 20 oz. If 20 oz cost $2.20, then 1 oz costs $0.11.

25% More Crackers
For the same low price of $2.20

crackers

The 16-oz box is the better buy.

Read each advertisement. Determine which is the better buy. Use a calculator.

1. Juice A:
Now 30% off
Usually 48 oz for $3.20

Juice B:
Now 30% more juice
Usually 48 oz for $3.20

____

2. Spaghetti Sauce A:
Now 10% off
Usually 10 oz for $1.69

Spaghetti Sauce B:
Now 10% more spaghetti
Usually 10 oz for $1.69

____

3. Cereal A:
Now 15% off
Usually 16 oz for $2.89

Cereal B:
Now 15% more cereal
Usually 16 oz for $2.89

____

4. A box of 20 plastic forks usually sells for $2.00. It is on sale for 20% off the regular price. Another box holds 20% more forks. Set a price for the second box so that neither box is a better buy. ______________________________

Use with text page 294.

Name ______________________________

Applying Percent: Finding a Number From a Percent

82% of what number is 492?

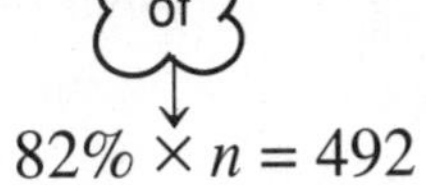

Write the equation. $82\% \times n = 492$

Write the percent as a decimal. $0.82 \times n = 492$

Solve for n.

This quotient is 1.
$1 \times n = n$

$\frac{0.82}{0.82} \times n = \frac{492}{0.82}$

$n = 600$

Write and solve an equation for each problem.

1. 60% of what number is 9?

$60\% \times n = 9$

$\frac{0.60}{0.60} \times n = \frac{9}{0.60}$

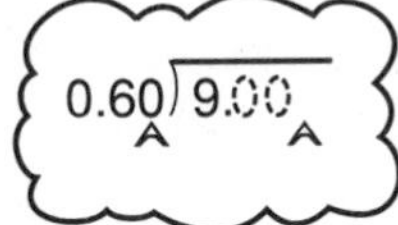

$n =$ 15

2. 62% of what number is 15.5?

$62\% \times n =$ ______

$n =$ ______

3. 20% of what number is 44?

$20\% \times n = 44$

$n =$ ______

4. 15% of what number is 6?

$n =$ ______

5. 24% of what number is 18?

$n =$ ______

6. 66% of what number is 165?

$n =$ ______

7. 80% of what number is 12.8?

$n =$ ______

8. 3% of what number is 4.68?

$n =$ ______

Name ______________________________

Discount and Sale Prices

Find the discount and the sales price of the typewriter.

Regular Price $460.00
15% OFF

Discount

Discount Percent x Regular Price = Discount
15% × $460 = Discount
0.15 × $460 = $69
The **discount** is $69.

Sale Price

Regular Price – Discount = Sale Price
$460 – $69 = Sale Price
$460 – $69 = $391
The **sale price** is $391.

Use a calculator to find the discount and the sale price for each item

		Discount	Sale Price
1.	Regular Price: $80 Discount Percent: 30%	30% of $80 = Discount 0.30 × $80 = $24	discount $80 – $24 = $56
2.	Regular Price: $65 Discount Percent: 20%		
3.	Regular Price: $50 Discount Percent: 30%		
4.	Regular Price: $90 Discount Percent: 40%		
5.	Regular Price: $75 Discount Percent: 28%		
6.	Regular Price: $250 Discount Percent: 50%		
7.	Regular Price: $10.50 Discount Percent: 20%		
8.	Regular Price: $3,200 Discount Percent: 50%		

Name ______________________________

Making Circle Graphs

To make a circle graph:

Step 1: Draw a circle and mark the center point.

Step 2: Use a calculator to find the number of degrees in each central angle. Round to the nearest degree.

> To find the number of degrees in each central angle:
>
> 360 × percent = number of degrees in the central angle

Step 3: Use a protractor to draw each central angle.

Step 4: Label each sector and title the graph.

Use the data from each survey to make a circle graph. Use a calculator to help find the number of degrees in each central angle.

1. What is your favorite subject?

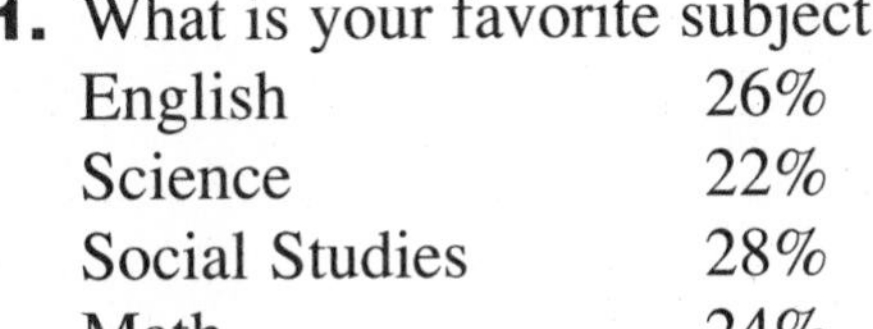

English	26%
Science	22%
Social Studies	28%
Math	24%

2. How many hours a day do you spend reading?

Less than 1	17%
Between 1 and 2	32%
Between 2 and 3	25%
More than 3	26%

Name ____________________

Exploring Algebra: Solving Percent Problems

Translating words into equations can help solve percent problems.

Examples:

Remember:
n is the part you are looking for;
is means "equals";
of means "multiply."

What is 95% of 60?

$n = 95\% \times 60$

$n = 0.95 \times 60$

$n = 57$

60 is what percent of 150?

$60 = n \times 150$

$\frac{60}{150} = n$

$0.4 = n$

$n = 40\%$

2 out of 50 is what percent?

$\frac{2}{50} = n$

$0.04 = n$

$n = 4\%$

Translate to an equation and solve.

1. 40% of 75 is what number? ____________________

2. What number is 18% of 400? ____________________

3. 63 out of 300 is what percent? ____________________

4. 60% of what number is 75? ____________________

5. 7 out of 20 is what percent? ____________________

6. What number is 55% of 70? ____________________

7. 72% of 300 is what number? ____________________

8. 47 is 50% of what number? ____________________

9. 120 out of 150 is what percent? ____________________

10. 85% of 200 is what number? ____________________

11. What percent is 27 of 90? ____________________

12. 60 is what percent of 150? ____________________

Name ______________________________

Problems without Solutions

Some problems do not have solutions.

José parks cars for Café Italiano. José has to park 4 cars in a row. The length of the row is 55 feet. The cars must fill the entire row. How many of each type of car did José park in each row?

Types of Cars	Length
Compact	12 feet
Midsize	14 feet
Luxury	16 feet

Compact	Midsize	Luxury	Total Feet
4	0	0	48
3	1	0	50
3	0	1	52
2	2	0	52
2	2	0	52
2	0	2	56
2	1	1	54
1	3	0	54
1	0	3	60
1	2	1	56
1	1	2	58
0	4	0	56
0	0	4	64
0	3	1	58
0	1	3	62
0	2	2	60

You can make a list to help you check the possibilities.

The list shows that no combination of 4 cars will completely fill the row.

Solve. If there is no solution, tell why.

1. Dinners at the restaurant cost $8.95, $9.95 or $11.95. Three people had dinner. They gave the waiter $30 and received $1.15 change. What dinners did they eat?

____

____

2. Seven friends had lunch at the restaurant. They each contributed the same amount toward the waitress's tip. They tipped the waitress $17. How much did each contribute?

____

____

3. Café Italiano has tables that seat 2, 4, or 6. Fifteen people enter the restaurant. How many types of full tables will seat them?

____

____

4. José made $22 in tips. He has 6 bills in his pocket. What bills does he have in his pocket?

____

____

Name ______________________________

Understanding Integers

To determine the opposite of an integer:

Plot the integer on a number line.	→	Determine the distance the integer is from zero.	→	The opposite of that integer is the same distance from 0 in the other direction.

Example: Find the opposite of 5.

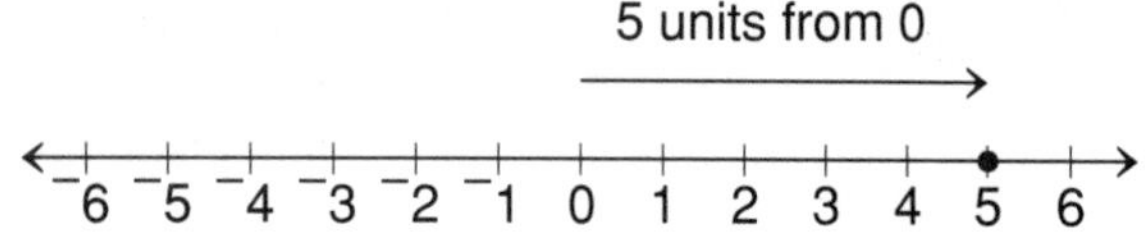

5 is 5 units to the right of 0 (in the positive direction).

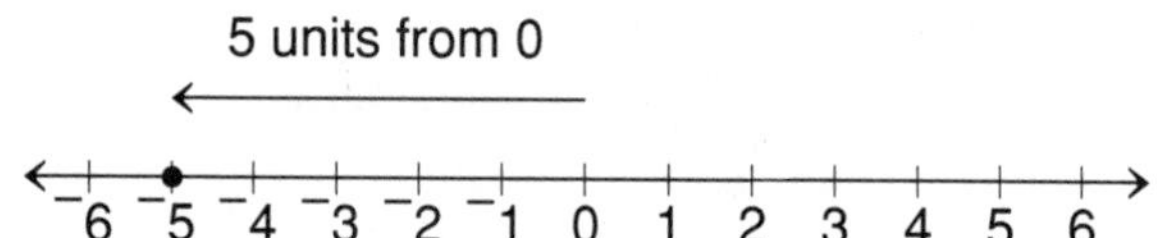

Find the integer that is 5 units to left of 0 (in the negative direction).

The opposite of 5 is ⁻5.

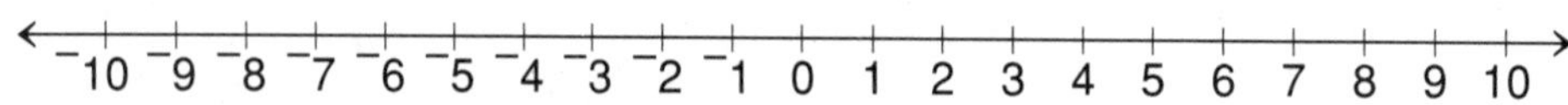

Use the number line to help identify the opposite of each integer.

1. ⁺7 ______ **2.** ⁻9 ______ **3.** ⁻1 ______

4. ⁻3 ______ **5.** 0 ______ **6.** ⁺1 ______

7. ⁻4 ______ **8.** ⁺2 ______ **9.** ⁻10 ______

10. ⁺8 ______ **11.** ⁻6 ______ **12.** ⁺4 ______

For each situation, give the suggested integer and its opposite.

13. spend $7 __________ **14.** lose 1 pound __________

15. forget 1 glove __________ **16.** 5 minutes more __________

Name ______________________________

Properties of Integers

Use each property to identify the missing integers.

Opposites Property
A number + its opposite = 0
example: $5 + {}^{-}5 = 0$

1. $^{+}11 + {}^{-}11 =$ ______

2. $^{-}20 +$ ______ $= 0$

Zero Property for Addition
a number + 0 = the same number
example: $18 + 0 = 18$

3. $^{-}10 + 0 =$ ______

4. ______ $+ 22 = 22$

One Property for Multiplication
a number • 1 = the same number
example: $6 \cdot 1 = 6$

5. $^{-}5 \cdot {}^{+}1 =$ ______

6. $^{+}14 \cdot$ ______ $= {}^{+}14$

Use each property to write the addends or factors in a different way.

Commutative Property
$^{-}5 + 7 = 7 + {}^{-}5$
$2 \cdot 10 = 10 \cdot 2$

7. $^{-}14 \cdot {}^{+}8 =$ ____________

8. $^{+}12 + {}^{-}3 =$ ____________

Associative Property
$(4 + 9) + 6 = 4 + (9+6)$
$({}^{-}8 \cdot 14) \cdot 2 = {}^{-}8 \cdot (14 \cdot 2)$

9. $^{+}15 + ({}^{-}1 + {}^{+}7) =$ ____________

10. $^{+}9 \cdot ({}^{+}11 \cdot {}^{-}5) =$ ____________

Distributive Property
$6(13 + {}^{-}2) = 6 \cdot 13 + 6 \cdot {}^{-}2$

11. $^{+}14({}^{-}7 + {}^{+}10) =$ ____________

12. $^{-}16({}^{+}5 + {}^{+}12) =$ ____________

Name ______________________________

Adding Integers

To add integers using counting chips:

Let each white chip represent $^{+}1$. Let each red chip represent $^{-}1$. → White chip + red chip = 0. Cancel the pairs of opposites. → Evaluate the remaining chips.

Add: $^{-}5 + ^{+}3$

$^{-}5 + ^{+}3 = ^{-}2$

Add: $^{+}4 + ^{-}3$

$^{+}4 + ^{-}3 = ^{+}1$

Use chips to model each sum. Complete each equation.

1. $^{-}6 + 2 =$ 4

2. $7 + ^{-}5 =$ ____

3. $4 + ^{-}2 =$ ____

4. $^{-}5 + 2 =$ ____

5. $^{-}7 + 4 =$ ____

6. $8 + ^{-}5 =$ ____

7. $6 + ^{-}2 =$ ____

8. $^{-}4 + 1 =$ ____

9. $^{-}3 + 3 =$ ____

10. $^{-}6 + 5 =$ ____

11. $5 + ^{-}7 =$ ____

12. $^{-}8 + 2 =$ ____

13. $6 + ^{-}1 =$ ____

14. $7 + ^{-}6 =$ ____

15. $^{-}5 + 2 =$ ____

16. $^{-}2 + 7 =$ ____

17. $^{-}9 + 5 =$ ____

18. $5 + ^{-}8 =$ ____

19. $^{-}4 + 8 =$ ____

20. $^{-}7 + 6 =$ ____

21. $9 + ^{-}5 =$ ____

22. $6 + ^{-}5 =$ ____

23. $^{-}10 + 5 =$ ____

Name ______________________________

Subtracting Integers

To subtract integers using counting chips:

Use red (negative) chips or white (positive) chips to show the first integer.	→	If necessary, add pairs of positive and negative chips.	→	Take away the appropriate chips.	→	Evaluate the remaining chips.

Subtract: $^{-}6 - {}^{-}2$

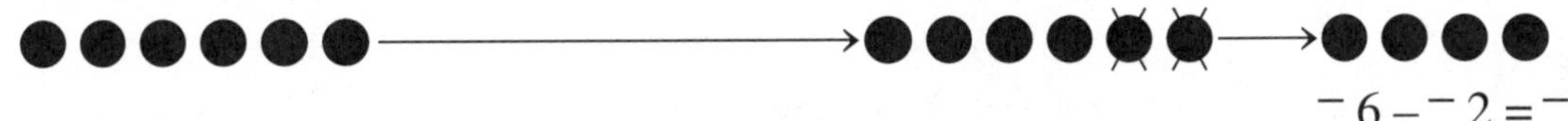

$^{-}6 - {}^{-}2 = {}^{-}4$

Subtract: $2 - {}^{-}5$

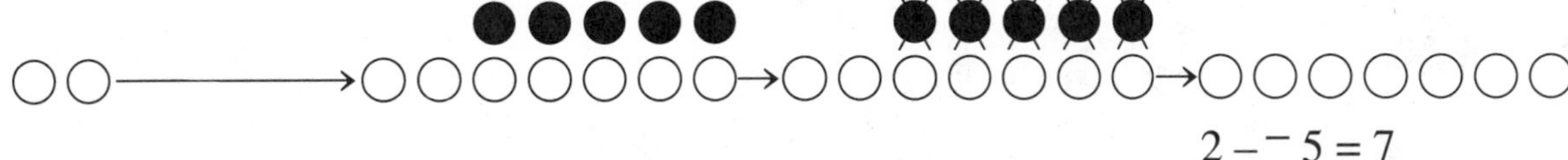

$2 - {}^{-}5 = 7$

Write a subtraction equation for each model.

1.  ______________

2. ______________

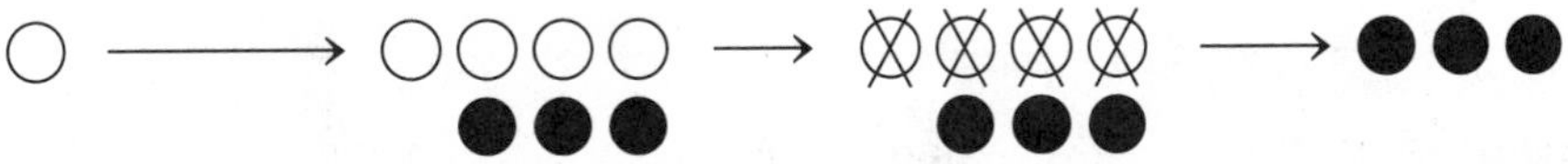

Subtract. Use counting chips if necessary.

3. $^{-}6 - 9 =$ ______ **4.** $6 - 9 =$ ______ **5.** $^{-}5 - 7 =$ ______

6. $5 - 8 =$ ______ **7.** $^{-}4 - 6 =$ ______ **8.** $4 - 6 =$ ______

9. $^{-}3 - 9 =$ ______ **10.** $3 - 9 =$ ______ **11.** $^{-}9 - 3 =$ ______

12. $9 - {}^{-}3 =$ ______ **13.** $^{-}3 - {}^{-}9 =$ ______ **14.** $^{-}9 - {}^{-}3 =$ ______

15. $^{-}4 - 8 =$ ______ **16.** $4 - {}^{-}8 =$ ______ **17.** $^{-}9 - 2 =$ ______

Name ____________________

Integer Multiplication Patterns

Multiply. Look at the signs of the factors and products.

$4 \times 4 = 16$		$4 \times {}^{-}3 =$ ____	
	-4		$+3$
$4 \times 3 = 12$		$3 \times {}^{-}3 =$ ____	
	-4		____
$4 \times 2 = 8$		$2 \times {}^{-}3 =$ ____	
	-4		____
$4 \times 1 = 4$		$1 \times {}^{-}3 =$ ____	
	-4		____
$4 \times 0 = 0$		$0 \times {}^{-}3 =$ ____	
$4 \times {}^{-}1 =$ ____		${}^{-}1 \times {}^{-}3 =$ ____	
$4 \times$ ___ $=$ ____		___ $\times {}^{-}3 =$ ____	
$4 \times$ ___ $=$ ____		___ $\times {}^{-}3 =$ ____	
$4 \times$ ___ $=$ ____		___ $\times {}^{-}3 =$ ____	

Conclusion: When one negative integer and one positive integer are multiplied, the product is ____________.

Conclusion: When two negative integers are multiplied together the product is ____________.

Use the patterns you have discovered to find these product.

1. 6×2 ____ **2.** $6 \times {}^{-}2$ ____ **3.** ${}^{-}6 \times {}^{-}2$ ____

4. 9×5 ____ **5.** ${}^{-}9 \times 5$ ____ **6.** ${}^{-}9 \times {}^{-}5$ ____

Name ____________________

Multiplying Integers

When multiplying integers:

If the signs are alike, the product is positive.

alike: $^{-}3 \cdot {}^{-}2 = 6m$

alike: $4 \cdot 6 = 24$

If the signs are unlike, the product is negative.

unlike: $^{-}3 \cdot 5 = {}^{-}15$

unlike: $2 \cdot {}^{-}6 = f12$

Multiply.

1. (unlike) $7 \cdot {}^{-}2 =$ $^{-}14$	**2.** (alike) $5 \cdot 4 =$ 20	**3.** (unlike) $^{-}6 \cdot 3 =$ ______
4. $5 \cdot 8 =$ ______	**5.** $5 \cdot {}^{-}8 =$ ______	**6.** $^{-}5 \cdot {}^{-}8 =$ ______
7. $9 \cdot {}^{-}3 =$ ______	**8.** $^{-}3 \cdot {}^{-}8 =$ ______	**9.** $4 \cdot {}^{-}7 =$ ______
10. $5 \cdot {}^{-}3 =$ ______	**11.** $6 \cdot {}^{-}9 =$ ______	**12.** $^{-}7 \cdot {}^{-}8 =$ ______
13. $^{-}8 \cdot 6 =$ ______	**14.** $^{-}9 \cdot {}^{-}5 =$ ______	**15.** $6 \cdot {}^{-}4$ ______
16. $^{-}5 \cdot {}^{-}3 =$ ______	**17.** $^{-}7 \cdot 9 =$ ______	**18.** $^{-}8 \cdot {}^{-}4 =$ ______
19. $4 \cdot 8 =$ ______	**20.** $^{-}3 \cdot {}^{-}7 =$ ______	**21.** $^{-}9 \cdot 4 =$ ______
22. $^{-}2 \cdot {}^{-}9 =$ ______	**23.** $^{-}5 \cdot 7 =$ ______	**24.** $7 \cdot {}^{-}9 =$ ______
25. $^{-}3 \cdot {}^{-}6 =$ ______	**26.** $^{-}6 \cdot {}^{-}9 =$ ______	**27.** $8 \cdot 7 =$ ______
28. $^{-}9 \cdot 6 =$ ______	**29.** $^{-}4 \cdot 8 =$ ______	**30.** $^{-}6 \cdot {}^{-}5 =$ ______

Name ______________________________

Dividing Integers

When dividing integers:

If the signs are **alike**, the quotient is positive.

If the signs are **unlike**, the quotient is negative.

alike	alike	unlike	unlike
$^{-}30 \div {}^{-}6 = 5$	$16 \div 8 = 2$	$^{-}21 \div 7 = {}^{-}3$	$36 \div {}^{-}9 = {}^{-}36$

Divide.

unlike **1.** $^{-}18 \div 6$ $^{-}3$	alike **2.** $^{-}9 \div {}^{-}3$ 3	unlike **3.** $15 \div {}^{-}5$ ______
4. $^{-}4 \div 2$ ______	**5.** $^{-}6 \div {}^{-}2$ ______	**6.** $^{-}70 \div 7$ ______
7. $15 \div 5$ ______	**8.** $^{-}60 \div {}^{-}20$ ______	**9.** $^{-}64 \div 8$ ______
10. $^{-}14 \div 2$ ______	**11.** $^{-}20 \div 4$ ______	**12.** $5 \div 5$ ______
13. $^{-}12 \div {}^{-}3$ ______	**14.** $40 \div {}^{-}8$ ______	**15.** $^{-}50 \div 5$ ______
16. $8 \div {}^{-}2$ ______	**17.** $32 \div {}^{-}16$ ______	**18.** $^{-}9 \div 9$ ______
19. $^{-}25 \div 5$ ______	**20.** $^{-}14 \div 7$ ______	**21.** $^{-}27 \div {}^{-}9$ ______
22. $3 \div {}^{-}3$ ______	**23.** $^{-}36 \div 4$ ______	**24.** $18 \div {}^{-}1$ ______
25. $^{-}16 \div {}^{-}8$ ______	**26.** $^{-}24 \div 6$ ______	**27.** $^{-}32 \div {}^{-}4$ ______
28. $36 \div {}^{-}6$ ______	**29.** $^{-}42 \div 6$ ______	**30.** $^{-}18 \div {}^{-}3$ ______

Name ______________________________

Graphing Integer Coordinates

The **coordinates** of a point give its location.

Point *A*→ Start at zero. 2 spaces right: 2 4 spaces down: ⁻4 →(2,⁻4)

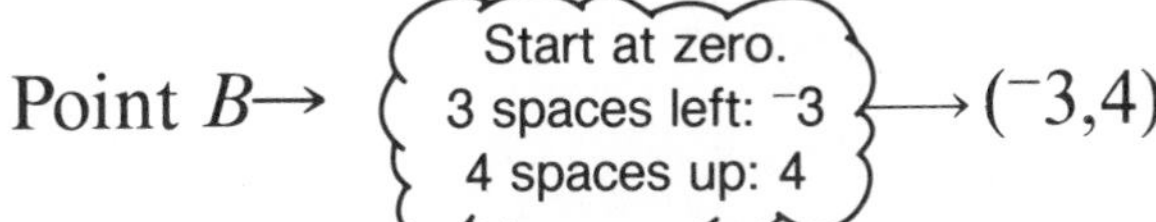

Point *B*→ Start at zero. 3 spaces left: ⁻3 4 spaces up: 4 →(⁻3,4)

Point *C*→ Start at zero. 4 spaces left: ⁻4 2 spaces down: ⁻2 →(⁻4,⁻2)

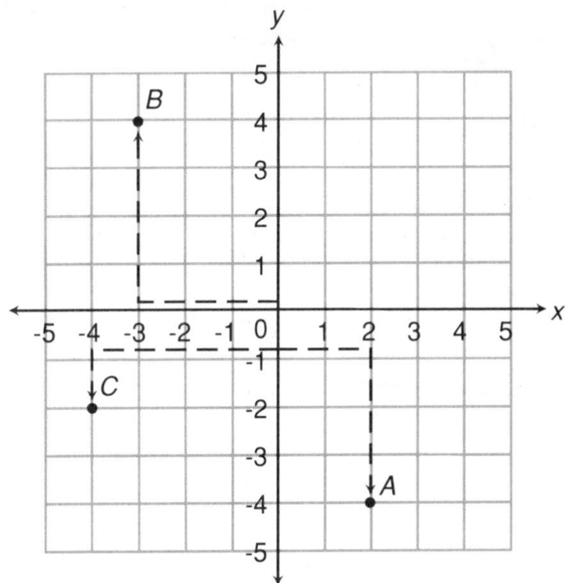

Give the coordinates for each point.

1. *D* (5,⁻1) — Start at zero. Move right 5 spaces, then down 1 space.

2. *G* (⁻2,⁻2) — Start at zero. Move left 2 spaces, then down 2 spaces.

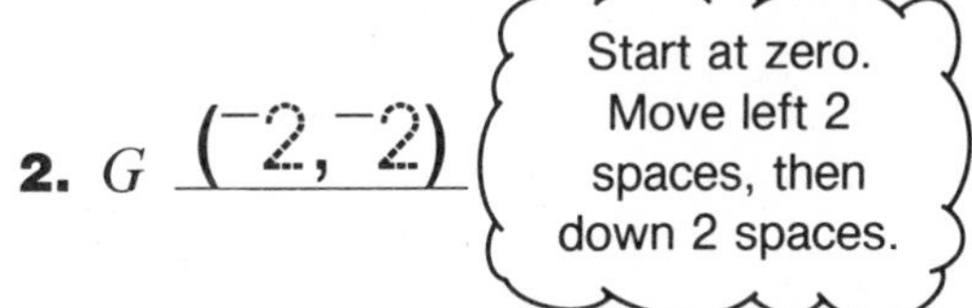

3. *E* ________ **15.** *S* ________

4. *A* ________ **16.** *P* ________

5. *C* ________ **17.** *L* ________

6. *M* ________ **18.** *R* ________

7. *K* ________ **19.** *U* ________

8. *T* ________ **20.** *W* ________

9. *H* ________ **21.** *Y* ________

10. *X* ________ **22.** *V* ________

11. *N* ________ **23.** *J* ________

12. *F* ________ **24.** *B* ________

13. *Q* ________ **25.** *O* ________

14. *I* ________ **26.** *Z* ________

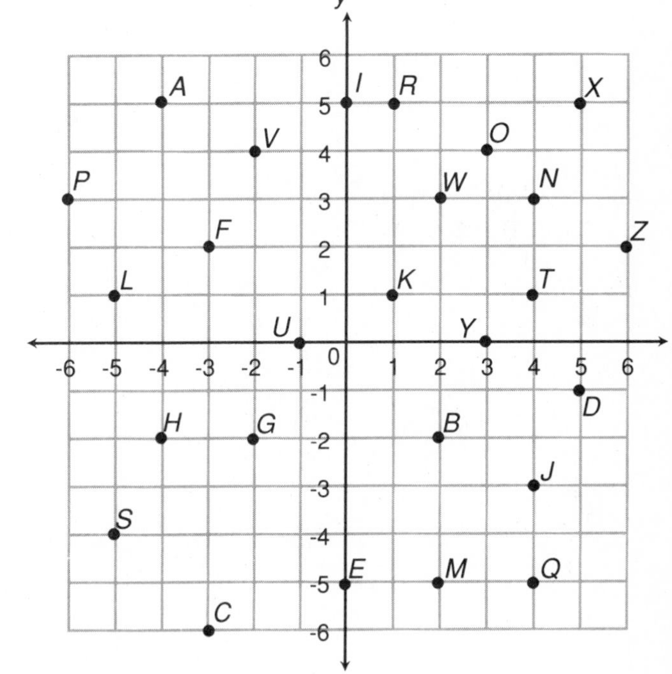

Name ______________________________

Exploring Algebra: Graphing Equations

To graph a linear equation:

Choose at least 3 values for the variable *x*.	→	Put each value of *x* into the equation to get a value for *y*.	→	Graph each of the coordinate pairs.	→	Connect the points.

Example: Graph the equation: $y = x - 4$

Let $x = {}^-2$	Let $x = 0$	Let $x = 6$
$y = {}^-2 - 4$	$y = 0 - 4$	$y = 6 - 4$
$y = {}^-6$	$y = {}^-4$	$y = 2$
$({}^-2, {}^-6)$ is a solution.	$(0, {}^-4)$ is a solution.	$(6, 2)$ is a solution.

Now graph the ordered pairs and draw a line through the points.

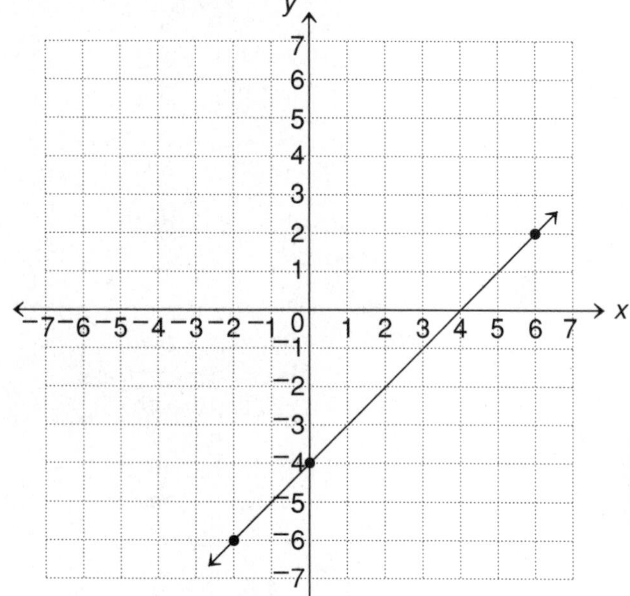

Complete the table of ordered pairs and graph the equation.

Equation: $y = 5 - x$

x	⁻3	⁻1	0	2	5	7
y	8	6	5	3	0	-2
(*x*,*y*)	⁻3,8	⁻1,6	0,5	2,3	5,0	7,⁻2

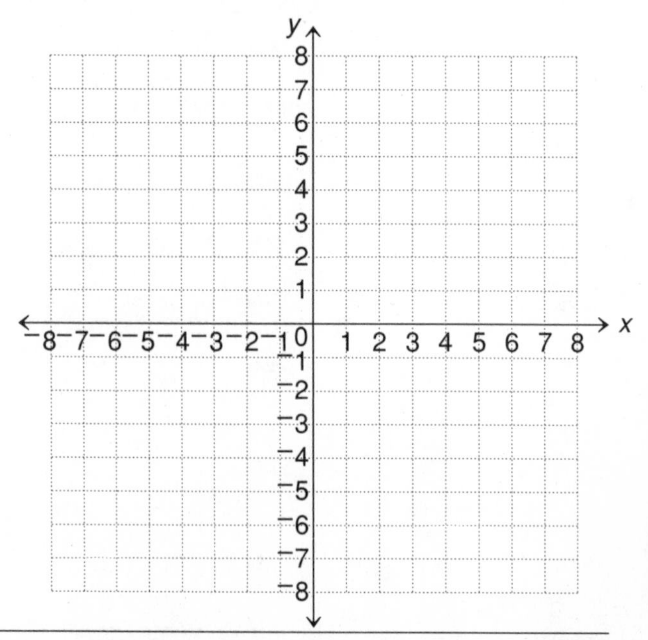

Name ______________________________

Using the Strategies

Be sure that you completely solve a problem.

Ask: Is there more than one answer to this problem? → Use the problem solving strategies to determine every possible answer. → Give all possible answers.

Example:

Shannon and Erin belong to the same gym. Shannon goes every other day and Erin goes every third day. Both are there on May 3. On what other days in May will they both be at the gym?

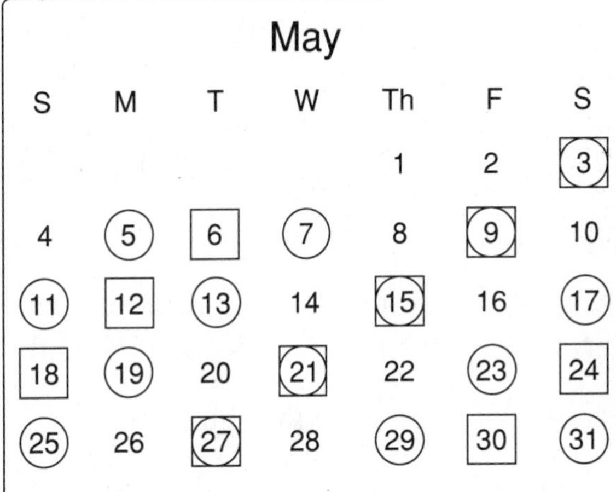

○ days that Shannon is at the gym

□ days that Erin is at the gym

Think: Is there more than one answer? The word *days* suggests there may be more.

Do: Use the problem solving strategies. Make an Organized List and Draw a Picture.

Solution: Erin and Shannon will be at the gym together on May 9, May 15, May 21, and May 27.

Solve. Check for more than one answer.

1. Sutan and Siobhan both work at a health food store. Sutan works every fifth day and Siobhan works every other day. They both worked on June 4. On what other days in June will they work together?

____

2. Using only slices that are parallel or perpendicular to the sides, how many cuts do you need to make to divide a rectangular loaf of bread into 8 pieces?

____

Name ______________________________

Chance Events

The line at the right can be used to picture the likelihood of an event occurring. Decide where each event should be shown on the line.

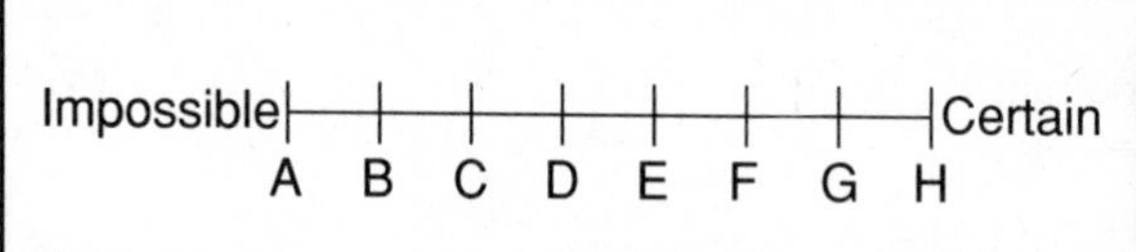

Example: Where should spinning an A or a D be shown on the line?

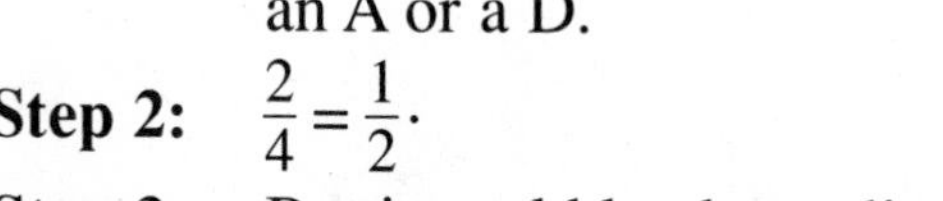

Step 1: You have 2 chances out of 4 to spin an A or a D.

Step 2: $\frac{2}{4} = \frac{1}{2}$.

Step 3: But it could land on a line.

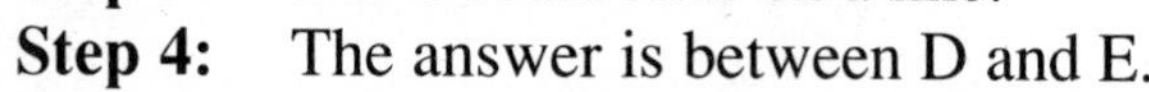

Step 4: The answer is between D and E.

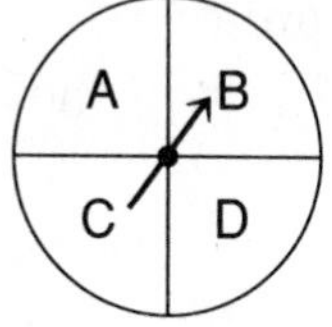

Exercises 1 to 6 refer to the spinner.

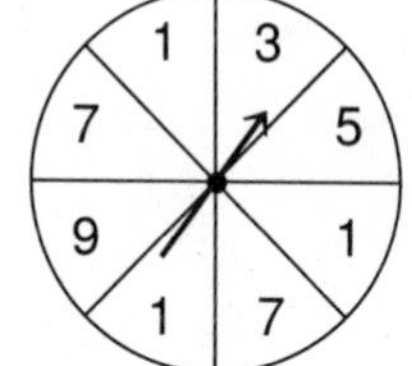

1. Spinning a 1. ______________

2. Spinning a 7. ______________

3. Spinning an odd number. ______________

4. Spinning an even number. ______________

5. Spinning a 7 or a 9. ______________

6. Spinning a number greater than 4. ______________

Exercises 7 to 10 refer to the number cube. Its faces are numbered 1 to 6.

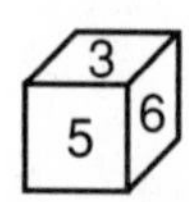

7. Throwing an odd number. ______________

8. Throwing a number less than 7. ______________

9. Throwing a prime number. ______________

10. Throwing a 1 or a 6. ______________

Name ______________________________

Sample Spaces

A card is drawn from the hat at the same time that the spinner is spun. List the sample space of all the outcomes for the events that follow.

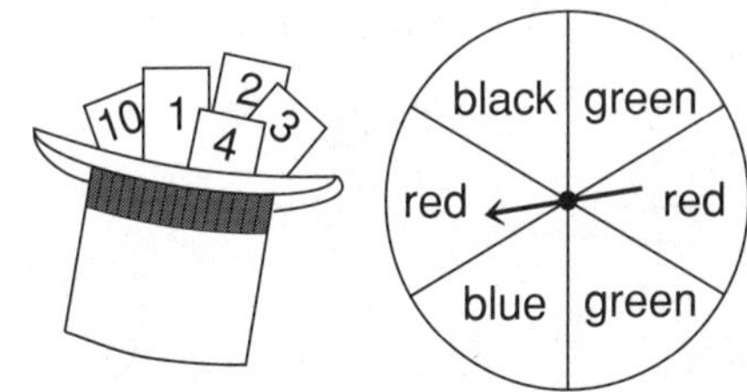

Example: What outcomes make the sample space of getting a number less than 3 and a green segment?

Step 1: Find the numbers less than 3: 1 and 2.

Step 2: Make pairs of these numbers and *green*.

Step 3: (1, green), (2, green)

1. What outcomes make the event of getting an even number and a red segment?

   ____

   ____

2. What outcomes make the event of getting a multiple of 2 and a green or red?

   ____

   ____

A normal coin and a cube with numbers 1 to 6 on its faces are used. If they are tossed at the same time, give the outcomes that make each event.

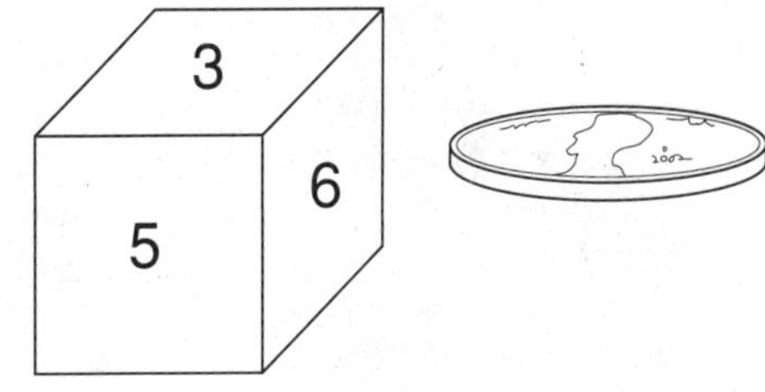

3. A 6 and a tail. __________

4. A number less than 4 and a tail. ______________

5. An odd number and a tail. ______________

6. A composite number and a head. __________

A cube with numbers 1 to 6 on its faces is tossed at the same time that a number card is drawn from the hat above.

7. What outcomes make the event of getting a difference of 2 between the card and the cube?

   ____

8. What outcomes make the event of getting one number less on the card than on the cube?

   ____

Name ______________________________

Probability of an Event

Spin the spinner.

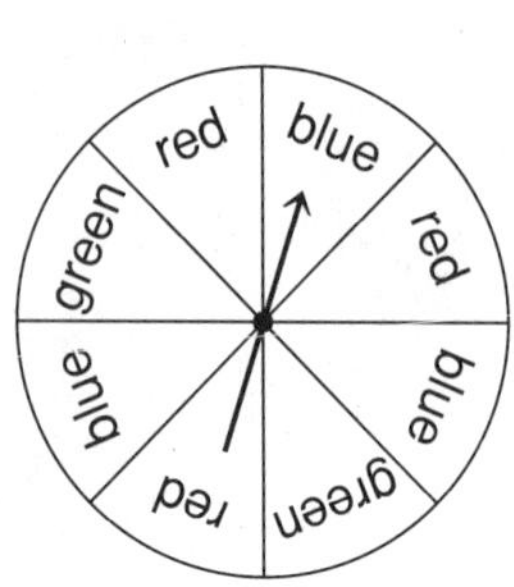

Chance	Probability
There are **3** chances in **8** of stopping on red. ⟶	Probability of red = $\frac{3}{8}$ P(red) = $\frac{3}{8}$
There are **2** chances in **8** of stopping on green. ⟶	P(green) = $\frac{2}{8}$ or $\frac{1}{4}$
There are **0** chances in **8** of stopping on yellow. ⟶	P(yellow) = $\frac{0}{8}$ or 0

Write each probability.

One of these names is to be drawn from a hat.

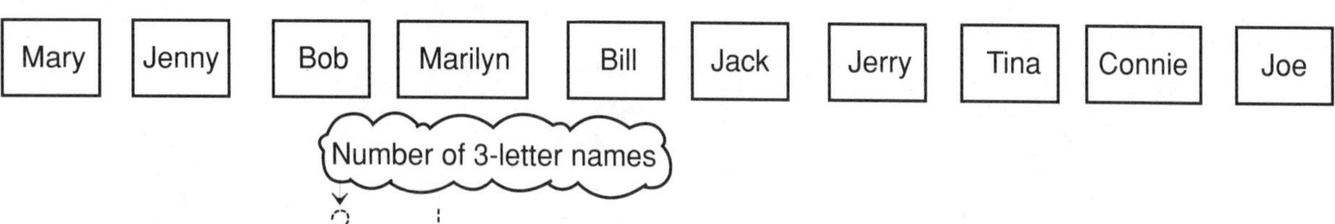

Number of 3-letter names

1. P(3-letter name) = $\frac{2}{10}$ or $\frac{1}{5}$

What is the probability of drawing a 3-letter name?

Total number of names

2. P(4-letter name) = $\frac{4}{10}$ or $\frac{2}{5}$

3. P(name starting with B) = $\frac{2}{10}$ or $\frac{1}{5}$

4. P(name starting with T) = ______

5. P(7-letter name) = ______

6. P(name starting with S) = ______

7. P(name ending with Y) = ______

One of these cards will be drawn without looking.

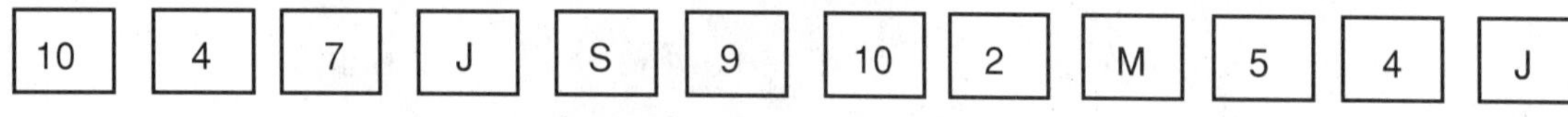

8. P(2) = $\frac{\_\_\_}{\_\_\_\_\_\_}$ ⟵ number of twos / ⟵ total number of cards

9. P(5) = ______

10. P(J) = ______

11. P(a number) = ______

12. P(4) = ______

13. P(T) = ______

14. P(a letter) = ______

Name ______________________________

Probability Experiments

Find the experimental probability of each event.

Example: A spinner lands on red 14 times and on green 10 times. What is the experimental probability of it landing on red?

Step 1: Find the total number of spins: $14 + 10 = 24$

Step 1: Write the number of times the spinner landed on red over the total number of spins: $\frac{14}{24}$

Step 1: Find lowest terms, if necessary: $\frac{14}{24} = \frac{7}{12}$

Exp P (red) is $\frac{7}{12}$.

---

1. Two number cubes are tossed 18 times. A sum of 5 appears 6 times.

Exp P (sum of 5) = ____________

2. 24 paper clips are in a bag. 8 pink paper clips are drawn; 10 purple paper clips are drawn.

Exp P (purple) = ____________

Exp P (pink) = ____________

3. A spinner lands on brown 3 times, on purple 6 times, and on blue 5 times.

Exp P (purple) = ____________

Exp P (brown) = ____________

Exp P (blue) = ____________

4. A spinner is spun 12 times. It lands on the number 6 three times, on the number 4 six times, and on the number 3, three times.

Exp P (even number) = ____________

Refer to the table below. Use a calculator to determine the experimental probability for each student. Round to the nearest thousandth.

Ron ____________

Keisha ____________

Eric ____________

Ron:	43 heads in 92 tosses
Keisha:	109 heads in 221 tosses
Eric:	38 heads in 73 tosses

Who had the experimental probability closest to 0.5? ____________

Name ______________________________

Using Critical Thinking: Analyzing and Testing Formulas

Formulas can be used to describe physical events. The formula below drescribes an experimental method to approximate the value of π, or 3.14.

$\pi \approx$ **Drops × 2 ÷ Hits**

Needle

miss

hit

Example:

What is the purpose of the tally boxes at the bottom of the diagram?

to keep an accurate count of hits and misses in order to use the data in the formula

HITS	MISSES
|||| ||||	|||| |||

1. Why does the diagram show the needle perpendicular to the two lines?

____

____

2. If the needle hits the line and bounces off, can it be counted as a "hit."

____

____

3. Do the experiment shown above using a toothpick and paper with proportionately spaced lines. Drop the toothpick 40 times and tally your results. Is the result close to 3.14?

____

If not, how far away was your result?

____

4. Compare your tally at 30 drops with your tally at 40 drops. At which number are you closer to 3.14 as the value of π?

____

Name ____________________

Exploring Algebra: Inequalities

Draw graphs for these inequalities.

Example: $x \leq 18$

Step 1: $<$ means less than } Use an empty dot on a graph. ○
$>$ means greater than
$\leq$ means less than or equal to } Use a filled-in dot on a graph. ●
$\geq$ means greater than or equal to

Step 2: Graph

x
0 18

1. $x \geq 12$

2. $d < 8$

3. $n \leq 13$

4. $y > 21$

Write the inequality for each statement.

Example: Length L is at least 24.

Step 1: Reword. L has to be equal to or greater than 24.

Step 2: Write using mathematical symbols. $L \geq 24$.

5. Cost c is less than $3.19. ____________

6. Time t is greater than 5 hours. ____________

7. Price p will be at least $112. ____________

8. Width w is at most 10 feet. ____________

9. Ratio r is greater than $\frac{3}{7}$. ____________

Write inequalities for these graphs.

10.

____

11.

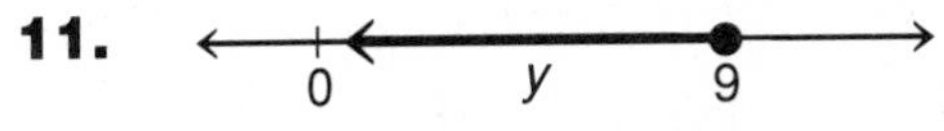

____

Name ______________________________

Tree Diagrams and Compound Events

Use this tree diagram.

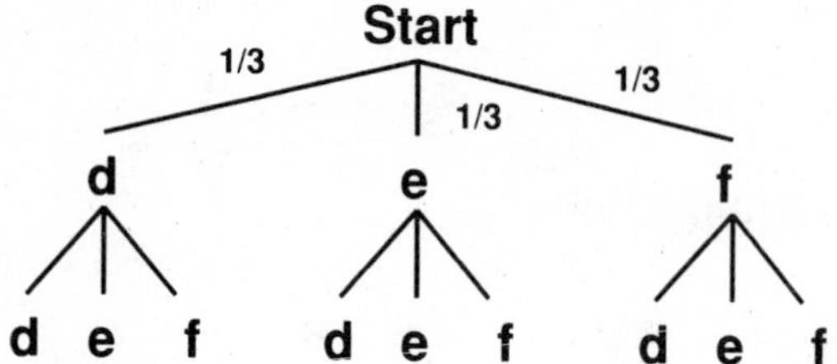

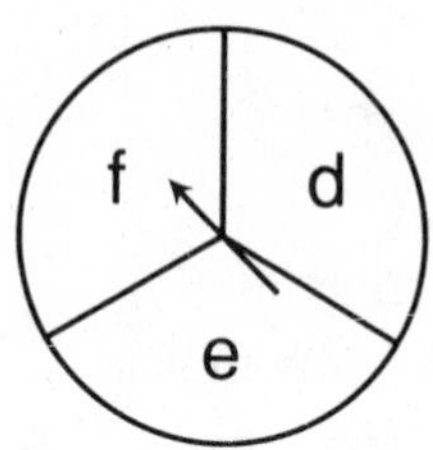

$P(d) = \frac{1}{3}$

$P(e) = \frac{1}{3}$

$P(f) = \frac{1}{3}$

Example:

P (2 letters the same) = __________

Step 1: Outcomes are (d,d), (d,e), (d,f), (e,d), (e,e), (e,f), (f,d), (f,e), and (f,f).

Step 2: Count the pairs with the same letters: (d,d), (e,e), and (f,f). There are 3.

Step 3: Put 3 over 9 because there are 9 possible outcomes.

Step 4: The answer is 3/9 or 1/3.

1. P (2 letters different) = __________

2. P (2 consonants) = __________

Use the tree diagram.

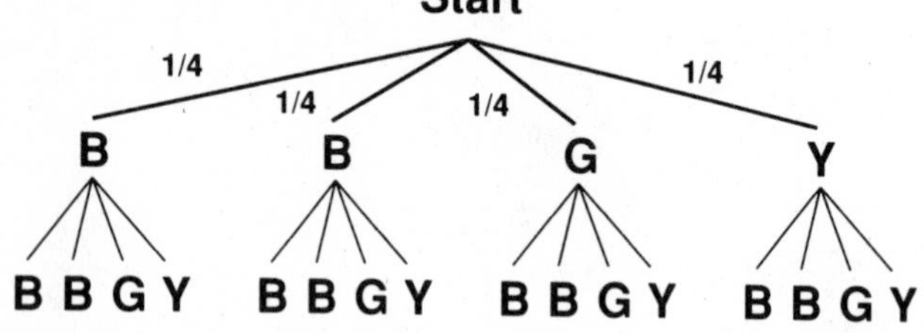

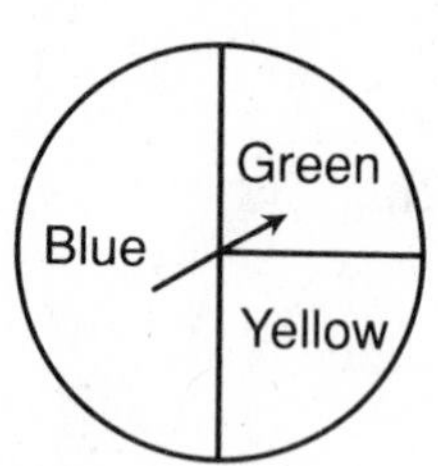

$P(B) = \frac{1}{2}$

$P(G) = \frac{1}{4}$

$P(Y) = \frac{1}{4}$

3. P (2 different colors) = __________

4. P (B,B) = __________

5. P (G,G) = __________

6. P (Y,Y) = __________

7. P (2 identical colors) = __________

8. P (both blue or both green) = __________

Name ______________________________

Finding Related Problems

When you have a problem to solve, thinking of a related problem can help.

Make a diagram. → Start with the first category. → Link each item/person in the first category with each in the second. → Repeat for each additional category.

John, Sandra, and Marie, who are good at math, will study with Lisa, Errol, and Tom, who are good at science. How many different study-group pairs could they form?

There are 9 different study-group pairs possible.

Jack decided to cancel the day's soccer games because of rain. He called 2 players and asked each of them to call 2 more, and so on. Including Jack, how many people knew about the cancellation by the end of the third set of calls?

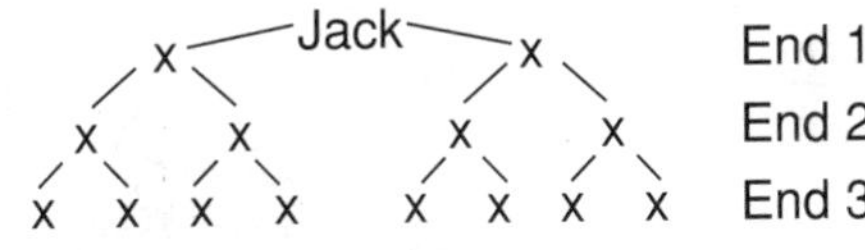

By the end of the third set of calls, 15 people knew.

Read all four problems. Which pairs are related?

______ and ______ , ______ and ______

Solve. Use any strategy.

1. Tyson has to mail a package to his cousin. He knows the first three numbers of the zip code but has forgotten the other two. How many guesses might he make before he gets the correct zip code? ______________

2. Karen saw 6 different shirts in a store. She bought 2. How many different combinations of 2 different shirts could she have bought?

____

3. Each player in a game starts with 50 points. Five points are added for each correct answer; 2 points are subtracted for each incorrect answer. If a player answers 5 questions and has a total score of 61, how many questions did he or she answer correctly?

____

4. Mark has a base pay of $10 a day. He receives a $1.50 bonus for each crate of eggs he packs without breaking any eggs. For each crate that has broken eggs, $0.50 is deducted. One day he packed 20 crates. Mark broke eggs in 4 crates. How much money did he make that day? ______________

Name ______________________________

Expected Value

Find the expected value by making a table. Find the expected value for this spinner and 30 spins.

Step 1: Find $\frac{1}{2}$ (the probability) of 30 (the number of spins).
Multiply by 3 points. 45 points

Step 2: Find $\frac{1}{3}$ of 30.
Multiply by 4 points. 40 points

Step 3: Find $\frac{1}{6}$ of 30
Multiply by 5. 25 points

Step 4: Add the points. 110 points

Step 5: Divide by 30 (the number of spins). $110 \div 30 = 3\frac{2}{3}$

3 points
4 points
5 points

$P(3) = \frac{1}{2}$

$P(4) = \frac{1}{3}$

$P(5) = \frac{1}{6}$

Spin 30 times

Outcome	Number Expected in 30 Spins	Total Points
3 points	$\frac{1}{2} \times 30 = 15$	45
4 points	$\frac{1}{3} \times 30 = 10$	40
5 points	$\frac{1}{6} \times 30 = 5$	25
	Total of all spins	110
	Expected Value	$3\frac{2}{3}$

1.

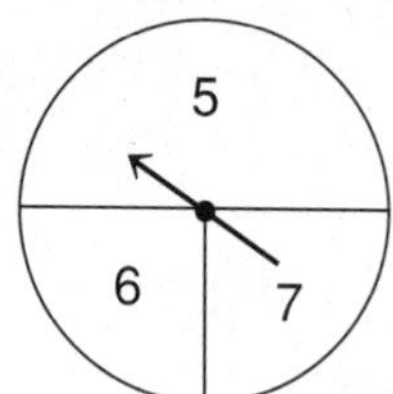

$P(5) = \frac{1}{2}$

$P(6) = \frac{1}{4}$

$P(7) = \frac{1}{4}$

Spin 72 times
Expected value ______________

2.

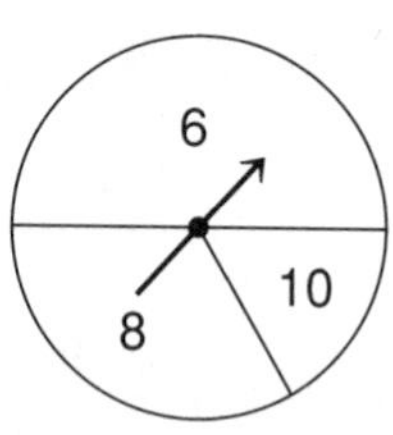

$P(6) = \frac{1}{2}$

$P(8) = \frac{1}{3}$

$P(10) = \frac{1}{6}$

Spin 60 times
Expected value ______________

Name ______________________________

Exploring the Concept of Area

To find the area of a figure:

Divide the figure into rectangles and triangles.	→	Determine the number of square units contained in each region.	→	Add the area of each region to find the area of the figure.

Find the area of the figure below.

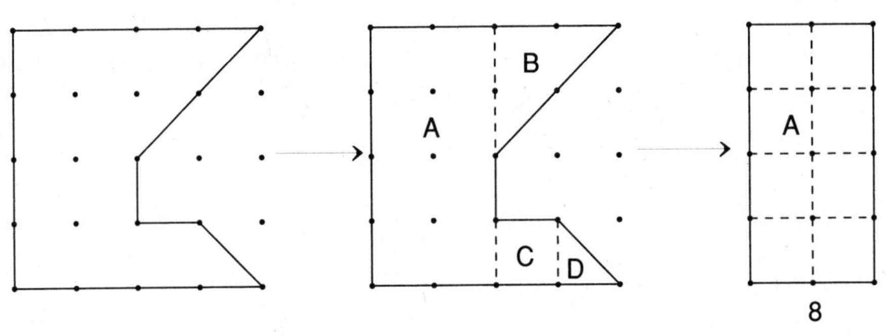

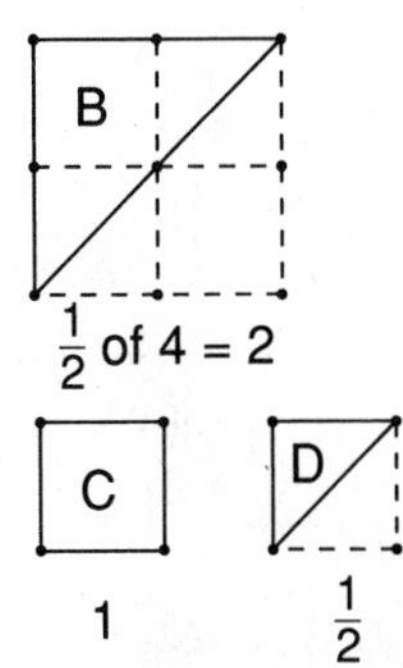

$8 + 2 + 1 + \frac{1}{2} = 11\frac{1}{2}$

The area of the figure is $11\frac{1}{2}$ square units.

Divide each figure into rectangles and triangles. Then find the area.

1. 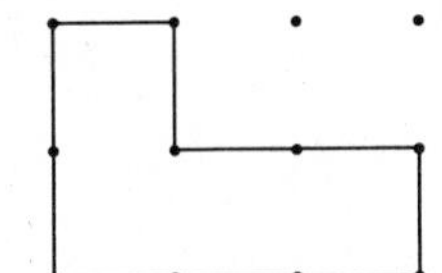 ______________

2. 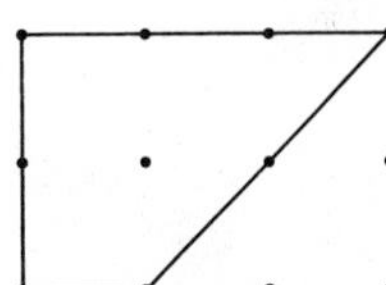 ______________

3. 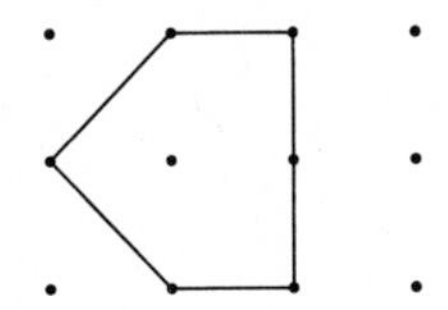 ______________

4. 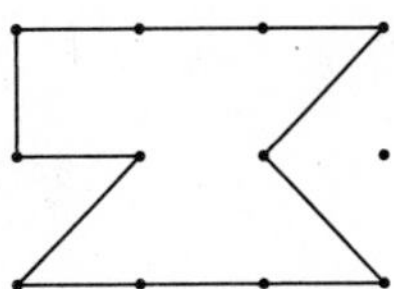 ______________

5. 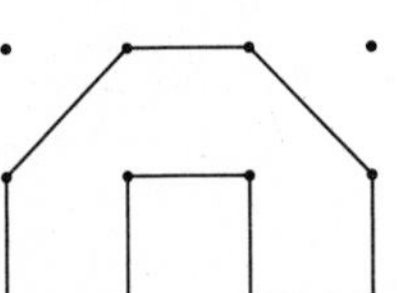 ______________

2. 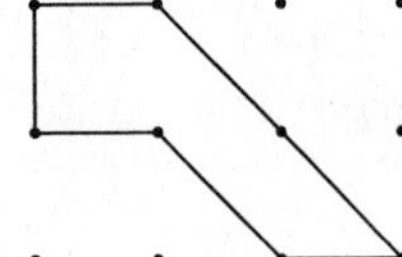 ______________

Name ____

Area of Rectangles and Parallelograms

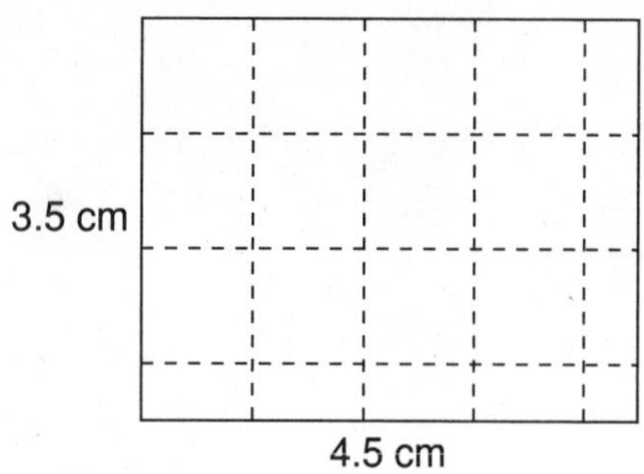

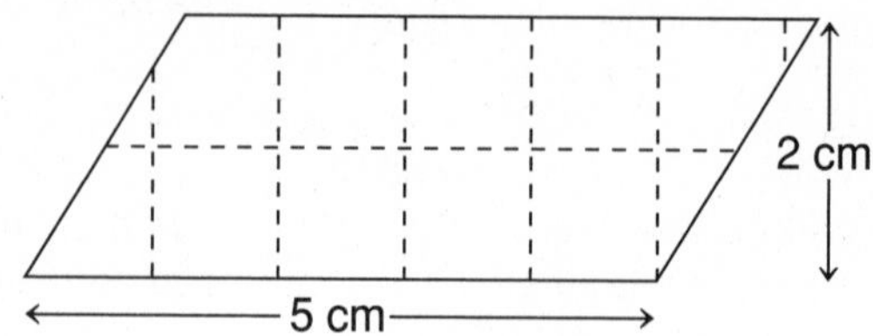

Area of a Rectangle
Area = length × width

$A = lw$

$A = 3.5 \times 4.5$

$A = 15.75\ cm^2$

Area is measured in square units.

Area of a Paralleogram
Area = base × height

$A = bh$

$A = 5 \times 2$

$A = 10\ cm^2$

Find the areas.

1. How much linoleum is needed to cover a rectangular floor that is 2.4 m wide and 3.8 m long?

$A = lw$

$A = 2.4 \times 38$

A = ____________ m^2

2. How many square meters of sod will be needed to cover a lawn in the shape of a parallelogram with a base of 23 m and a height of 26 m?

$A = bh$

A = 2 3 × ____________

A = ____________

3. A rectangle has a length of 8.2 in and a width of 4 m.

Area = ____________

4. A parallelogram has a base of 7.5 cm and a height of 3 cm.

Area = ____________

5. If 25 m^2 of carpet were bought to carpet a rectangular floor 5.2 m by 4.5 m, how much carpet would be left over?

____

6. A flower bed is in the shape of a parallelogram with a base of 2.8 m and a height of 1.5 m. What is the area of the flower bed?

____

Name ______________________________

Area of Triangles and Trapezoids

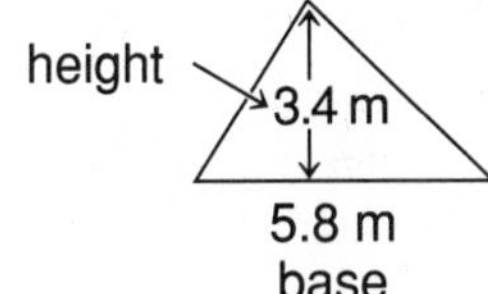

$b_2 = 4$ cm
$h = 2$ cm
$b_1 = 9$ cm

Area of a Triangle	Area of a Trapezoid
Area $= \frac{1}{2} \times$ base $\times$ height	Area $= \frac{1}{2} \times$ height $\times$ (base$_1$ + base$_2$)
$A = \frac{1}{2}bh$	$A = \frac{1}{2}h\,(b_1 + b_2)$
$A = \frac{1}{2} \times 5.8 \times 3.4$	$A = \frac{1}{2} \times 2\,(9 + 4)$
$A = 9.86\text{ m}^2$	$A = 13\text{ cm}^2$

Find the areas.

1. $h = 3.5$ cm, $b = 5.2$ cm

$A = \frac{1}{2}bh$

$A = \frac{1}{2} \times 5.2 \times 3.5$

$A = \frac{1}{2} \times 18.2$

$A =$ 9.1 cm^2

2. $b_2 = 3.2$ m, $h = 6$ m, $b_1 = 9.8$ m

$A = \frac{1}{2} \times h\,(b_1 + b_2)$

$A = \frac{1}{2} \times 6\,(9.8 + 3.2)$

$A = \frac{1}{2} \times 6 \times$ ______

$A =$ ____________

3.

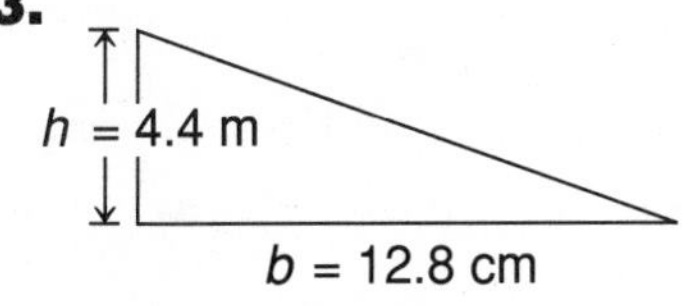

$A =$ ____________

4.

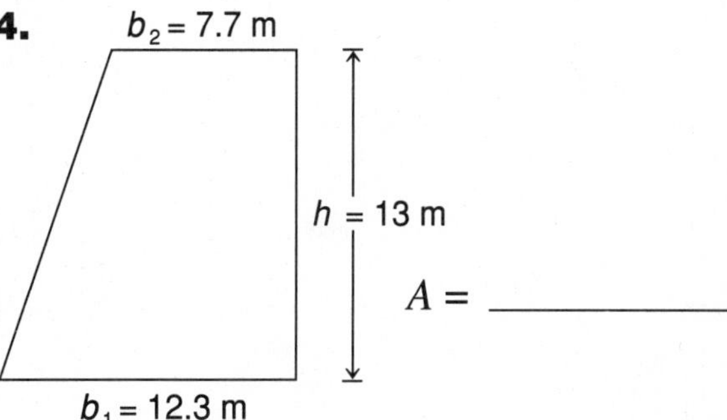

$A =$ ____________

5.

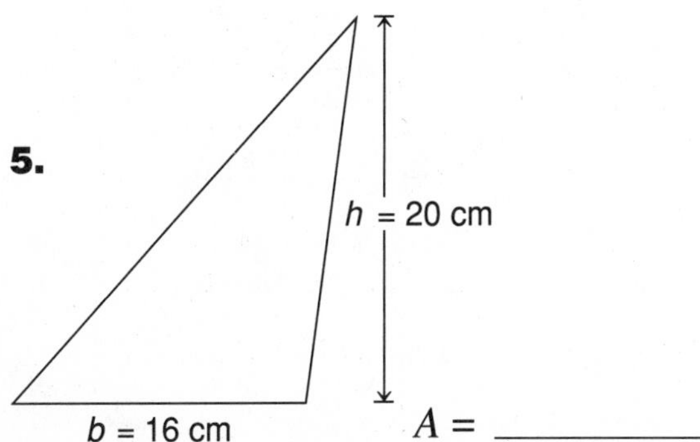

$A =$ ____________

6.

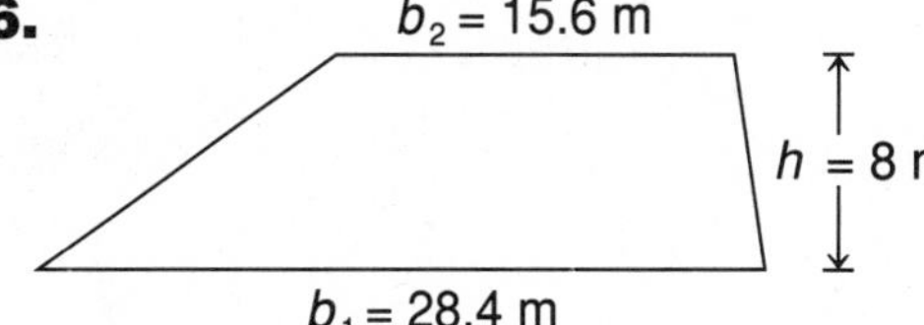

$A =$ ____________

Name ______________________________

Area of Circles

Find the approximate area of a circle whose radius is 3 cm.

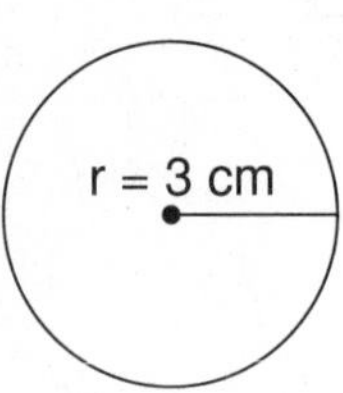

Area = π × radius squared

Area = πr^2
Area ≈ 3.14×3^2
Area ≈ 3.14×9
Area ≈ 28.26 cm^2

π ≈ 3.14

Find the approximate area of each circle. Use a calculator.

1. $r = 0.6$ m

$A = \pi r^2$

$A \approx 3.14 \times (0.6)^2$

$A \approx 3.14 \times 0.36$

$A \approx$ 1.1304 m^2

2. $d = 16$ mm

Divide 16 mm by 2.

$r = 8$

$A = \pi r^2$

$A \approx 3.14 \times$ ______

$A \approx$ __________ mm^2

3. $d = 6.8$ m

$r = 3.4$

$A = \pi r^2$

$A \approx$ ______ × ______

$A \approx$ __________

4.

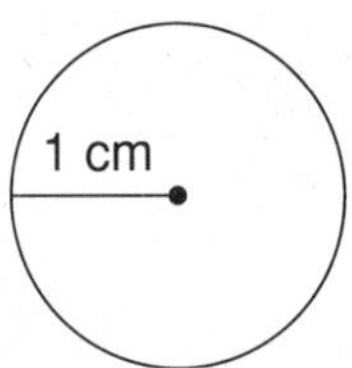

$A \approx$ __________

5.

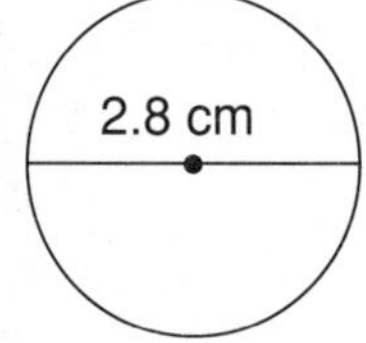
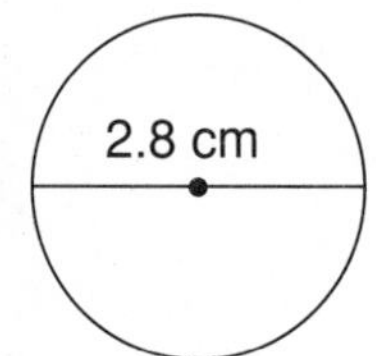

$A \approx$ __________

6.

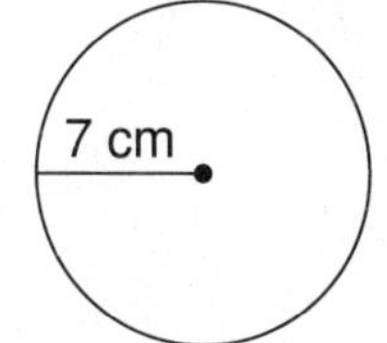

$A \approx$ __________

7. $r = 2$ cm

$A \approx$ __________

8. $d = 40$ mm

$A \approx$ __________

9. $r = 0.8$ m

$A \approx$ __________

10. $d = 10$ cm

$A \approx$ __________

11. $r = 30$ m

$A \approx$ __________

12. $d = 22$ mm

$A \approx$ __________

13. $r = 15$ m

$A \approx$ __________

14. $d = 5.6$ cm

$A \approx$ __________

15. $r = 29$ cm

$A \approx$ __________

Name ______________________________

Area of Irregular Shaped Figures

To find the area of irregular shaped figures:

Divide the figures into shapes that you know. → Find the area of each shape. → Add and/or subtract these areas, depending on the figure.

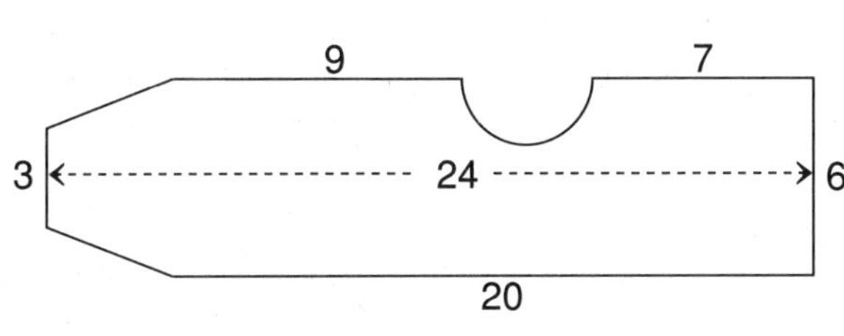

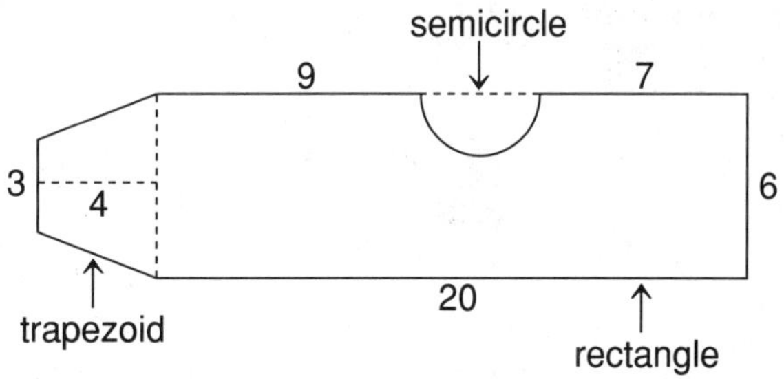

Area of figure = Area of rectangle + Area of trapezoid – Area of semicircle

$= (20 \cdot 6) + [\frac{1}{2}(6 + 3)\ 4] - (\frac{1}{2} \cdot 2 \cdot 2 \cdot \pi)$

$= 120 + 18 - 6.28$

$= 131.72$ square units

Calculate the areas of these figures. All lengths are in meters.

1.

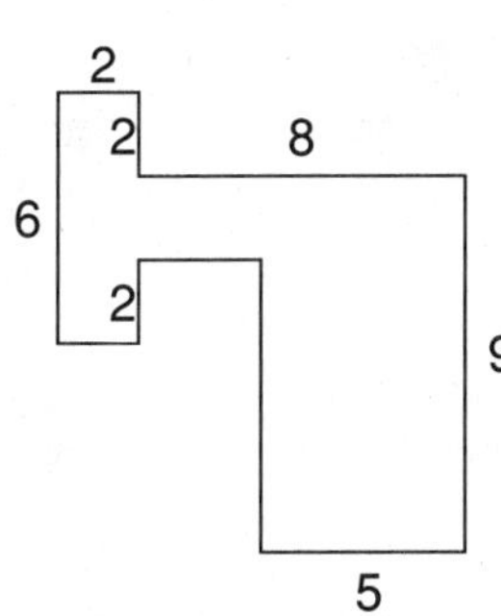

2.

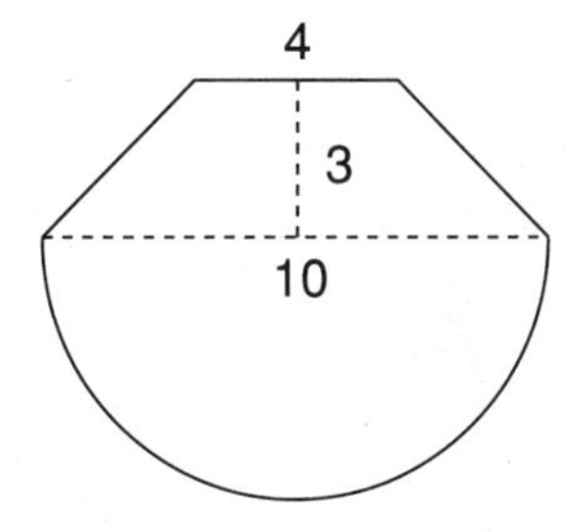

3.

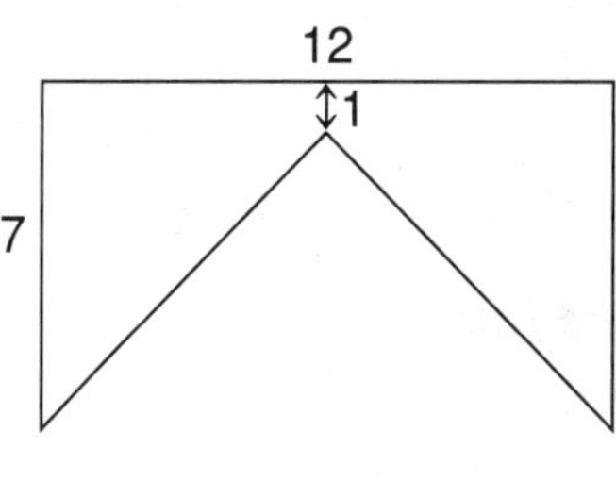

__________ __________ __________

Name ______________________________

Developing a Plan

To solve problems that require more than one strategy:

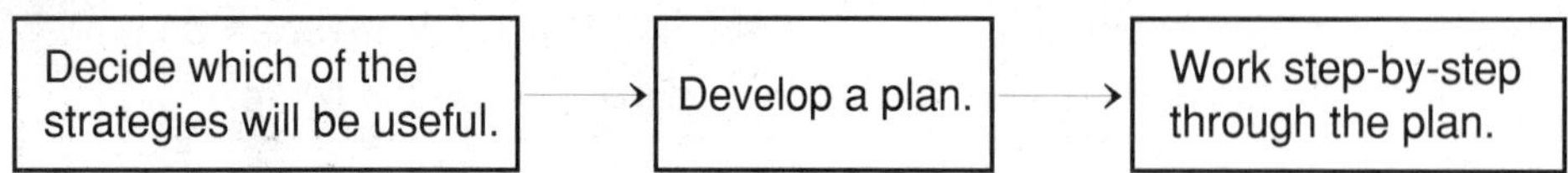

Example: Seven girls play on Ellen's basketball team. How many different sets of five girls can make up the starting team?

Try Use Objects, Make an Organized List, and Look for a Pattern.

A Use objects. ① ② ③ ④ ⑤ ⑥ ⑦

B Make an organized list. Make a list of the different combinations

When 1 sits out, then 2, and so on. Do not repeat combinations

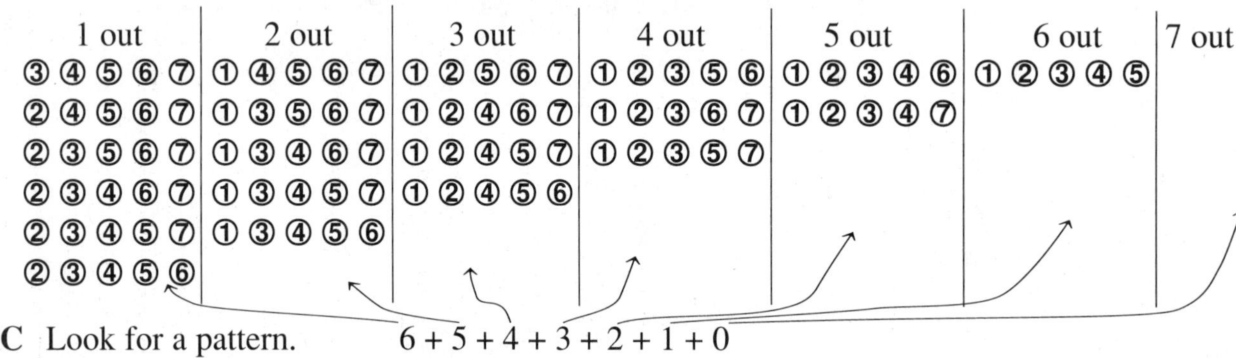

1 out	2 out	3 out	4 out	5 out	6 out	7 out
③ ④ ⑤ ⑥ ⑦	① ④ ⑤ ⑥ ⑦	① ② ⑤ ⑥ ⑦	① ② ③ ⑤ ⑥	① ② ③ ④ ⑥	① ② ③ ④ ⑤	
② ④ ⑤ ⑥ ⑦	① ③ ⑤ ⑥ ⑦	① ② ④ ⑥ ⑦	① ② ③ ⑥ ⑦	① ② ③ ④ ⑦		
② ③ ⑤ ⑥ ⑦	① ③ ④ ⑥ ⑦	① ② ④ ⑤ ⑦	① ② ③ ⑤ ⑦			
② ③ ④ ⑥ ⑦	① ③ ④ ⑤ ⑦	① ② ④ ⑤ ⑥				
② ③ ④ ⑤ ⑦	① ③ ④ ⑤ ⑥					
② ③ ④ ⑤ ⑥						

C Look for a pattern. 6 + 5 + 4 + 3 + 2 + 1 + 0

There are 21 possible combinations of the seven girls for the starting five.

Using the strategies, develop a plan and solve the problem.

1. Regular polygons can be divided into triangles by drawing every possible diagonal from one vertex of the polygon. How many triangles can be formed in a 12-sided polygon?

   ______

2. Karen sets the table on even days. Joel sets the table on odd days. On how many combinations of days in the year will Joel set the table 2 days in a row?

   ______

Name ______________________________

Using Critical Thinking

To compare the area of figures if you are given their dimensions:

Use the dimensions to find the areas of the figures.	›	Compare their areas.

Look at circle *A* and circle *B* at the right. The area of how many circle *A*s will equal the area of circle *B*?

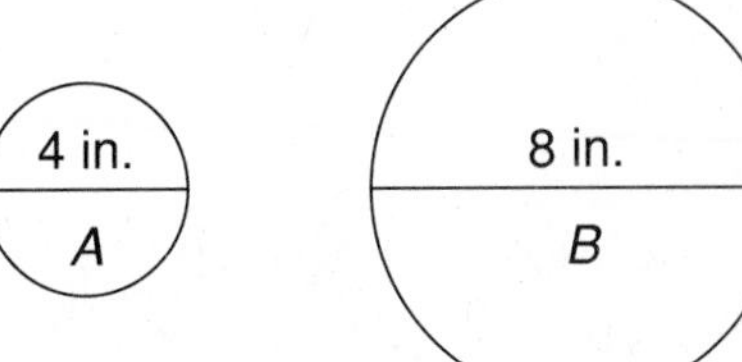

Area of circle $A = 2^2\pi \quad = 4\pi \quad \approx 12.57 \text{ in}^2$.

Area of circle $B = 4^2\pi \quad = 16\pi \quad \approx 50.27 \text{ in}^2$.

The diameter of circle *B* is twice that of circle *A*, but it would take 4 times the area of circle *A* to equal the area of circle *B*.

Use the given dimensions to help compare the areas of the circles.

1. The areas of how many circles of radius 6 m are needed to equal a circle of radius 18 m?

____

2. The areas of how many circles with a diameter of 20 in. are needed to equal the area of a circle with a diameter of 100 in.?

____

3. The areas of how many circles with a radius of 5 cm are needed to equal the area of a circle with a radius of 20 cm?

____

4. The area of a circle with a radius of _____ cm is four times as large as a circle with an area of 78.5 cm.

5. The area of a circle with a radius of 15 cm is _____ times as large as a circle with an area of 78.5 cm.

Name ______________________________

Exploring Algebra: Solving a Formula for a Given Variable

To solve a formula for a given variable:

> Rewrite the formula so that the variable stands alone on one side of the equals sign.

Example: What is the base of a parallelogram with an area of 357 cm² and a height of 25.5 cm?

The formula for the area of a parallelogram is $A = bh$. In this case, the area and the height are given, and the base is unknown. The formula needs to be rewritten to solve for the base, b.

$$A = bh \qquad \frac{A}{h} = \frac{bh}{h} \qquad \frac{A}{h} = b$$

Now evaluate the new formula for $A = 357$ and $h = 25.5$.

$$\frac{357}{25.5} = b \qquad 14 = b \qquad b = 14 \text{ cm}$$

A parallelogram with an area of 357cm² and a height of 25.5cm has a base of 14cm.

Rewrite each formula for the stated variables.

1. $A = bh;\ h$ __________

2. $A = lw;\ l$ __________

3. $A = lw;\ w$ __________

4. $A = \frac{1}{2}bh;\ b$ __________

5. $A = \frac{1}{2}bh;\ h$ __________

6. $A = \frac{1}{2}(b_1 + b_2)h;\ h$ __________

7. $A = \pi r^2;\ r$ __________

8. $A = s^2;\ s$ __________

Find the missing dimensions.

9. 12.5 cm; 37.5 cm²; w

____

10. 7 mm; h; 40 mm²; 9 mm

____

Name ______________________________

Surface Area of Prisms and Cylinders

To find the surface area of any prism or cylinder:

Mentally break the prism or cylinder down into separate parts. → Find the area of each part. → Add all areas.

Example: Find the surface area of the cylinder at the right.

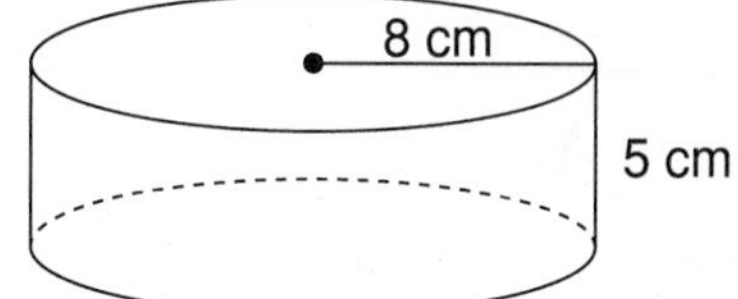

Any cylinder can be broken down into three parts:

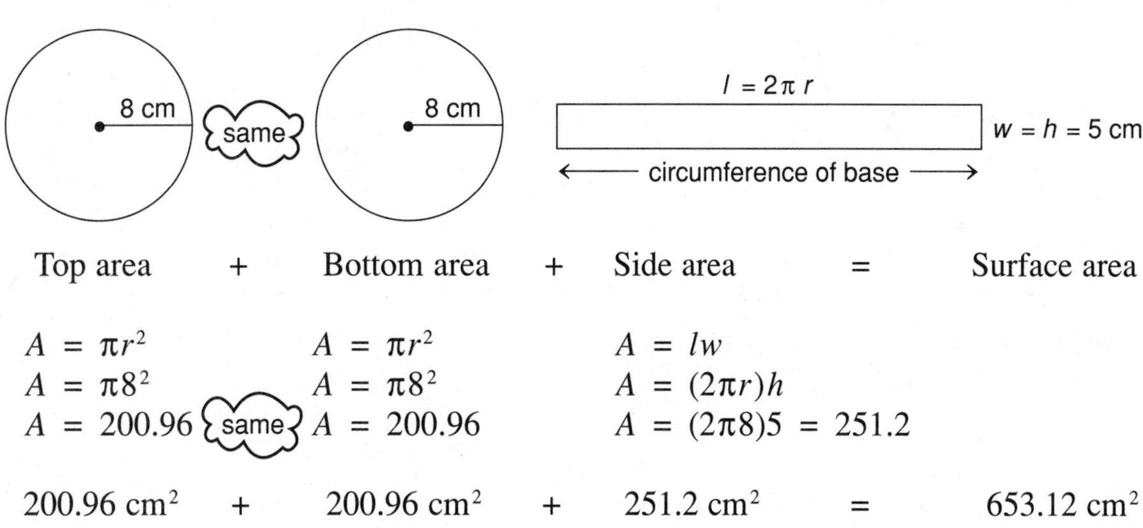

Top area	+	Bottom area	+	Side area	=	Surface area
$A = \pi r^2$		$A = \pi r^2$		$A = lw$		
$A = \pi 8^2$		$A = \pi 8^2$		$A = (2\pi r)h$		
$A = 200.96$	same	$A = 200.96$		$A = (2\pi 8)5 = 251.2$		
$200.96\ cm^2$	+	$200.96\ cm^2$	+	$251.2\ cm^2$	=	$653.12\ cm^2$

The top and the bottom have the same area, so a formula for the surface area of a cylinder is:

Surface area $= 2\pi r^2 + 2\pi rh$

Find the surface area of the three figures below.

1. __________

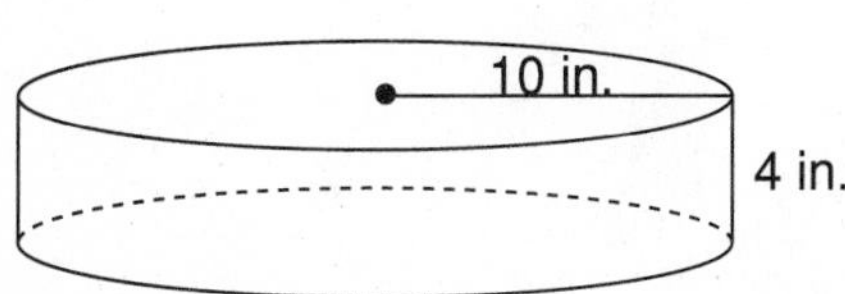

2. __________

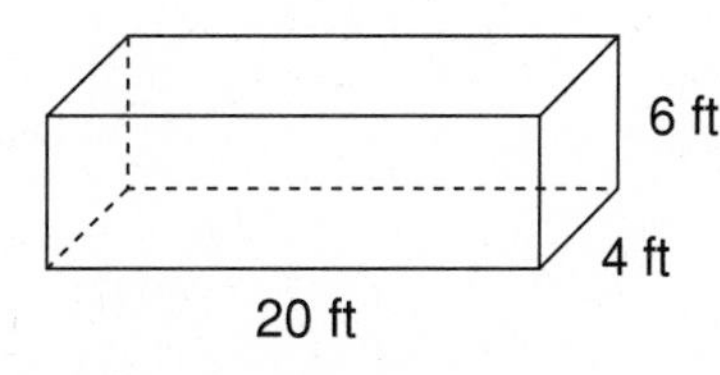

3. __________

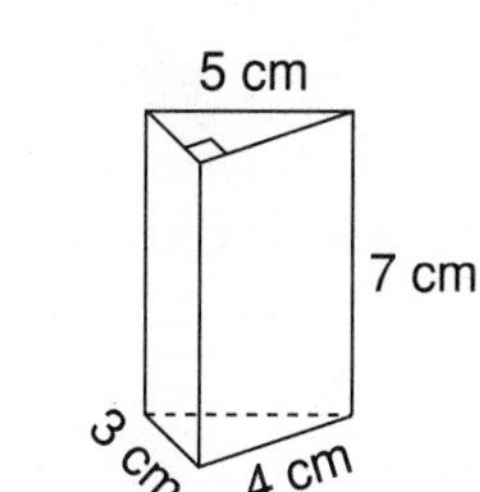

Name ______________________________

Exploring the Concept of Volume

A cubic unit is a cube with each edge one unit long. Volume is measured in terms of cubic units.

cubic unit

To find the volume of a space figure, count the number of cubic units.

Example: Find the volume of the figure at the right. Each "block" is a cubic unit. There are 13 blocks, so the volume of the figure is 13 cubic units or 13 units ^{3}.

Imagine a back view of the same figure

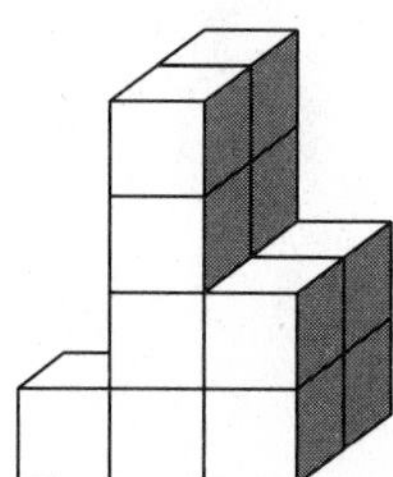

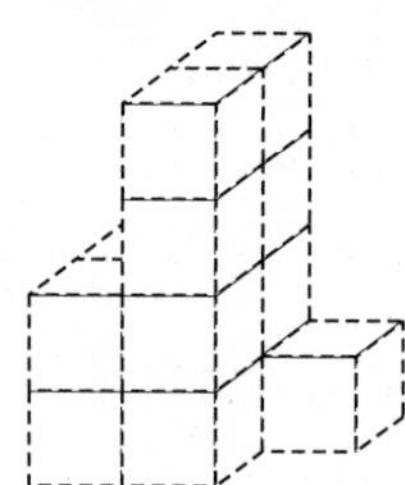

Find the volume of each figure below. The hidden back view looks like the corner of a box.

1.

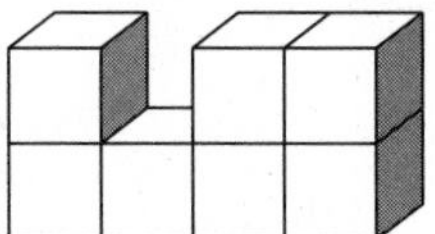

____

2.

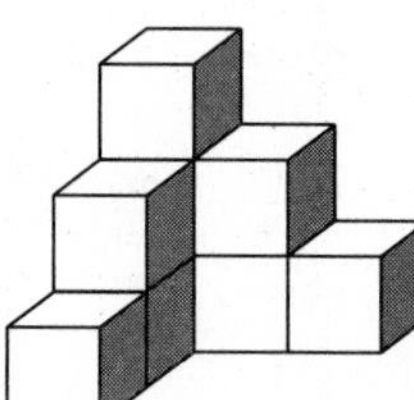

____

3.

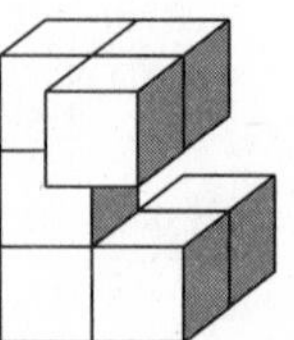

____

4.

____

Name ______________________________

Volume of Prisms

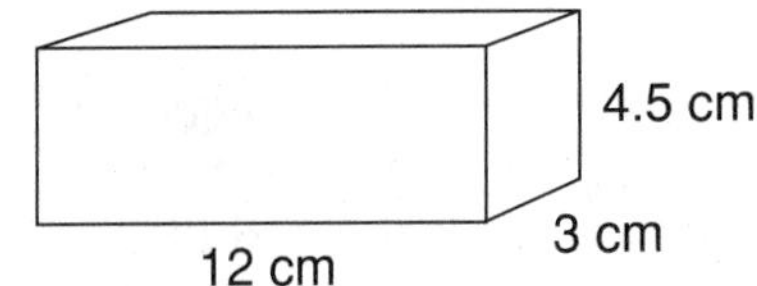

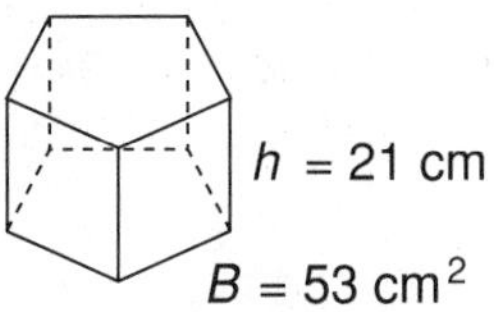

Volume of a rectangular prism

Volume = length × width × height

$V = lwh$

$V = 12 \times 3 \times 4.5$

$V = 162 \text{ cm}^3$ ← Volume is measured in cubic units.

Volume of any prism

Volume = Area of base × height

$V = Bh$

$V = 53 \times 21$

$V = 1{,}113 \text{ cm}^3$

Find the volume of each prism.

1.

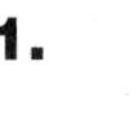

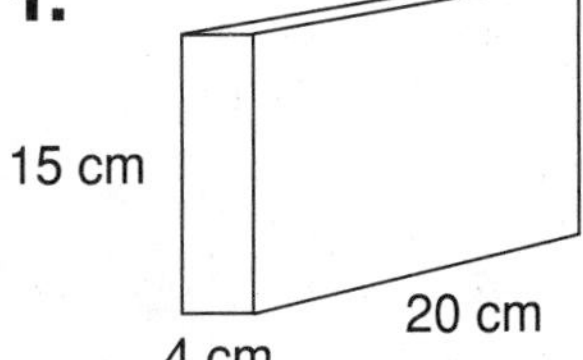

$V = lwh$

$V =$ 20 × 4 × 15

$V =$ 12000 cm^3

2.

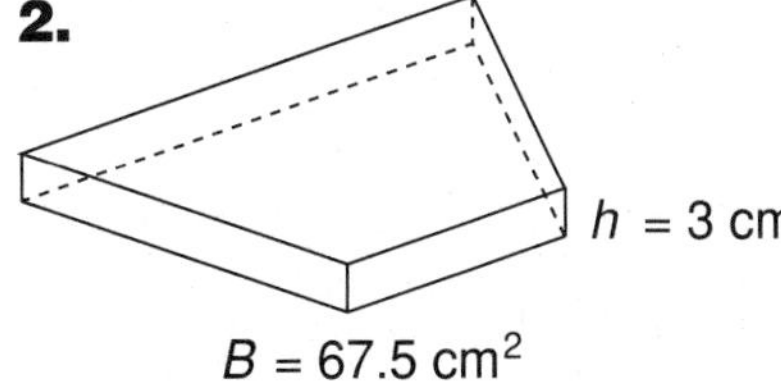

$V = Bh$

$V =$ 67.5 × ______

$V =$ ______

3.

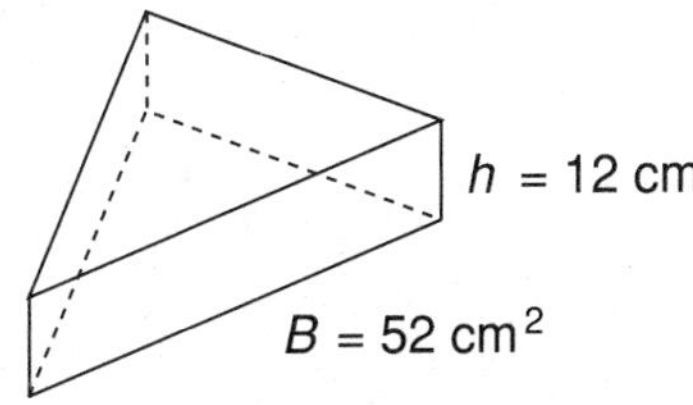

$V =$ ______

4.

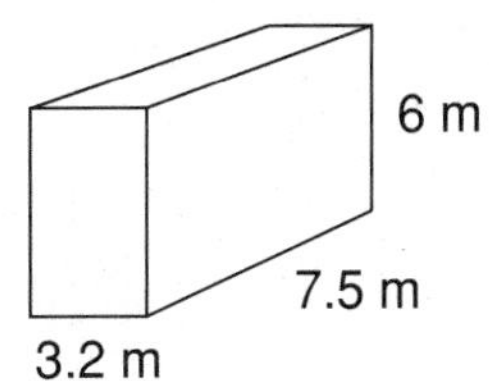

$V =$ ______

5.

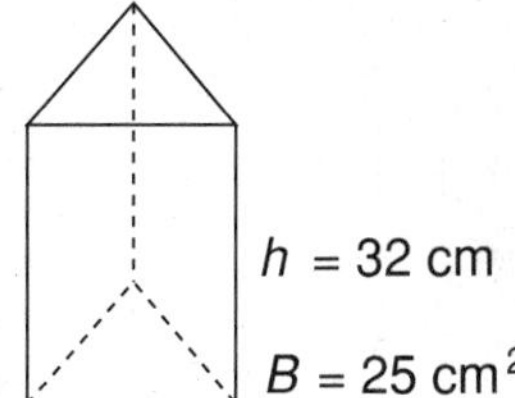

$V =$ ______

6.

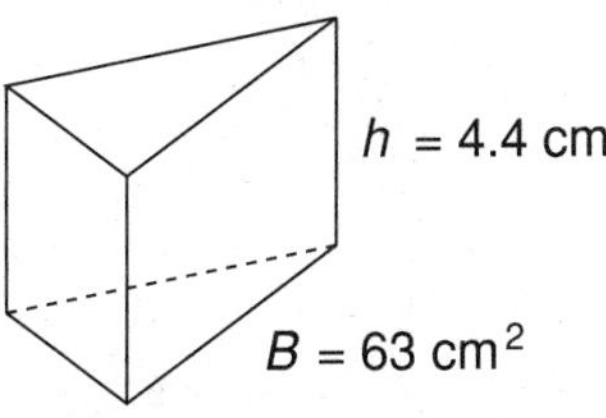

$V =$ ______

7.

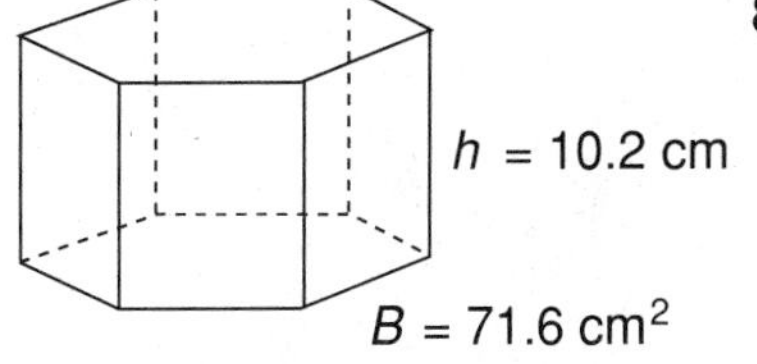

$V =$ ______

8.

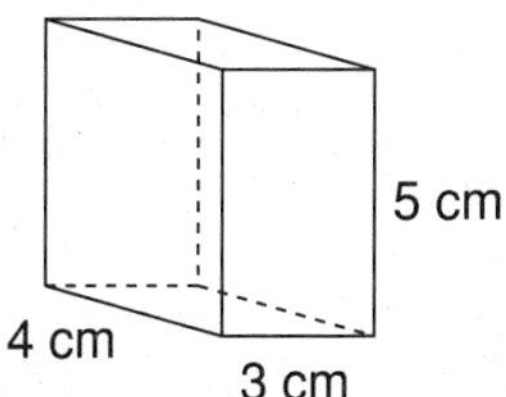

$V =$ ______

Name ______________________________

Volume of a Cylinder

Find the volume of a cylinder whose radius is 9 cm and height is 20 cm.

h = 20 cm

r = 9 cm

Volume = Area of base × height

Volume = $\underbrace{\pi \times \text{radius squared}}_{\text{area of base}}$ × height

$V = \pi r^2 h$

$V \approx 3.14 \times 9^2 \times 20$

$V \approx 3.14 \times 81 \times 20$

$V \approx 5{,}086.80 \text{ cm}^3$ ← cubic centimeters

Find the volume of each cylinder.
Use a calculator. Use 3.14 for π.

1.

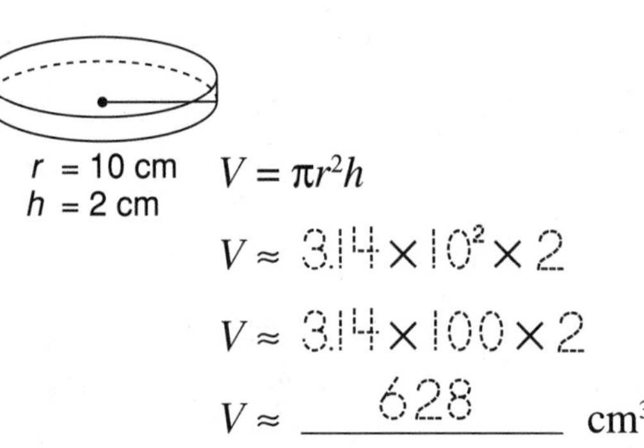

r = 10 cm
h = 2 cm

$V = \pi r^2 h$

$V \approx 3.14 \times 10^2 \times 2$

$V \approx 3.14 \times 100 \times 2$

$V \approx$ 628 cm³

2.

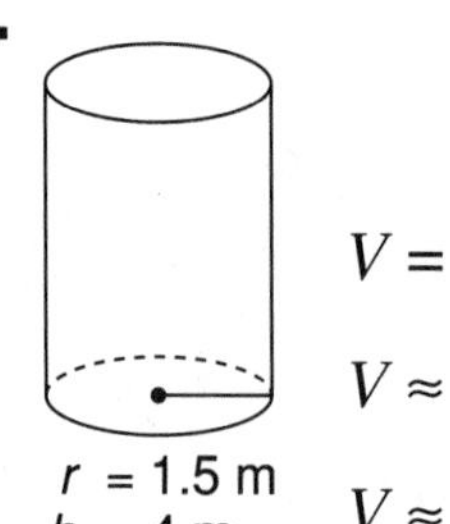

r = 1.5 m
h = 4 m

$V = \pi r^2 h$

$V \approx 3.14 \times (\_\_\_\_)^2 \times \_\_\_\_$

$V \approx$ ______________

3.

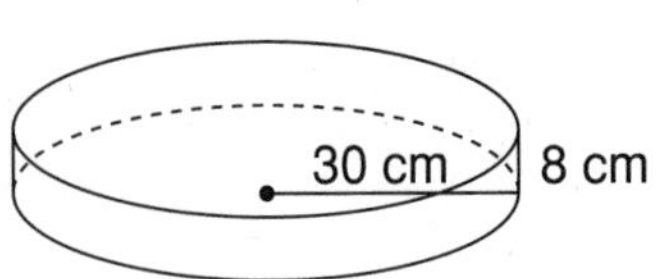

$V \approx$ ______________

4.

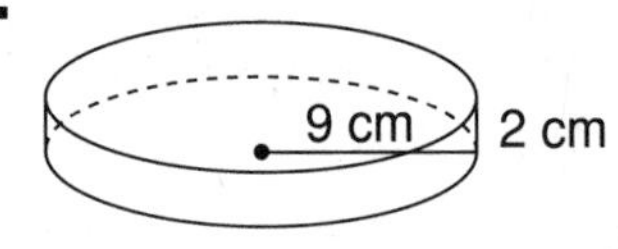

$V \approx$ ______________

5.

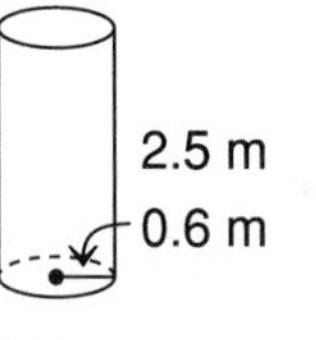

$V \approx$ ______________

6. r = 10 cm
h = 10 cm

$V \approx$ ______________

7. r = 1.5 cm
h = 3.0 cm

$V \approx$ ______________

8. r = 1.2 m
h = 2.5 m

$V \approx$ ______________

9. r = 4 cm
h = 6 cm

$V \approx$ ______________

10. r = 0.5 cm
h = 1.0 cm

$V \approx$ ______________

11. r = 12 mm
h = 8 mm

$V \approx$ ______________

Name ______________________________

Volume of Pyramids and Cones

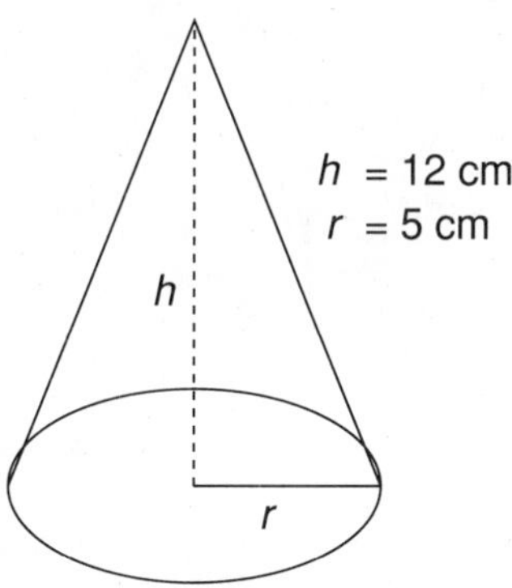

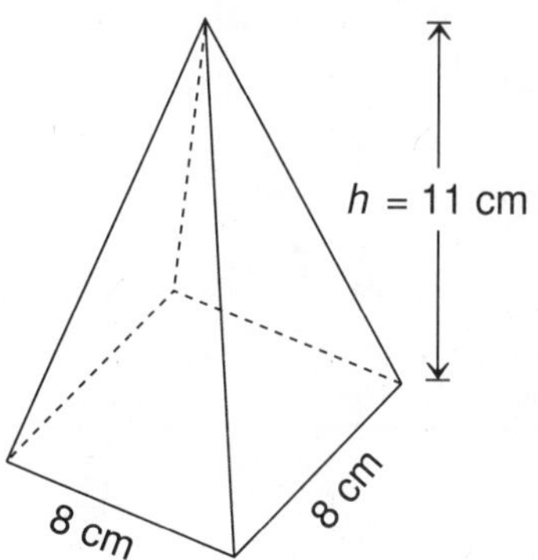

A **cone** has a circular base. A **pyramid** has a polygonal base.

To find the volume of a cone or a pyramid:

Find the area of the base (B).	→	Use the formula $V = \frac{1}{3}Bh$.

Example: Find the volumes of the figures above.

Volume of the cone:

$B = \pi r^2 = 3.14 \times 5 \times 5 = 78.5 \text{ cm}^2$

$V = \frac{1}{3}Bh = \frac{1}{3} \times 78.5 \times 12$

$V = 314 \text{ cm}^3$

Volume of the pyramid:

$B = lw = 8 \times 8 = 64 \text{ cm}^2$

$V = \frac{1}{3}Bh = \frac{1}{3} \times 64 \times 11$

$V = 234.67 \text{ cm}^3$

Find the volumes of the figures below.

1. ____________

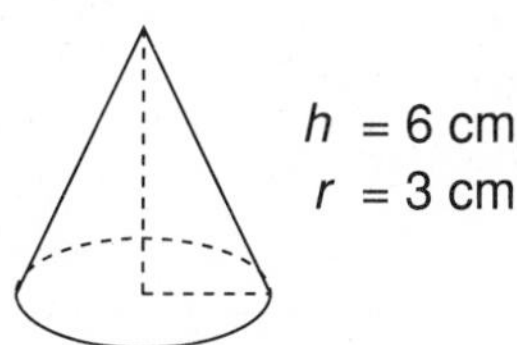

2. ____________

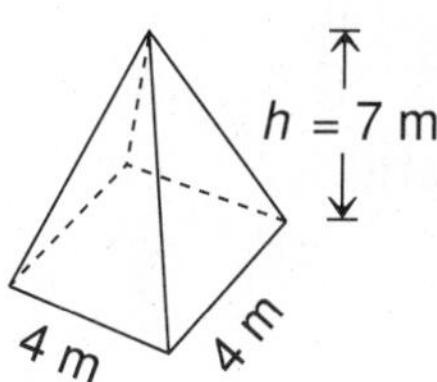

3. pyramid
$B = 12 \text{ m}^2$
$h = 5 \text{ m}$

____

4. cone
$r = 6 \text{ cm}$
$h = 7 \text{ cm}$

____

5. pyramid
$B = 18 \text{ dm}^2$
$h = 3 \text{ dm}$

____

Name ____________________

Data from a Blueprint

This blueprint shows the floor plan of a music shop.

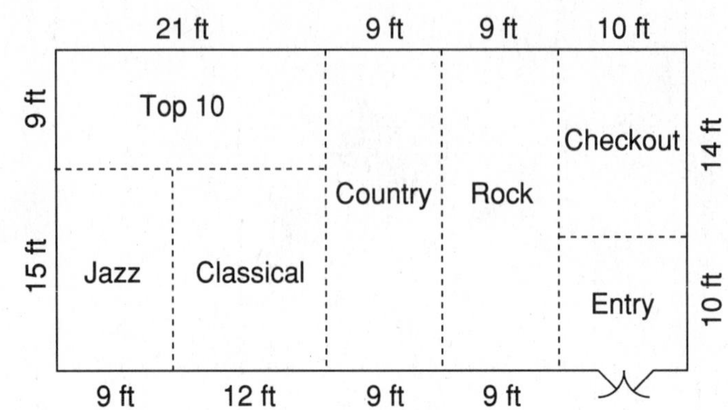

How many square yards of carpet are needed for the jazz section?

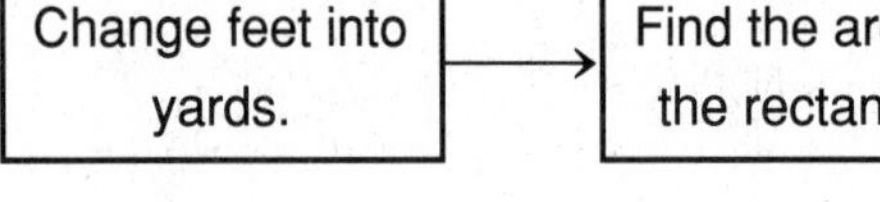

15 ft by 9 ft

$15 \div 3 = 5$
$9 \div 3 = 3$

$3 \times 5 = 15$ yd^2

15 yd^2 of carpet are needed for the jazz section.

Find the surface area of the three figures below.

1. Classical

$l =$ _____ $w =$ _____

_____ $\div 3 =$ _____ yards

_____ $\div 3 =$ _____ yards

Area: _____ $\times$ _____ $=$ _____

2. Top 10

$l =$ _____ $w =$ _____

____

____

Area: ____________________

3. Country

____

____

____

Area: ____________________

4. How many square feet of tile are needed for the entry and checkout sections?

____

5. Find the total area of the store in square feet. Verify that this area is also the sum of the areas of all the sections.

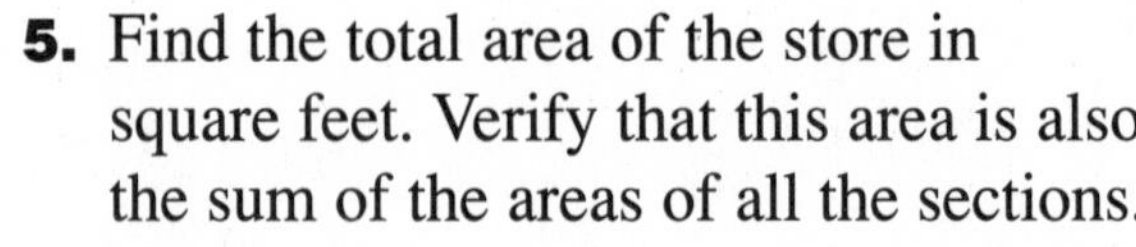

____

____

____

Name ______________________________

Lines of Symmetry

This figure has one **line of symmetry.**

This figure has two **lines of symmetry.**

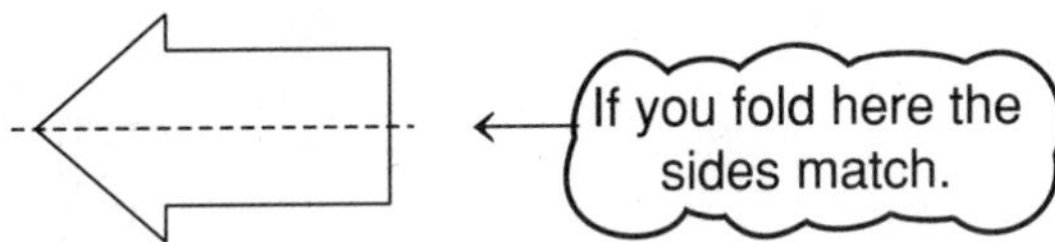

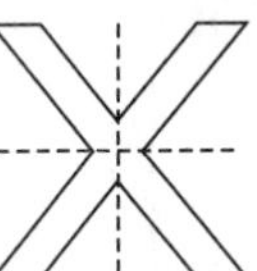

Think of folding each figure on the dotted line.
Is the dotted line a line of symmetry? Write yes or no.

1. 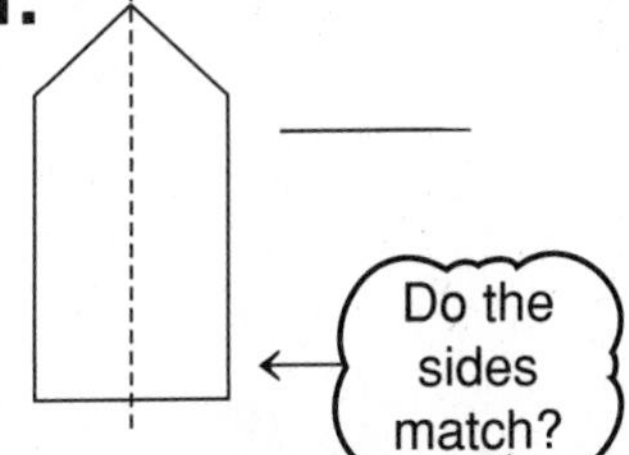

____

2. 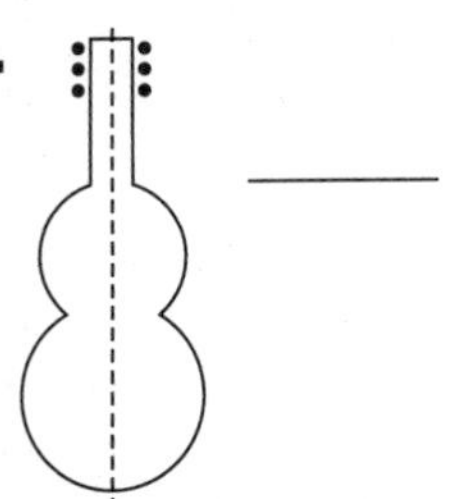 ________

3. 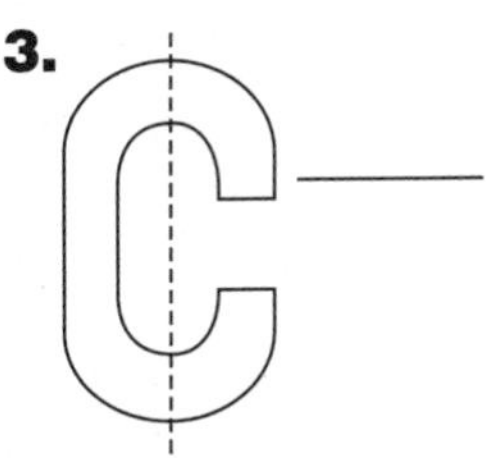 ________

4. 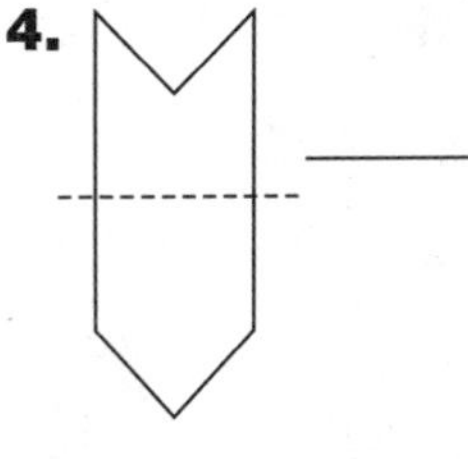 ________

Draw all the lines of symmetry for each figure. Some figures do not have a line of symmetry.

5. 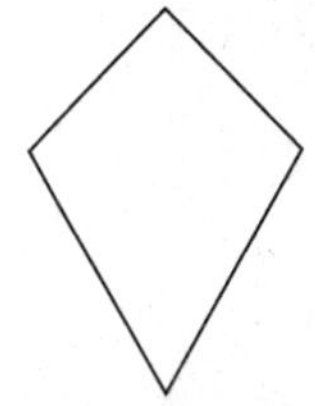

6. 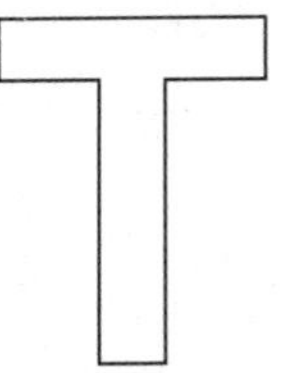

7. 

8. 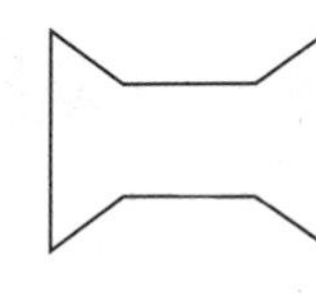

9. 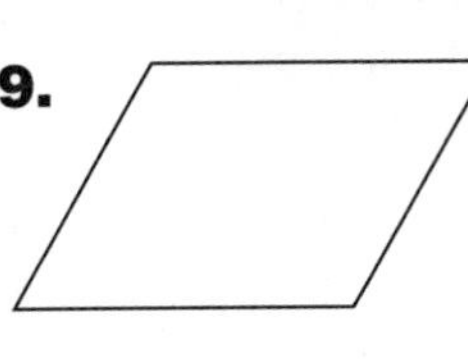

10. 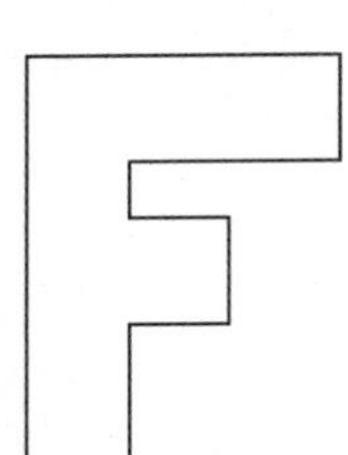

11. 

12. 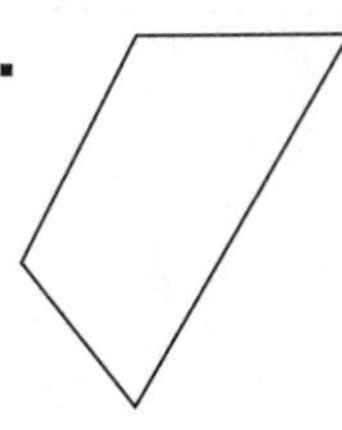

13. 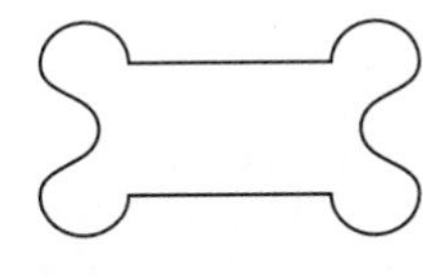

14. 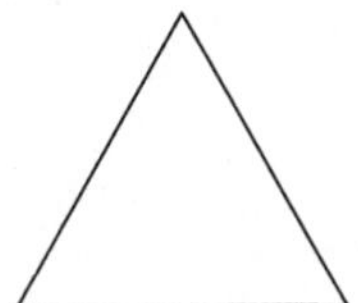

15. 

16. 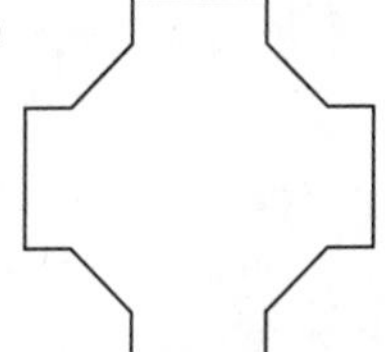

Name ______________________________

Reflection in a Line

Look at the figure to the right. $A'B'C'D'$ is called the **reflection image** of quadrilateral *ABCD*. If you fold the paper along line *l*, $A'B'C'D'$ will fall on top of *ABCD*.

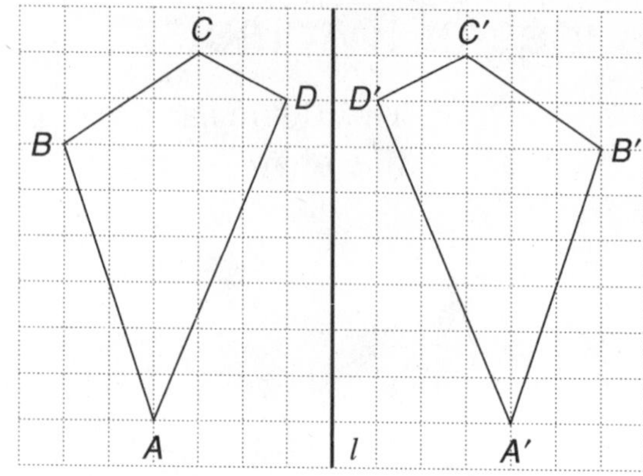

Draw the reflection image of each figure in line *l*.

1.

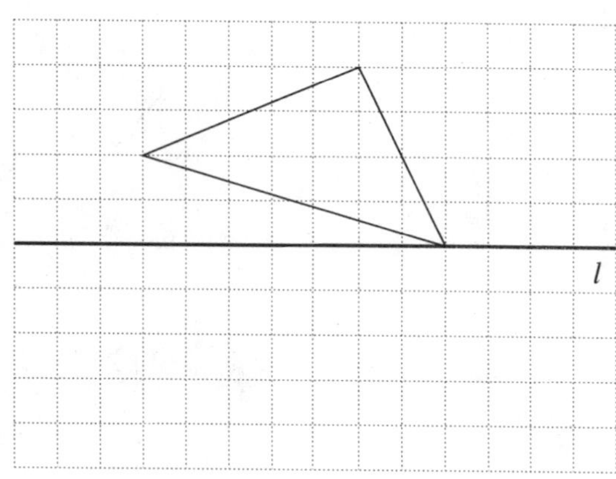

2.

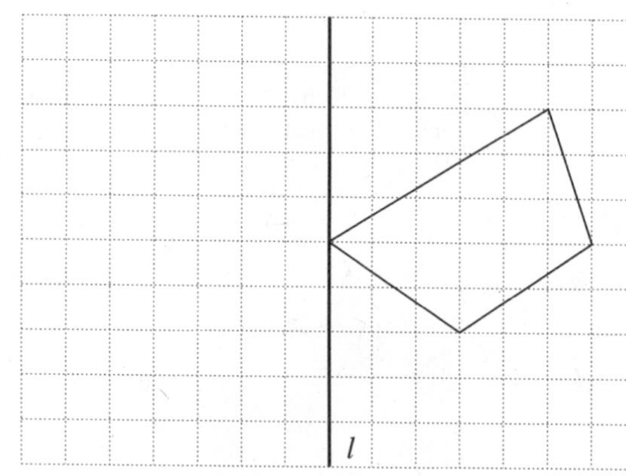

3.

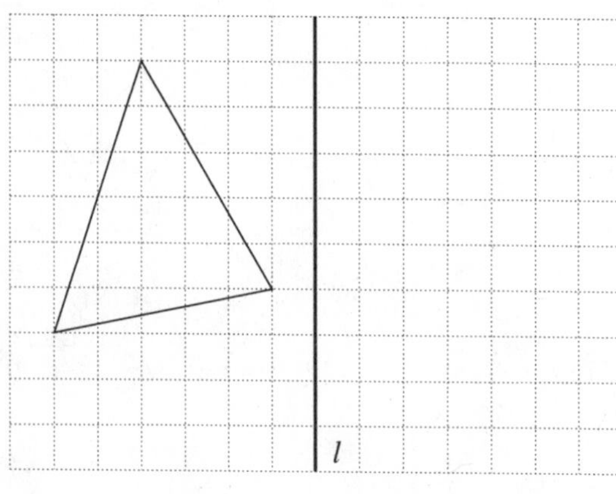

4.

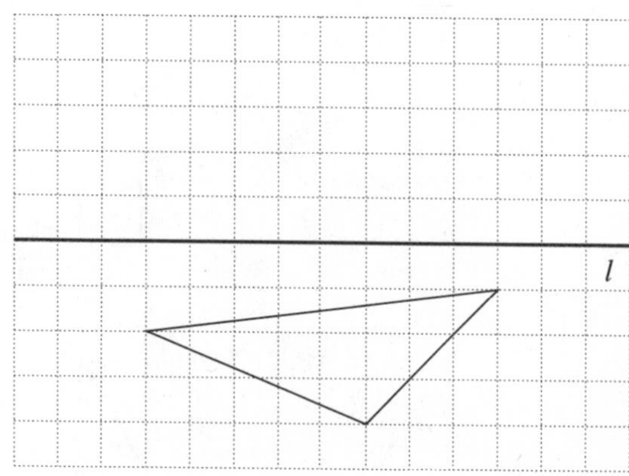

Name ________________________________

Turn Symmetry

To test a figure for turn symmetry, first trace the figure. Then hold the center point fixed and turn the tracing. See what *fraction* of a turn it takes for the traced figure to coincide with the original figure. If the figure must be turned a full 360°, the figure does not have turn symmetry.

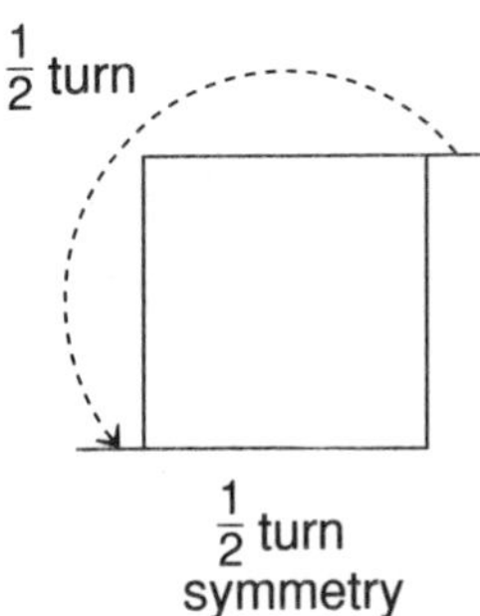

$\frac{1}{2}$ turn symmetry

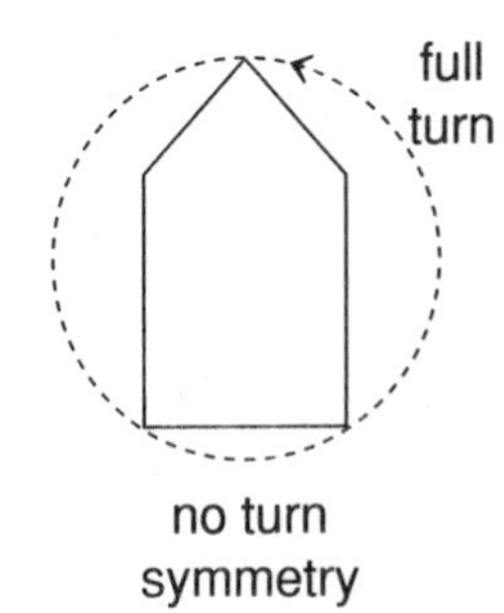

no turn symmetry

Does the figure have turn symmetry?

1.

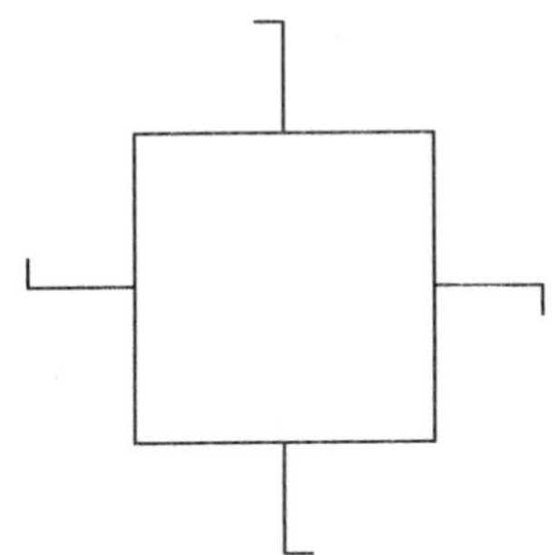

2.

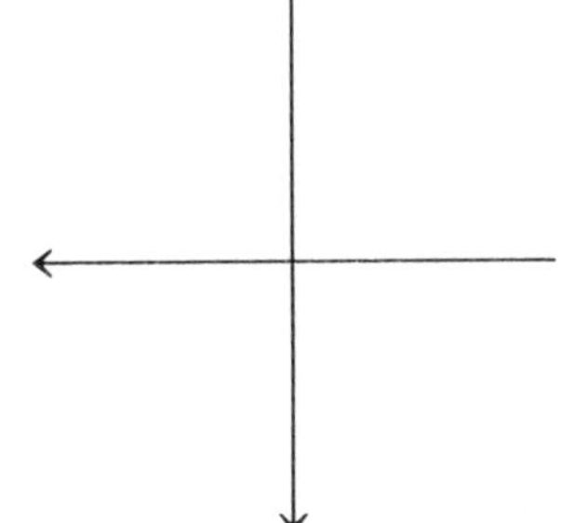

3.

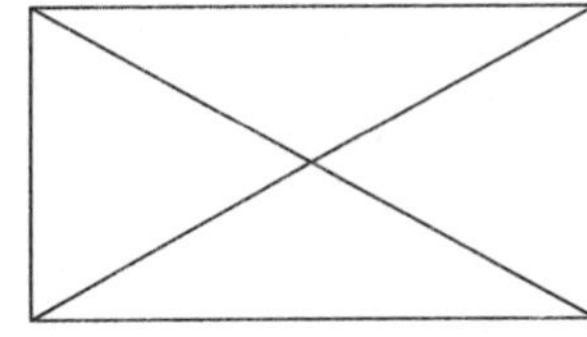

_____________ _____________ _____________

The turn symmetry of each figure is what fraction of a full turn?

4.

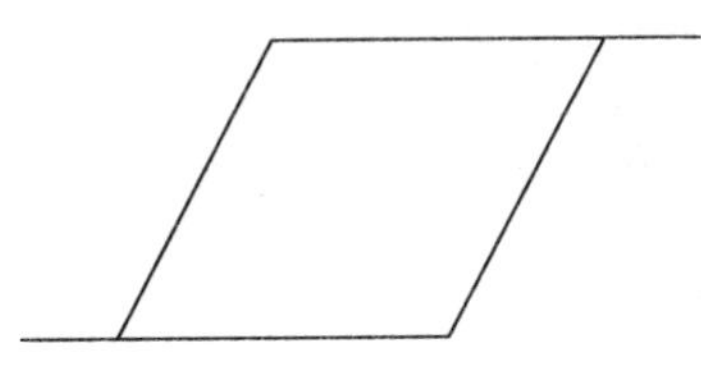

5.

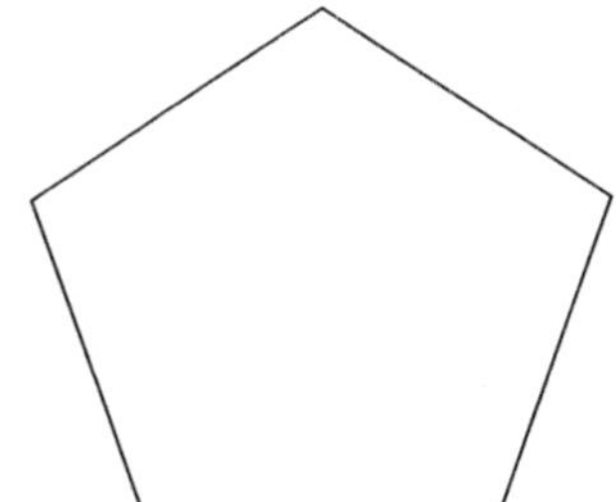

6.

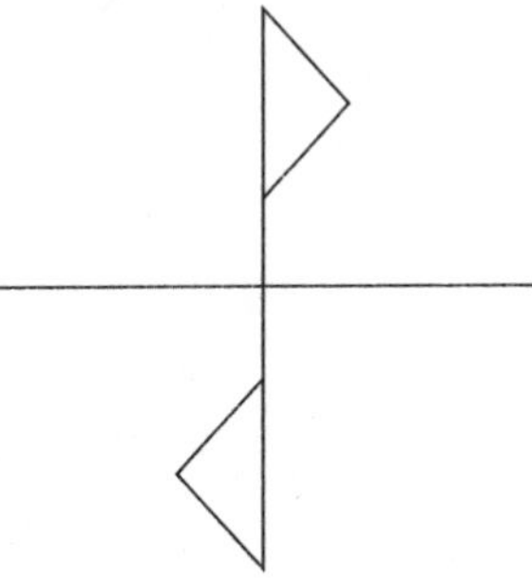

_____________ _____________ _____________

Name ______________________________

Rotations

Look at the figures.

The top row shows a $\frac{1}{4}$ turn image of the triangle.

The bottom row shows a $\frac{1}{2}$ turn image of the triangle.

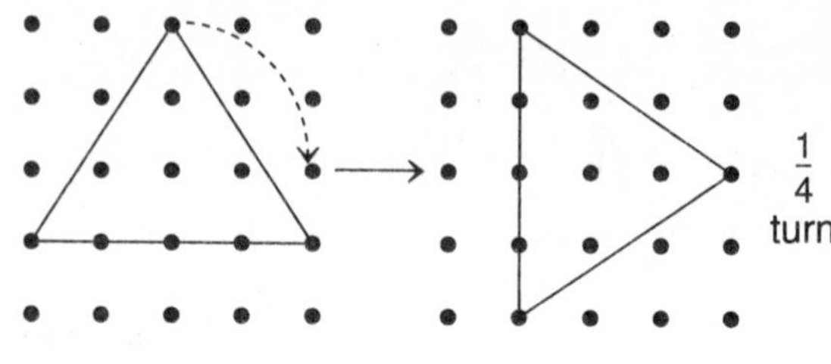

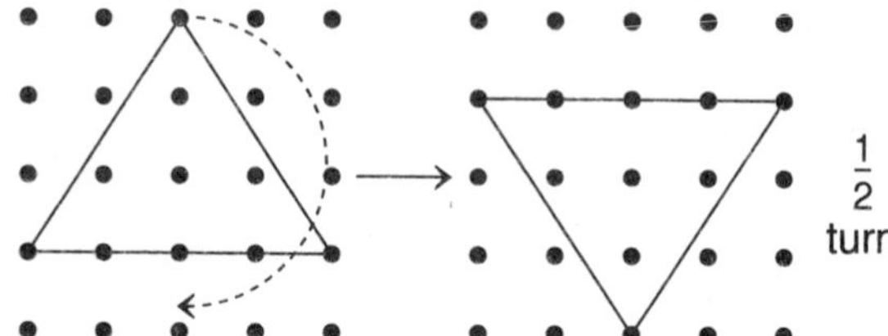

Draw the $\frac{1}{2}$ turn image of each figure.

1. 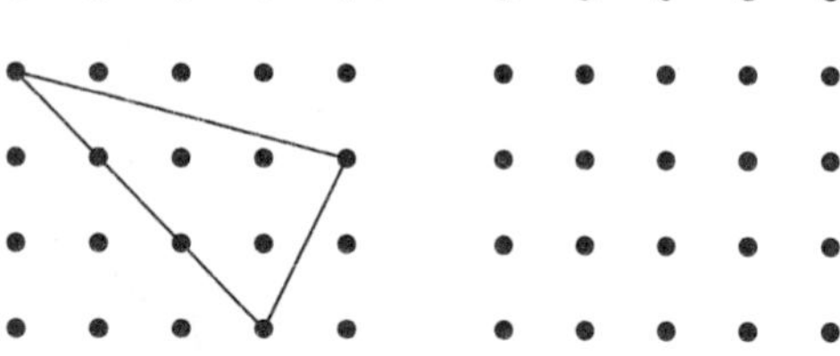

2. 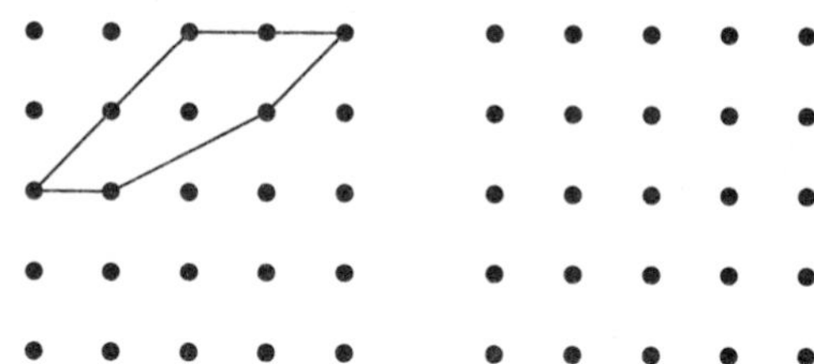

3. 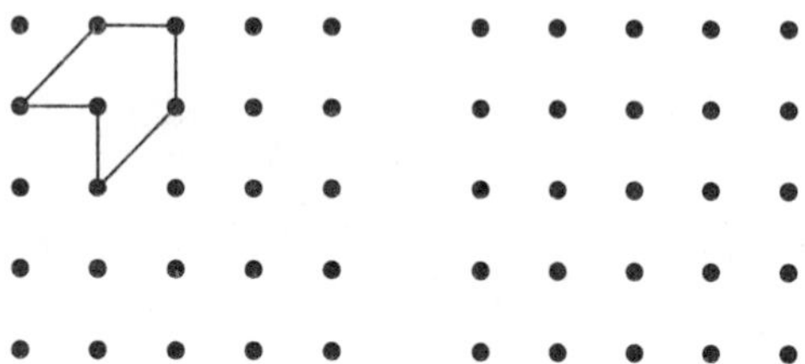

4. 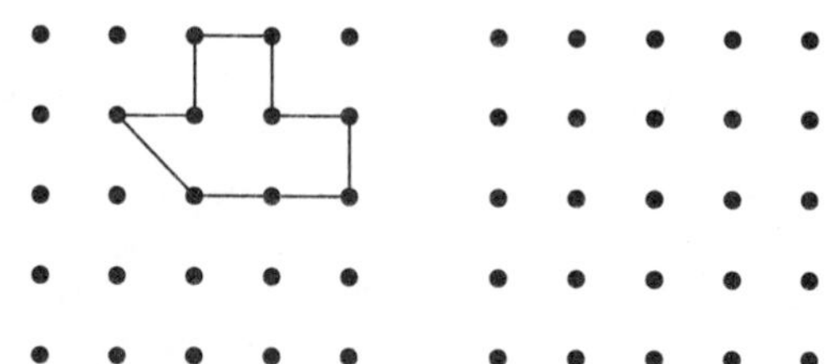

Draw the $\frac{1}{4}$ turn image of each figure.

5. 

6. 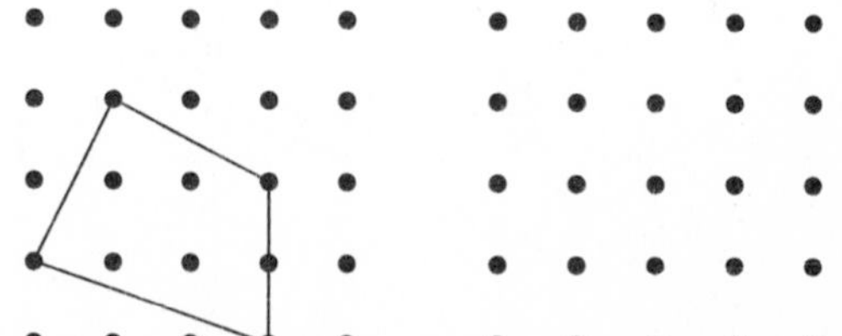

Use with text pages 410–411.

Name ______________________________

Exploring Algebra: More Patterns and Functions

To complete the table shown, substitute each value for x and solve.

x	0	1	2	3
$y = x^2 - 1$	$^-1$			

Let $x = 1$, then:
$y = 1^2 - 1$
$y = 1 - 1$
$y = 0$

Let $x = 2$, then:
$y = 2^2 - 1$
$y = 4 - 1$
$y = 3$

Let $x = 3$, then:
$y = 3^2 - 1$
$y = 9 - 1$
$y = 8$

Complete each table.

1.

x	0	1	2	3
$y = x^2 + 5$				

2.

x	0	5	10	15
$y = x^2 + 7x$				

3.

x	2	10	200	500
$y = 2x - 2$				

4.

x	0	5	10	20
$y = x^2 + x + 4$				

5.

x	0	3	10	12
$y = 2x^2 + x + 6$				

6.

x	2	6	8	15
$y = 2x^2 + x + 2$				

Make a table showing 4 solutions for each equation.

7. $y = 2x^2 + 3x - 1$

8. $y = x^2 + 3x + 10$

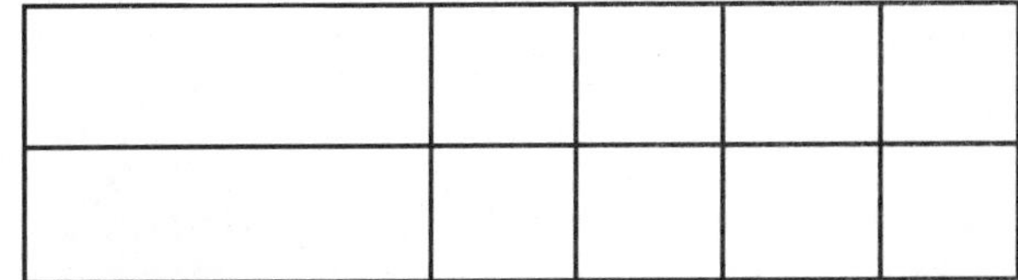

9. $y = x^2 + 2x + 1$

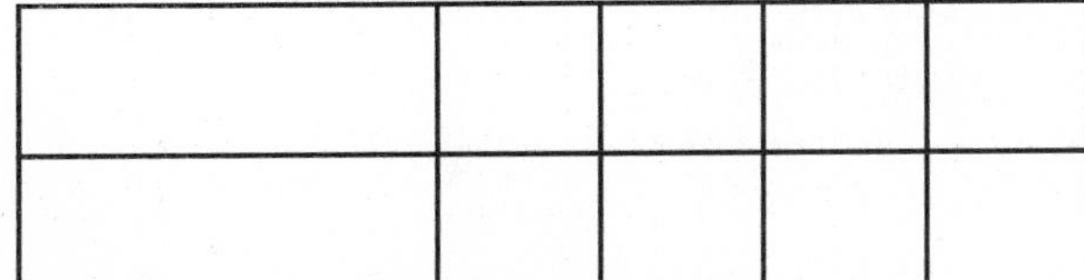

10. $y = (x^2 \div 2) + 1$

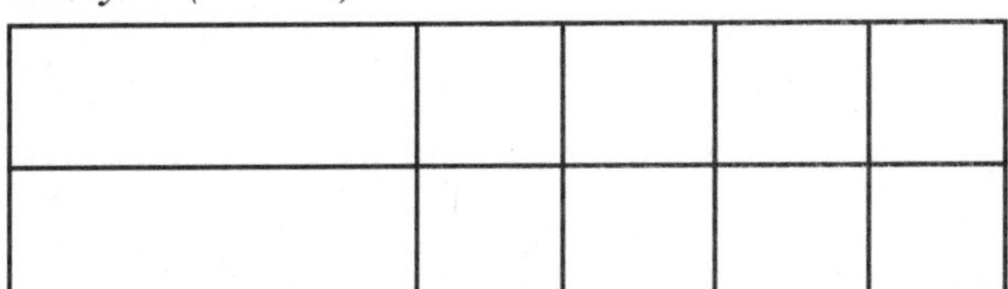

Use with text page 412.

Name ________________

Using the Strategies

A rectangular container is 60 cm wide, 50 cm long, and 40 cm tall. Find the volume of the container.

Next find the volume of liquid in the container if its depth is 20 cm. Then change the depth to 10 cm and find the volume.

What effect does changing the depth have on the volume?

Width	Length	Depth	Volume in cu units
60	50	40	120,000
60	50	20 (÷2)	60,000
60	50	10 (÷2)	30,000

As the depth is halved, so is the volume.

Solve.

1. A rectangular swimming pool has 4 ft of water in it. The length of the pool is 30 ft and the width of the pool is 20 ft. What is the volume of the water in the pool?

   ____

   How does the volume change if 4 more feet of water are added to the pool?

   ____

2. A square container has a length of 10 cm. a width of 10 cm, and a height of 10 cm. What is the volume of the container?

   ____

   What is the volume of water in the container if its depth is 6 cm?

   ____

3. A cylindrical tank is 40 ft high and 24 ft in diameter. If the diameter of the tank is changed to 48 ft, what happens to the volume?

   ____

4. A circular swimming pool has 6 ft of water in it. The diameter of the pool is 30 ft. If the depth of the water is decreased to 3 ft, what happens to the volume of water?

   ____

Name ______________________________

Translations

A slide or translation image can be found by moving a figure a certain number of units.

The translation image at the right has a path of 5 right and 3 down.

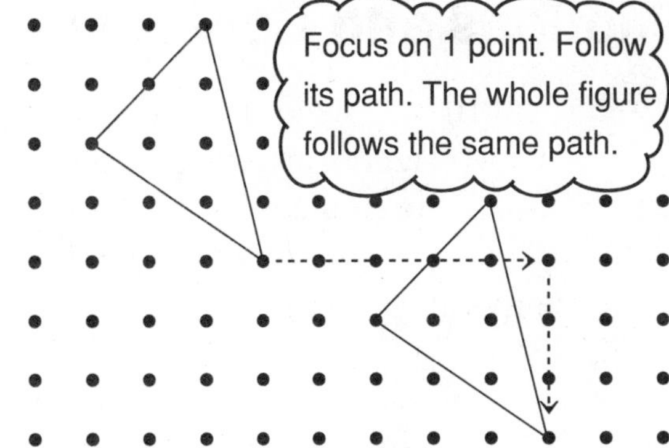

Describe each slide.

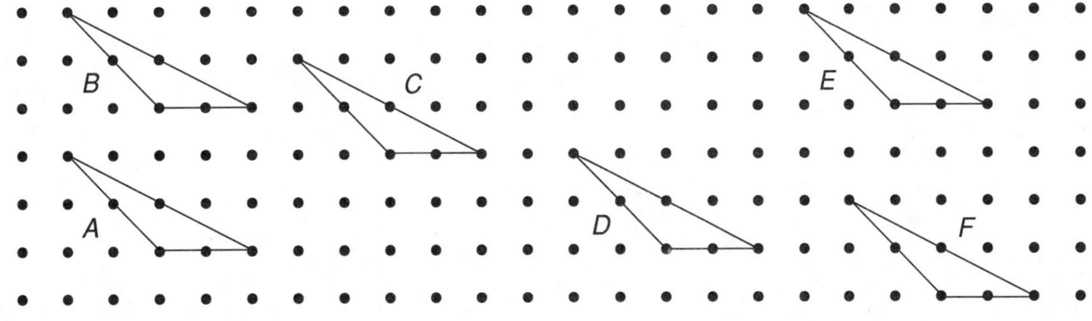

1. *A* to *D* ______________________________

2. *C* to *B* ______________________________

3. *F* to *E* ______________________________

4. *A* to *F* ______________________________

Draw the slide image of each figure.

5. (2 down, 4 right)

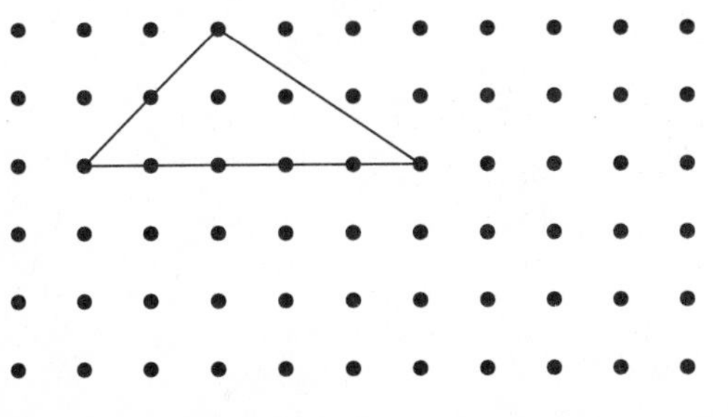

6. (5 left, 2 up)

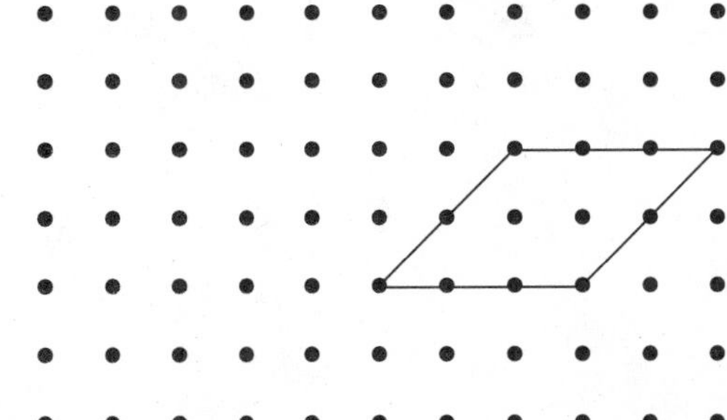

Name ______________________________

Motions and Congruence

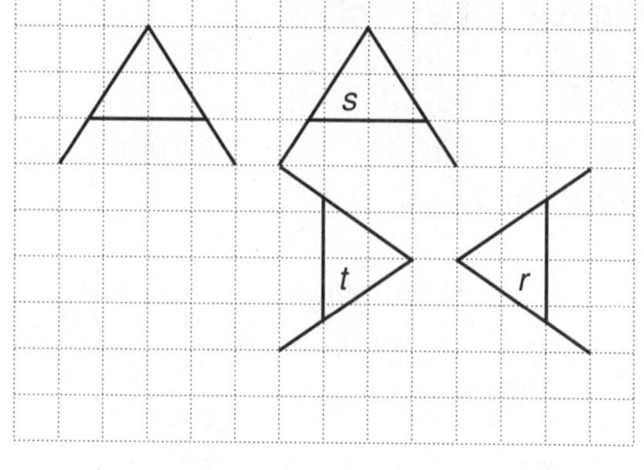

Congruent figures have the same size and shape. If two figures are congruent, one can be moved onto the other by a reflection, a turn, a slide, or a combination of these motions.

Are the figures congruent? If so, what motion or combination of motions moves one figure onto another?

1.

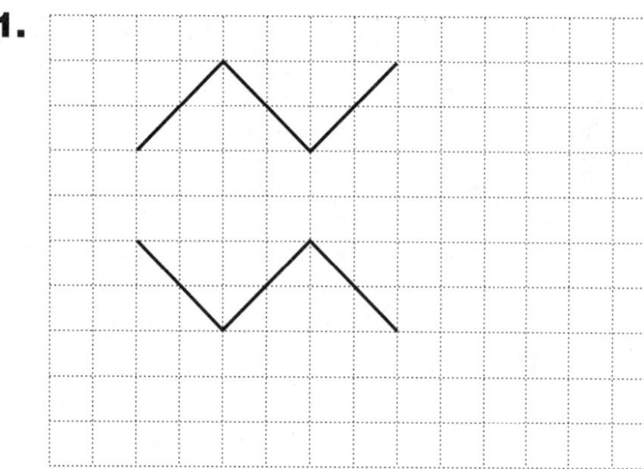

____

2.

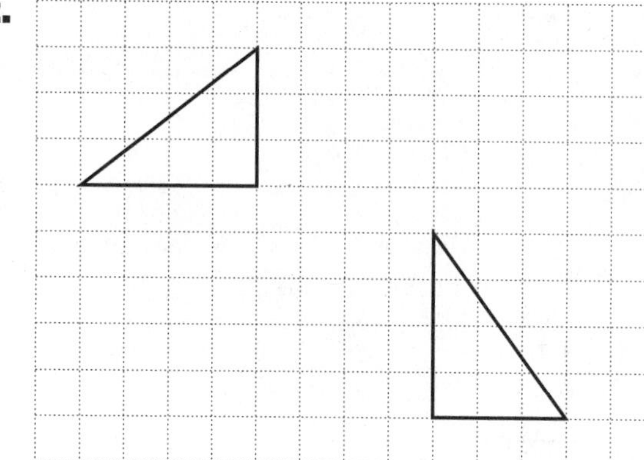

____

3.

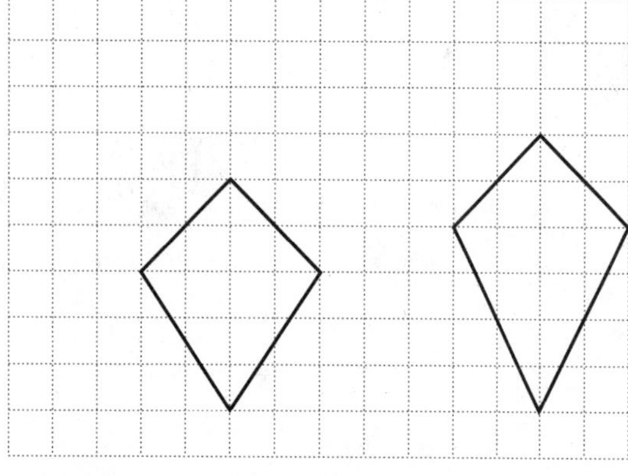

____

4.

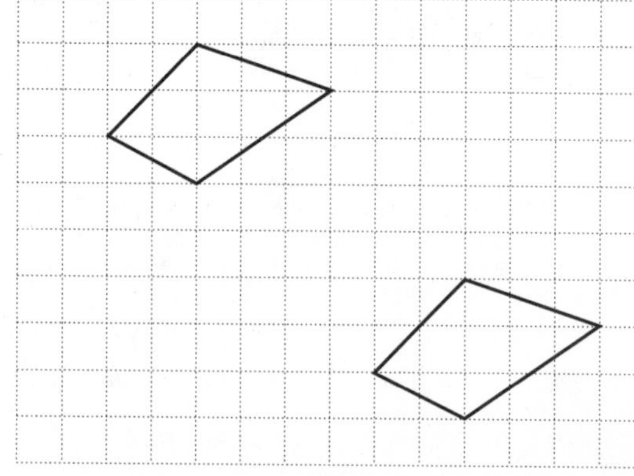

____

Name ______________________________

Using Critical Thinking

A figure can be divided into equal parts in many different ways depending on the assumptions you make. Divide this figure into two equal parts.

Assumption 1: Cuts must be diagonals from edge to opposite edge.
Result: 6 ways to make 2 equal parts

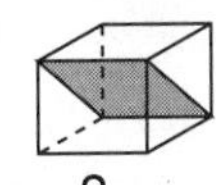
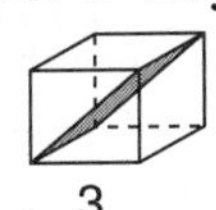
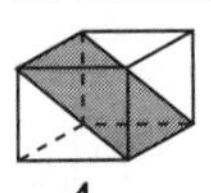
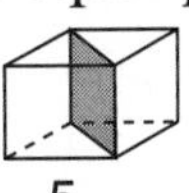
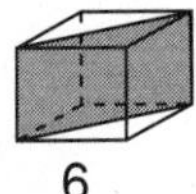

Assumption 2: Cuts must be diagonals from edge to opposite edge, and those that result in the same-shaped sections are the same.
Result: 3 ways to make 2 equal parts

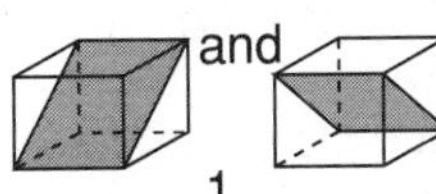

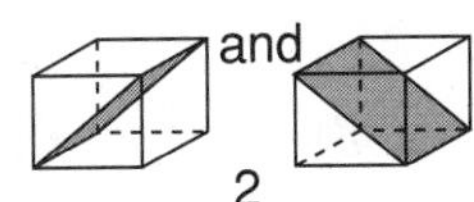

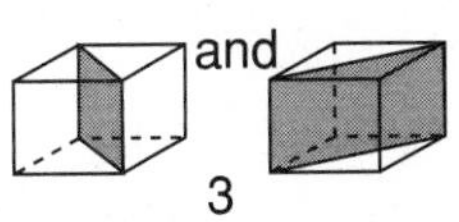

Find out how many ways each figure can be divided into two equal parts. List the assumptions you make.

A Number of ways: ______ Assumption: ______

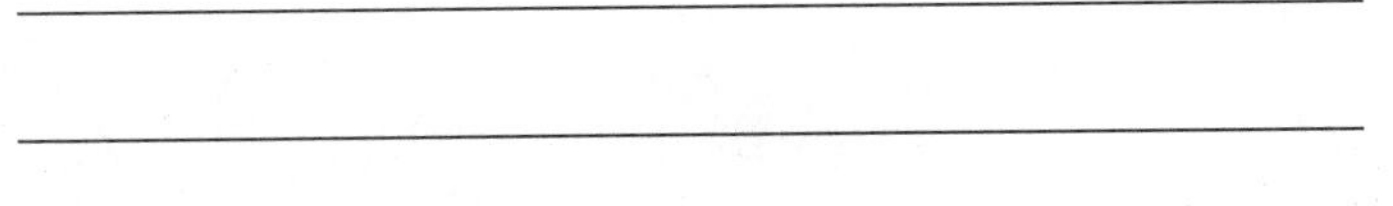

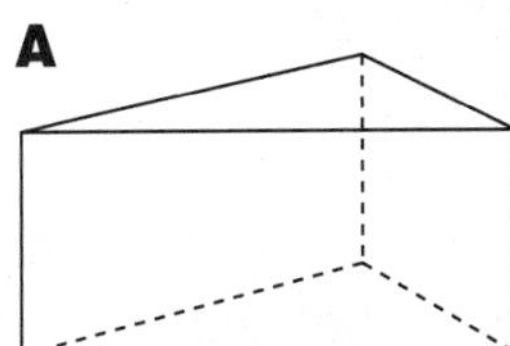

B Number of ways: ______ Assumption: ______

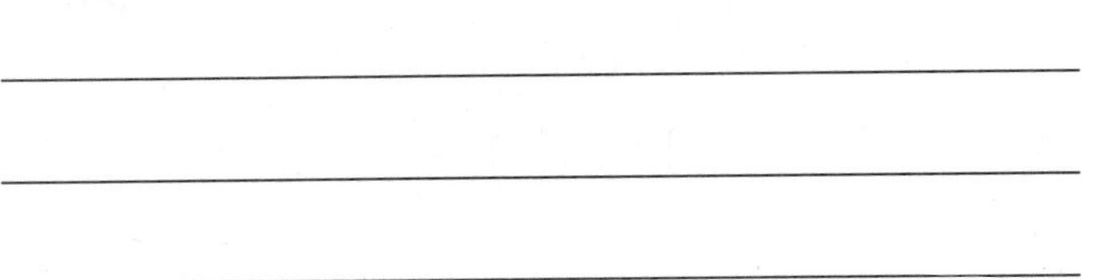

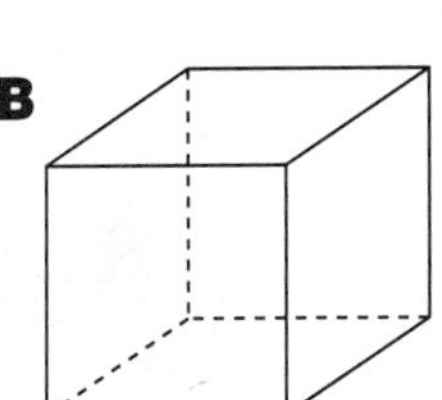

C Number of ways: ______ Assumption: ___

____

____

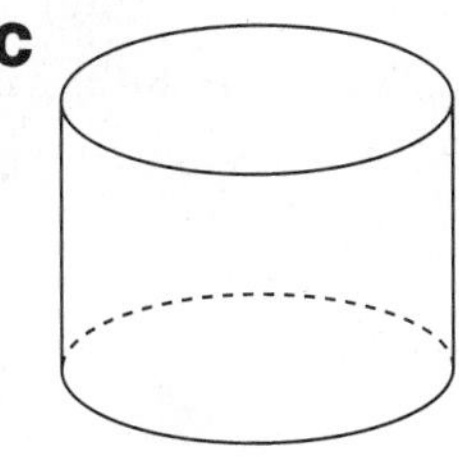

Name ___________________________________

Estimating Answers

When solving problems, you can estimate to see if your answer is reasonable.

Tyler bought a compact disk for $12.99, a book for $6.99, and a shirt for $8.99. The tax was $2.40. How much money did Tyler spend?

Estimate by rounding:

$13 + $7 + $9 + $2 = $31

The actual price is $31.37. It is a reasonable answer.

Before solving the problem, estimate the answer. Then solve the problem and decide if your answer is reasonable.

1. A theater sold 48 tickets at $39.99 each, 28 tickets at $29.99 each, and 19 tickets at $16.80 each. How much money did the theater receive?

Estimate: ____________________

Actual: ____________________

2. Mark rented a car for $33 a day plus $0.20 for each mile over 150 miles a day. Mark's bill was $103.80 for 3 days. How many miles did he drive over the 150 per day?

Estimate: ____________________

Actual: ____________________

3. Sean bought 4 tapes for $9.25 each. He gave the cashier $40. How much change did he get?

Estimate: ____________________

Actual: ____________________

4. A store sells pens packed in boxes. The store has 14,880 pens. Each box holds 20 dozen pens. How many boxes can be filled?

Estimate: ____________________

Actual: ____________________

5. Gianna read 240 pages on Monday, 76 pages on Tuesday, and 167 pages on Wednesday. How many pages did she read in all?

Estimate: ____________________

Actual: ____________________

6. Joe scored 76, 83, 92, 88, and 86 on his last 5 tests. What was his average test score?

Estimate: ____________________

Actual: ____________________

Name ______________________________

Extending Order of Operations

You can extend the rules for the order of operations to include exponents.

- ► Compute within grouping symbols first.
- ► Compute with exponents.
- ► Multiply and divide in order from left to right.
- ► Add and subtract in order from left to right.

Example:

Evaluate.

$(3 + 4)^2 - 3x^2 \div 3 + 6$ for $x = 3$ — Substitute 3 for x.

Solve.

$(3 + 4)^2 - 3(3)^2 \div 3 + 6$ — Compute inside parentheses.

$7^2 - 3(9) \div 3 + 6$ — Compute with exponents.

$49 - 27 \div 3 + 6$ — Multiply and divide in order.

$49 - 9 + 6 = 46$ — Add and subtract in order.

Evaluate each expression.

1. $36 \div (9 - 3) + 4$ ______

2. $(12 + 10) \bullet 5 - 1$ ______

3. $(4 \bullet 2)^2 - 3 + 2$ ______

4. $35 - 15 \bullet 2 + 6^2$ ______

5. $7(2 + a)$ for $a = 6$

____

6. $x + (6 \bullet 9) \div 2$ for $x = 3$

____

7. $23 + (6 - 4) \div w$ for $w = 2$

____

8. $40 - 3k^2 \div 4$ for $k = 4$

____

9. $y^2 - 4 \bullet 3 + 6$ for $y = 5$

____

10. $14 + (t^2 - 3) \div 6$ for $t = 3$

____

11. $3x^2 + x + 7$ for $x = 2$

____

12. $4w^2 - 12 \div 2$ for $w = 2$

____

Name ______________________________

Using Guess and Check to Solve Equations

You can use **Guess and Check** to solve equations.

The computer club has 14 members. This is 6 less than twice the number of members on the debate team. How many members are on the debate team?

Let n = the number of debate-team members. **Solve:** $2n - 6 = 14$

Try 12:	**Try 8:**	**Try 10:**
$2(12) - 6$	$2(8) - 6$	$2(10) - 6$
$24 - 6 = 18$ Too high	$16 - 6 = 10$ Too low	$20 - 6 = 14$ correct

The debate team has 10 members.

Solve. Use **Guess and Check.**

1. The drama club put on 8 shows in the first week. This is 8 less than 4 times the number of shows the second week. How many shows are there the second week? Let n = number of shows the second week.
Solve: $4n - 8 = 8$

____

2. Meryl bought 4 oranges and an apple. The apple cost $0.25. Meryl gave the cashier $1.45 for her purchase and received no change. How much did each orange cost? Let n = cost of an orange.
Solve: $4n + 0.25 = 1.45$

____

3. Mary Ann sold 24 glasses of juice on Friday. This was 16 less than 2 times the number of glasses she sold on Saturday. How many glasses of juice did she sell on Saturday?
Let n = number sold on Saturday.
Solve: $2n - 16 = 24$

____

4. The cost of tickets to Water World is $8 for adults and $6 for children. Sixty adults visited the park. The park took in $1,428. How many children entered the park?
Let n = number of children.
Solve: $6n + 480 = 1{,}428$

____

5. Joe's basketball team scored 58 points during a game. This was 12 more than 2 times the number scored by its opponent. How many points did the opposing team score?
Let n = score of opponent.
Solve: $2n + 12 = 58$

____

6. Matt bought 5 shirts and a watch. The total cost was $78. The watch cost $18. How much did each shirt cost?
Let n = price of each shirt.
Solve: $5n + 18 = 78$

____

Name ______________________________

Using Inverse Operations

To **build** an algebraic expression, start with a variable and combine it with numbers using arithmetic operations.

Start with y.	y
Multiply by 12.	$12y$
Subtract 3.	$12y - 3$

To **undo** an algebraic expression, use inverse operations in the reverse order to isolate to the variable.

Start with $12y - 3$.	$12y - 3$
Add 3.	$12y$
Divide by 12.	y

Show how to build and undo each expression.

1. $12x + 7$

Build: ______________________________ Undo: ______________________________

2. $9y - 3$

Build: ______________________________ Undo: ______________________________

3. $\frac{x}{6} + 5$

Build: ______________________________ Undo: ______________________________

4. $^{-}5w - 2$

Build: ______________________________ Undo: ______________________________

Name ______________________

Solving Two-step Equations

$\frac{x}{6} + 8 = 15$	First x was divided by 6. Then 8 was added.
$\frac{x}{6} + 8 - 8 = 15 - 8$	Undo adding 8 by subtracting 8 from both sides.
$\frac{x}{6} = 7$	
$6 \cdot \frac{x}{6} = 7 \cdot 6$	Multiply by 6 to undo dividing by 6.
$x = 42$	Check: $\frac{42}{6} + 8 = 15$

Solve and check.

1. $3x - 7 = 17$ ______

2. $4w - 36 = 0$ ______

3. $9y - 4 = 41$ ______

4. $9r + 6 = 24$ ______

5. $\frac{s}{5} + 7 = 13$ ______

6. $\frac{t}{7} - 3 = 2$ ______

7. $^{-}2k - 6 = {}^{-}8$ ______

8. $9t - 6 = 75$ ______

9. $\frac{q}{3} + 8 = 16$ ______

10. $6m - 8 = 28$ ______

11. $\frac{s}{7} + 3 = 6$ ______

12. $^{-}4x + 6 = {}^{-}14$ ______

13. $7w - 4 = {}^{-}18$ ______

14. $4t + 3 = {}^{-}21$ ______

15. $\frac{t}{3} + 3 = 12$ ______

16. $\frac{s}{8} + 9 = 14$ ______

Use the distributive property to help solve these equations. Show your work.

17. $5(4 + t) = 50$

______

18. $3(2h + 3) = 33$

______

19. $\frac{1}{2}(8 + r) = 46$

______

20. $2(x - 5) = {}^{-}4$

______

Name ______________________________

Inventing Activities with a Function Machine

The function machine to the right shows a number being input, applies the rule to the number, then prints an output.

Rule: $6n - 1$

Input 2: $6(2) - 1$

Output: 11

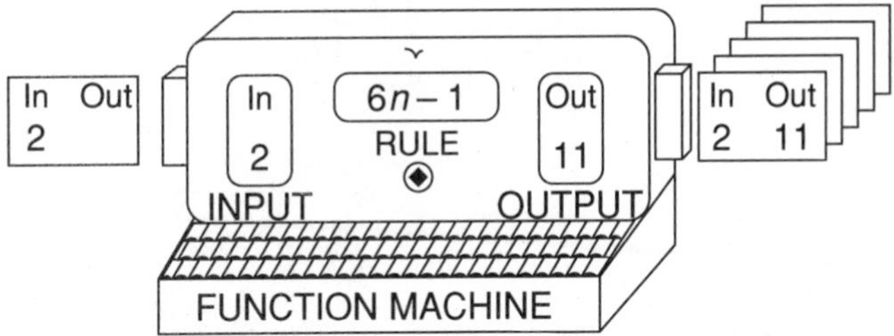

Find the output number for the given input numbers and rule.

1. input: 2, 12, 40; rule: $4n - 8$

____

2. input: 12, 60, 120; rule: $2n \div 3$

____

3. input: 8, 15, 20; rule: $12n + 5$

____

4. input: 0, 1, 2; rule: $5n - 1$

____

5. input: 10, 40, 80; rule: $n \div 5$

____

6. input: 50, 75, 100; rule: $7n - 40$

____

Find the input numbers for the given rule and output numbers.

7. rule: $3n + 3$; output: 3, 33, 63

____

8. rule: $n \div 4$; output: 3, 9, 15

____

9. rule: $2n - 1$; output: 1, 9, 17

____

10. rule: $17n \div 1$; output: 34, 170, 850

____

Look at the given input/output pairs and write a rule for the function machine.

11.

input	output
5	22
50	247
100	497

____

12.

input	output
0	0
1	1
2	2

____

Name ____________________

Graphing Inequalities

Look at the inequality. → Say it in words. → Draw what the words say.

Look at the inequality.	Say it in words.
$x < 2$	x is less than 2
$^{-}1 < x < 2$	x is greater than $^{-}1$ and less than 2
$x \geq 4$	x is greater than or equal to 4
$x \leq {}^{-}2$	x is less than or equal to $^{-}2$

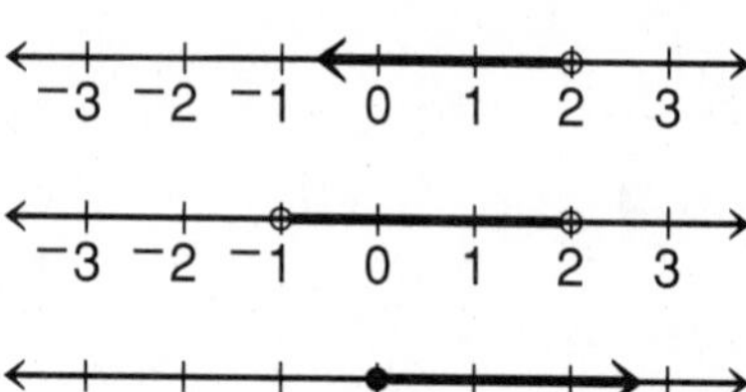

−5 −4 −3 −2 −1 0 1

Graph each inequality.

1. $x \leq 3$

0 1 2 3 4 5 6

2. $y \geq {}^{-}1$

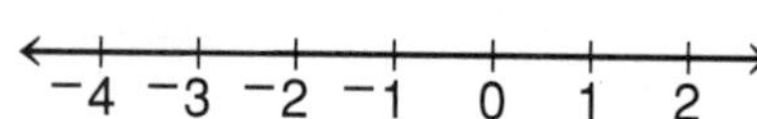

3. $^{-}2 > y$

−5 −4 −3 −2 −1 0 1

4. $5 \leq t$

2 3 4 5 6 7 8

5. $w > 12.2$

9 10 11 12 13 14 15

6. $s > 7\frac{2}{5}$

4 5 6 7 8 9 10

7. $d \leq {}^{-}2.3$

−5 −4 −3 −2 −1 0 1

8. $^{-}6 < y < {}^{-}1$

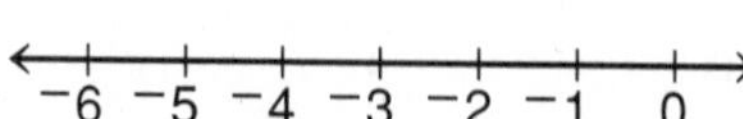

9. $4 \leq x < 6$

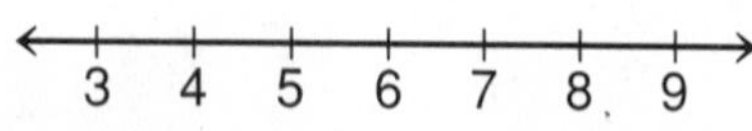

10. $^{-}2 \leq t \leq 2$

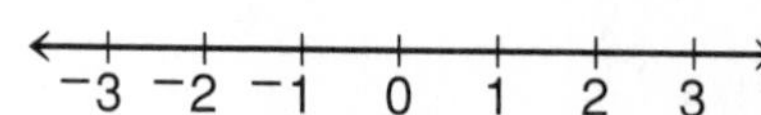

Name ______________________________

Solving Inequalities

You use the same method for solving inequalities as for solving equations.

Example:

$$x - 2 > 4$$
$$x - 2 + 2 > 4 + 2 \quad \text{Undo subtracting 2 by adding 2 to both sides.}$$
$$x > 6$$

Check the computation.	
Rewrite:	$x - 2 = 4$
Substitute:	$6 - 2 = 4$
	$4 = 4$ ✓

Check the inequality symbol.	
Choose a value from	$x > 6$.
Substitute:	$8 - 2 > 4$
	$6 > 4$ ✓

Solve and check.

1. $t + 5 < {}^-10$ ________

2. $n + 4 > 8$ ________

3. $q + 2 \geq 6$ ________

4. $s - 6 < 15$ ________

5. $p - 4 > {}^-2$ ________

6. $r + 3 < 5$ ________

7. $f + 6 \leq 10$ ________

8. $43 + n < 62$ ________

9. $w + 8 \geq 12$ ________

10. $r - 2 > 5$ ________

11. $t - 5 \geq 10$ ________

12. $4 + n < 6$ ________

13. $s - 2 < 4$ ________

14. $m - 10 \leq 0$ ________

15. $8 + n \geq 2$ ________

16. $r + 20 \geq 1$ ________

17. $m - 4 \geq {}^-2$ ________

18. $140 < t + 3$ ________

19. $x + 3 < {}^-1$ ________

20. $w - 1 > {}^-2$ ________

Name ________________________________

Equivalent Expressions

Write an equivalent expression for:	$2(x + 3) + 4x + 1$
Use the distributive property.	$2x + 6 + 4x + 1$
Add like terms $2x$ and $4x$.	$6x + 6 + 1$
Add numbers 6 and 1.	$6x + 7$

$2(x + 3) + 4x + 1$ and $6x + 7$ are equivalent expressions.

Write an equivalent expression.

1. $2x + 5 + x + 16$ __________

2. $(6x + 2) + (3x + 5)$ __________

3. $(4x + 3) + x + 9$ __________

4. $6(x + 8)$ __________

5. $5(2x + 3)$ __________

6. $2x(6 + 3)$ __________

7. $2 + 9x + 5 + 6x$ __________

8. $6(4x + 8)$ __________

9. $9(x + 7)$ __________

10. $4x + 2 + 2x$ __________

11. $(3x + 2) + (x + 1)$ __________

12. $8x + 3 + 4x + 2$ __________

13. $4x + 2 + 14x$ __________

14. $3x + 7x + 2x + 8$ __________

15. $2(x + 1) + 3x$ __________

16. $6(2x + 3) + 4$ __________

17. $2(x + 1) + 3x + 5$ __________

18. $3(2x + 3) + 2(3x + 2)$ __________

19. $4x + 5 + x + 2x$ __________

20. $(x + 2) + (x + 7)$ __________

Name ______________________________

Inductive Reasoning: Discovering Number Patterns

There are 15 soccer teams that play one another for practice games. How many games are played in all?

Team *A* vs. *B* (1 game)

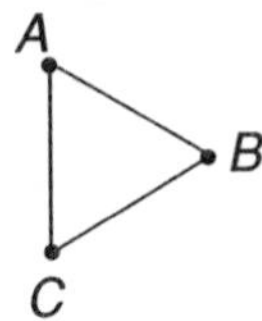

Team *A* vs. *B* vs. *C* (3 games)

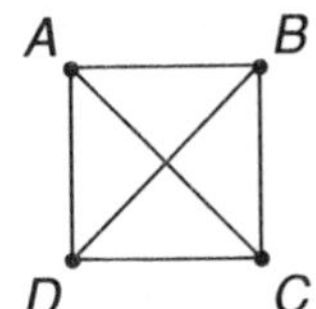

Team A vs. B vs. *C* vs. *D* (6 games)

Number of Teams	Number of Games	Pattern
2 (*A*, *B*)	1	**2** × 1 ÷ 2
3 (*A*, *B*, *C*)	3	**3** × 2 ÷ 2
4 (*A*, *B*, *C*, *D*)	6	**4** × 3 ÷ 2
5 (*A*, *B*, *C*, *D*, *E*)	10	**5** × 4 ÷ 2
. . .	. . .	. . .
15	105	**15** × 14 ÷ 2

The chart shows the games played for 2, 3, 4, and 5 teams. The same pattern works for these cases and probably works for all. When you make generalizations after discovering a pattern, you are using **inductive reasoning**.

Give the sum of each of the following.

1. the first 50 counting numbers ______

Number	1	2	3	. . .	50
Sum	1	3	6	. . .	
Pattern	$\frac{1 \times 2}{2}$	$\frac{2 \times 3}{2}$	$\frac{3 \times 4}{2}$	. . .	$\frac{50 \times 51}{2}$

2. The first 40 counting numbers ______

Number					
Sum					
Pattern					

3. the first 30 even numbers ______

Position	1st	2nd	3rd	. . .	30th
Even Number	2	4	6		
Sum	2	6		. . .	
Pattern	1 x 2	2 x 3	3 x__	. . .	30 x 31

4. the first 50 even numbers ______

Position					
Even Number					
Sum					
Pattern					

5. the first 45 odd numbers ______

Position	1st	2nd	3rd	. . .	45th
Odd Number	1	3	5		
Sum	1	4		. . .	
Pattern	1 x 1	2 x 2		. . .	45 x 45

6. the first 90 odd numbers ______

Position					
Odd Number					
Sum					
Pattern					

Name ______________________________

Inductive Reasoning: Discovering Geometric Patterns

Use isometric dot paper to make triangles with a comon vertex. Keep track of the number of exterior dots that make each triangle. How many dots will make the twentieth triangle?

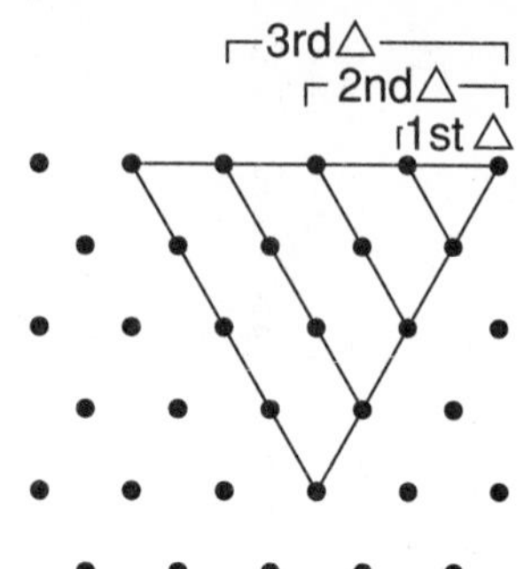

Start with the smallest triangle and draw the next 2 or 3 triangles

↓

Make a table and look for a pattern.

Triangle	Number of Dots	Pattern
1st	3	1 × 3
2nd	6	2 × 3
3rd	9	3 × 3
4th	12	4 × 3
. . .	. . .	. . .
20th		×

↓

Test the pattern to be sure it works.

↓

Use the pattern to solve the problem.

↓

The twentieth triangle will have 60 dots.

Draw pictures to help you solve these problems. Use inductive reasoning.

1. How many vertices would there be on a model like the ones shown but 50 "triangles high"?

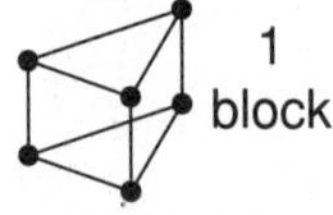

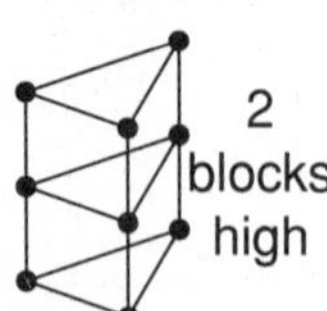

Blocks	Vertices	Pattern
1	6	2 × 3
2	9	3 × 3
3		×
. . .	. . .	. . .
50		×

2. How many vertices would there be on a model like the ones shown, but made from 64 triangles?

Blocks	Vertices	Pattern
1	6	2 × 3
2	8	×
3		×
. . .	. . .	. . .
64		×

3. How many vertices would there be on this pattern if 100 triangles were used?

______

Name ______________________________

Discovering Relationships

Look at Pierre's work. What type of numbers are the factors? What type of numbers are the products? What conclusion can you draw?

$2 \times 6 = 12$	$4 \times 8 = 32$
$10 \times 12 = 120$	$6 \times 4 = 24$

$824 \times 730 = 601{,}520$

$692 \times 84 = 58{,}128$

$554 \times 98 = 54{,}292$

The factors and products are even numbers.
The product of 2 even numbers is an even number.

Is the product of 5 even numbers even? ______

Explain your answer. ______________________________

Write even or odd. Justify your answer.

1. What is the product of 2 odd numbers?

2. What is the product of an even number of odd numbers?

3. What is the product of 5 odd numbers?

4. What is the product of an odd number of odd numbers?

5. What is the product of an odd and an even number?

6. What is the difference of an even and an odd number?

7. What is the difference of 2 odd numbers?

8. What is the difference of 2 even numbers?

Fibonacci first used this number sequence: 1, 1, 2, 3, 5, 8, 13, 21 . . .
It is now called the Fibonacci sequence.

9. Explain the relationship of the numbers in the sequence.

10. Find the next 5 numbers in the sequence.

Name ______________________________

Informal Proof in Algebra

An **informal proof** in algebra uses variables and operations to justify an outcome. This informal proof shows why a number trick works.

Number Trick	Trial	Informal Proof
Pick any number.	9	n
Add 6.	$9 + 6 = 15$	$n + 6$
Double your answer.	$15 \times 2 = 30$	$2(n + 6) = 2n + 12$
Subract 12.	$30 - 12 = 18$	$2n + 12 - 12 = 2n$
Divide by 2.	$18 \div 2 = 9$	$2n \div 2 = n$
You get the original number.	9	n

Try each number trick below. Then write an informal proof to show why each works.

1.

Pick any number.	9	n
Multiply by 3.		
Add 9.		
Subtract 6.		
Divide by 3.		
Subtract your number.		
The answer is 1.		

2.

Pick any number.	5	n
Add 12.		
Multiply by 3.		
Subtract 30		
Divide by 3.		
Subract your number.		
The answer is 2.		

3.

Pick any number	93	n
Multiply by 8.		
Add 64.		
Divide by 8		
Subtract your number.		
The answer is 8.		

4.

Pick any number.	19	n
Add 12.		
Subtract 6.		
Add 5.		
Subtract 11.		
You get the original number.		

Name ______________________________

Informal Proof in Geometry

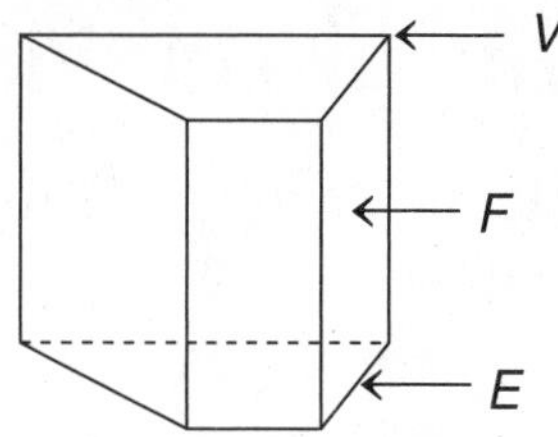

An **informal proof** in geometry uses variables and operations to justify an outcome. Step-by-step reasoning can help you prove a conclusion you have drawn.

Example:

Let V represent the number of vertices.
Let F represent the number of faces or sides.
Let E represent the number of edges.

Find $V + F - E$ for the figure above.

___ + ____ – ____ = ____

Use the pictures to complete the table.

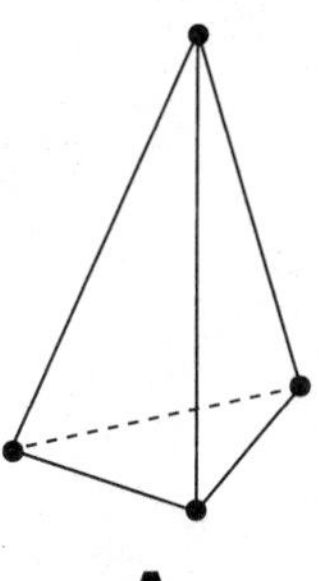

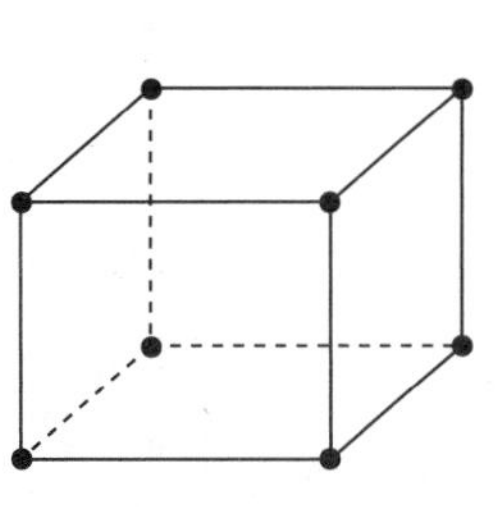

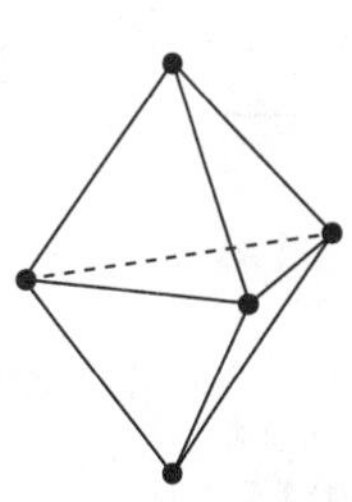

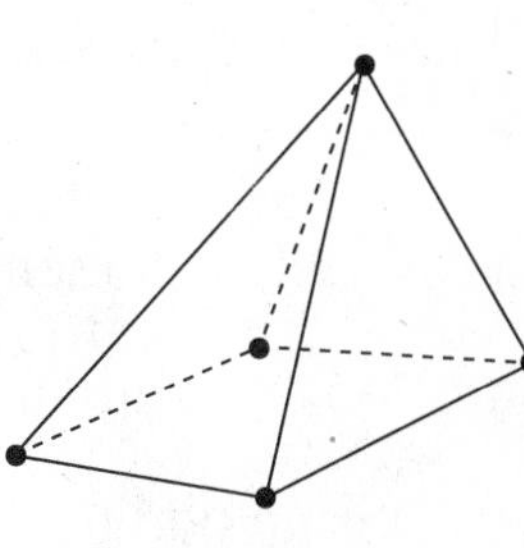

E

Figure	V	F	E	$V + F$	$V + F - E$
A	4	4	6		
B					
C					
D					
E					
F					

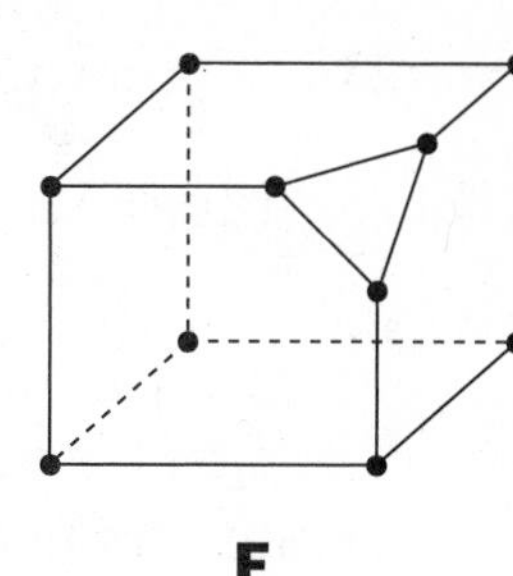

Write a conclusion based on the results of your table.

____

____

Will your conclusion work for a figure with 12 vertices, 8 faces, and 18 edges? Justify your answer.

____

____

Name ______________________________

Using Critical Thinking: The Language of Logic

Compound statements are made by joining two simple statements together. Check the chart to tell when the compound statement is true or false.

P and **Q**	True only when both **P** and **Q** are true
P or **Q**	False only when both **P** and **Q** are false
If **P**, then **Q**	False only when **P** is true and **Q** is false

Examples:

22 is an even number **and** 3 is an even number. false (**Q** is false.)
22 is an even number **or** 3 is an even number. true (**P** is true, even when **Q** is false)
If 22 is an even number, **then** 3 is an even number. false (**Q** is false.)

Label each statement **true** or **false**.

1. 23 is an odd number **or** 20 is an odd number.
2. 9 is an odd number **and** 155 is an odd number.
3. **If** 6 is an odd number, **then** 7 is an odd number.
4. 23 is a prime number **and** 23 = 6.
5. 13 > 45 **or** 56 < 123.
6. **If** 3 is a factor of 12, **then** 3 is a factor of 24.
7. There are 12 inches in one foot **and** there are 100 centimeters in one meter.
8. 56 is a multiple of 9 **or** 56 is a multiple of 8.
9. **If** $^{-}3 > ^{-}34$, **then** 9 > 4.
10. There are 7 days in a week **or** there are 10 items in a dozen.

Let **P:** $6 < 9$ **Q:** $4 + 5 = 10$ **R:** 3 is even **S:** $3^2 = 9$

Label each statement **true** or **false**.

11. P and Q _____ **12.** If P, the Q _____ **13.** P or Q _____ **14.** R and S _____

15. Q or S _____ **16.** If P, then S_____ **17.** If S, then P _____ **18.** Q and R _____

Name ______________________________

Logical Inference

You can chain statements to make new statements.

Examples:

A: Today is Monday. B: Tomorrow is Tuesday. C: I will have math class.

If today is Monday, then tomorrow is Tuesday. $A \to B$
If tomorrow is Tuesday, then I will have math class tomorrow. $B \to C$
Conclusion: If today is Monday, then I will have math class tomorrow. $A \to C$

P: n is even Q: $2n$ is even. R: $2n + 2$ is even

If n is even, then $2n$ is even. $P \to Q$
If $2n$ is even, then $2n + 2$ is even. $Q \to R$
Conclusion: If n is even, then $2n + 2$ is even. $P \to R$

Write the conclusion by chaining the statements.

1. If n is even, then $n + 1$ is odd. If $n + 1$ is odd, then $n + 2$ is even.
Conclusion:

____

____

2. If $n > 7$, then $2n > 14$. If $2n > 14$, then $2n — 1 > 13$.
Conclusion:

____

____

3. If it rains, then I will go shopping. If I go shopping, then dinner will be late.
Conclusion:

____

____

4. If Tom is shorter than Jan, then Tom is less than 5 feet tall. If Tom is less than 5 feet tall, then he will play soccer.
Conclusion:

____

____

5. If 7 is prime, then 2×7 is composite. If 2×7 is composite, then every multiple of 14 is composite. Conclusion:

____

____

6. If 3 is a factor of 21, then 21 is not prime. If 21 is not prime, then 21 is composite. Conclusion:

____

____

7. Write your own $B \to C$ statement and chain it with the $A \to B$ statement: If I study hard, then I will get good grades.

____

Name ______________________________

Reasoning from Graphs

Graphs are used to represent data visually.

Mr. Samuels bought an exercise bike and exercised every morning all week long. He gradually increased his exercise time until Thursday. After that his exercise time dropped slightly each day. By Saturday he was still exercising more than on Monday.

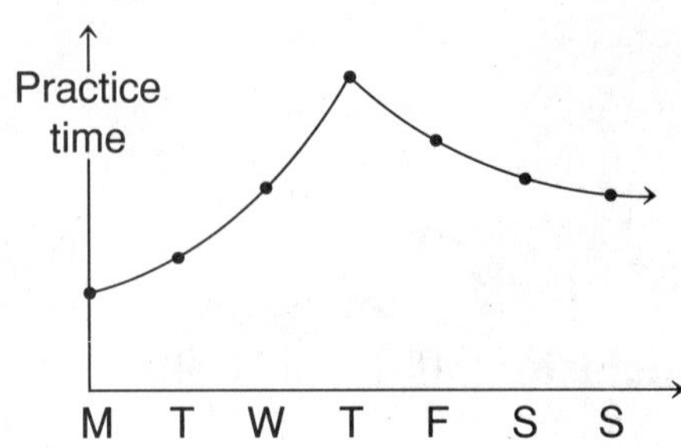

1. What is happening when the graph of exercise time slopes up? ______________________________

2. What is happening when the graph slopes down? ______________________________

3. Change the graph. Show that Mr. Samuels exercised the same amount of time from Thursday to Saturday.

Lois kept track of the temperatures in her city for one year.

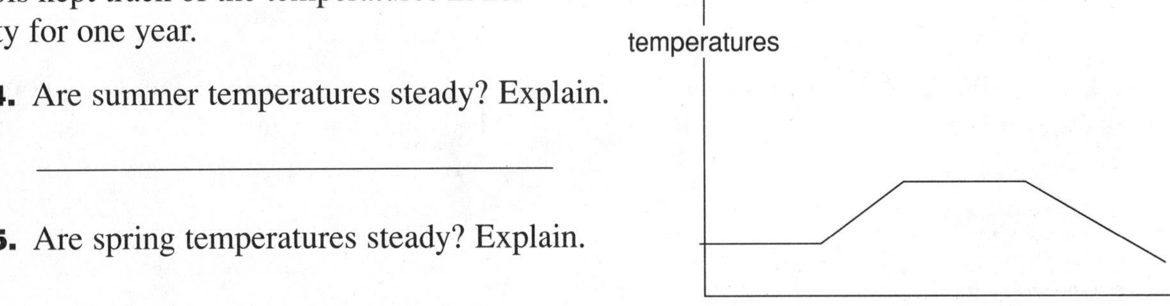

4. Are summer temperatures steady? Explain.

____

5. Are spring temperatures steady? Explain.

____

6. Change the graph. Show that spring temperatures rise more rapidly.

---

7. Unscramble this story of the gasoline level in an automobile tank. Place a letter on the graph to show each event.

A Ran out of gasoline in the morning
B Filled tank with gasoline
C Drove home after work
D Drove to work
E Stayed at work for 8 hours

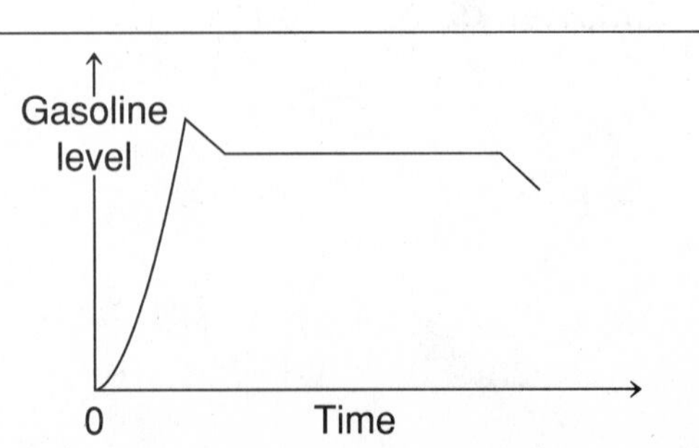

Name ______________________________

Finding Related Problems

To solve a problem, thinking of a related problem may help.

Example:

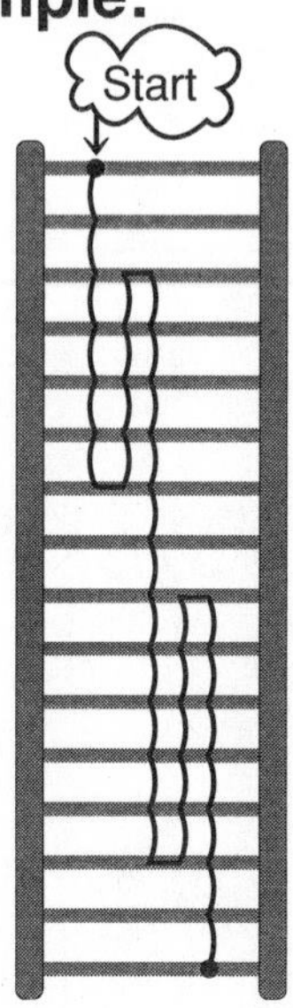

The painter stood on the top rung of the ladder. She then climbed down 6 rungs, up 4, down 11, and up 5. When she climbed down 7 rungs, she was on the last rung of the ladder. How many rungs does the ladder have?

____

A lizard fell into a hole 22 feet deep. It climbed 7 feet up the hole each day, but fell 2 feet each night. How many days did it take the lizard to climb out of the hole?

____

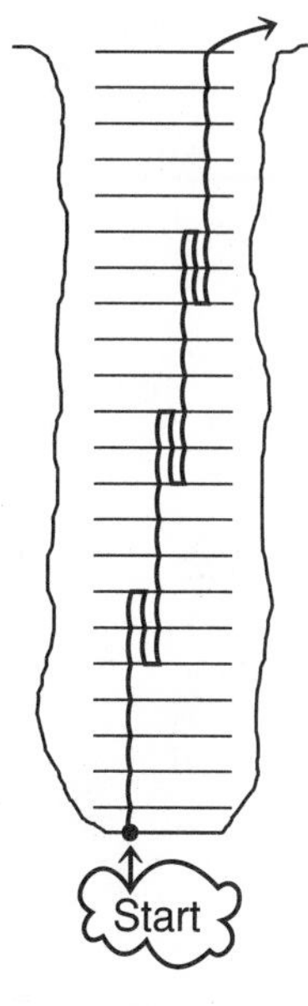

How are these problems related?

____

____

Read all the problems. Decide which problems are related. Then solve each problem.

1. There are 47 students in sports: 12 joined soccer and football, 25 joined only football. How many students joined only soccer?
Problem 1 is related to Problem ______.

____

2. Mike delivers 48 newspaper a day. In 1 hour he delievers half of them. In the next hour he delivers one fourth of the remaining newspapers. How many newspapers are left to deliver?
Problem 2 is related to Problem ______.

____

3. Cara assembles model cars. She assembled $\frac{1}{3}$ of the pieces on Friday and $\frac{1}{4}$ of the remaining pieces on Saturday. There are 9 pieces left. How many pieces did she have originally?
Problem 3 is related to Problem ______.

____

4. In Tim's survey he found that 22 people traveled to Texas and 10 people traveled to Georgia, and that 8 of the respondents had traveled to both states. How many people were surveyed?
Problem 4 is related to Problem ______.

____